500

CARAVAN &
CAMPSITES
in Britain

C000225130

This edition published 2007 by The Automobile
Association Development Limited

A CIP catalogue record for this book is
available from the British Library.

Directory generated by the AA Establishment
Database, Information Research.
Cover photo: AA /R Moore
All images are held in the Associations own photo
library (AA World Travel Library) and were taken
by the following photographers:
1 AA/R Victor; 5br AA

Typeset by Jamie Wiltshire
Printed in Italy by G.Canale & C.S.p.A.

The contents of this book are believed to be
correct at the time of printing. Nevertheless, the
Publisher cannot be held responsible for any
errors or omissions of for changes in the details
given in this guide or for the consequence of any
reliance on the information provided in the same.
This does not affect your statutory rights.

Assessments of the campsites are based on the
experience of the AA Caravan & Camping
Inspectors on the occasion of their visit(s) and
therefore descriptions given in this guide
necessarily contain an element of subjective
opinion which may not reflect or dictate a reader's
own opinion on another occasion.

Published by AA Publishing, which is a
trading name of Automobile Association
Developments Limited, whose registered office is
Fanum House, Basing View, Basingstoke,
Hampshire RG21 4EA. Registered number
1878835.

ISBN 13: 978-0-7495-5317-3
ISBN 10: 0-7495-5317-0

A03198

Welcome to the Guide

This pocket guide is aimed at families with children looking for the right caravan or camping park for their holiday. Within its pages you will find parks of all kinds, from busy, action-packed holiday centres to small sites handily located near beaches or other attractions. All of them are child friendly, and all offer at minimum a playing ground and/or designated playing area where children can safely let off steam. Every park is inspected annually by an unannounced visit from an experienced AA inspector, and the information which appears in this Guide, is also updated every year. Do check with a park when booking that all of your requirements will be met.

The AA Campsite Classification Scheme

AA parks are classified on a 5-point scale according to their style and range of facilities they offer. As the number of pennants increases, so the quality and variety of facilities is generally greater.

► One Pennant Parks offer a drinking water supply, chemical disposal point, and refuse collection. They may or may not have toilets and washing facilities.

►► Two Pennant Parks additionally offer seperate washrooms including at least 2 toilets and 2 wash basins per 30 pitches per sex, hot and cold water directly to each basin, and dishwashing facilities.

►►► Three Pennant Parks offer modern or modernised toilets with, additionally, at least one private shower cubicle per 35 pitches per sex, electric hook-ups, automatic laundry and children's playground.

►►►► Four Pennant Parks are of a very high quality, especially in the toilets which offer vanitory-style wash basins including some in lockable cubicles, or en suite shower/washing /toilet cubicles.

►►►►► Five Pennant Parks are some of an outstanding quality, and offer some fully-serviced pitches, along with first class toilet facilities including en suite cubicles.

A separate HOLIDAY CENTRE category indicates that full day and night holiday entertainment is offered, including sports, leisure and recreational facilities, and a choice of eating outlets.

The quality percentage score shows a comparison between sites within the same pennant rating. The score runs between 50% and 80%.

How to use this Guide

[1]- BOLVENTOR SX17

Colliford Tavern Campsite

[2]- ►►►► 78%

Colliford Lake St Neot PL14 6PZ

☎ 01208 821335 📠 01208 821335

email: info@colliford.com

www.colliford.com

[3]- **Dir:** *Exit A30 1.25m W of Bolventor onto unclass road signed Colliford Lake.*

[4]- * 🚐 £10 🚌 £10 ⛺ 10

Open: Etr-Sep, Booking advisable bank hols & Jul-Aug, Last arrival 22.30hrs Last departure 11.00hrs

[5]- An oasis on Bodmin Moor, a small site with spacious grassy pitches and very good quality facilities. The park is surrounded by mature trees and is very sheltered on the moor. Fly fishing is available at nearby Colliford Lake. A 3.5-acre site with 40 touring pitches.

[6]- **Facilities:** ⛺ 🚿 ☺ 🔌 ✲ ✆ 🐕 ♿

Services: 🍴 🍷 🚐 🔒 🍃 🛒 **Facilities found within 3 miles:** 🎣 **Notes:** Dogs

[7]- must be on leads

[1] **Locations** The guide is listed in country, county order, then by town/village alphabetically. Counties are listed down the side of each page. Map references are based on the National Grid.

[2] **AA Pennant Rating** Please see page 3 for an explanation.

[3] **Directions** are shown where provided by proprieters.

[4] **Charges** The prices given are the overnight cost for one tent or caravan, and one car with two adults, or one motor caravan and two adults. Some parks may charge separately for some facilities, including showers. There may be an extra charge for pitches with electricity. Prices in the republic of Ireland are given in Euros.

[5] **Pitches** The brief description of the site includes the number of touring pitches and hardstandings, as well as the number of static van pitches which gives an inditcation of the size of the park. Static

vans are not inspected, and are not part of the Pennant Scheme.

⑥ For symbols and abbreviations please see page 6.

⑦ **Notes** These are any restrictions the park has told us about.

Useful Information

It is advisable to book in advance at peak holiday times. Check whether a reservation entitles you to a particular pitch. Speak to the person in charge immediately if you have any complaints. If this personal approach fails and the matter is serious, you may decide to approach the local authority or tourist board.

Chemical Disposal Point

Most parks, except for those catering for tents only, will have one of these. It should have flushing, rinsing and soakaway facilities.

Electric Hook-Up

Most parks offer these, but if it is important to you, check with the park when booking.

Cables can usually be hired on a site, or a plug supplied to fit your own cable.

Restrictions

On many parks, unaccompanied young people, single-sex groups, single adults, and motorcycle groups are not accepted. Most parks accept dogs, though some will refuse certain breeds.

Key to symbols and abbreviations

🚐	Caravan	🍽	Restaurant
🚐	motorhome	🍷	Licensed bar
⛺	Tent	T	Toilet fluid
≋	Indoor swimming pool	⚓	dump thingy
≋	Outdoor swimming pool	🔌	Electric hook up
🎱	Games room	📟	Launderette
🎠	Children's playground	🔒	Calor gaz
📺	Separate TV room	🍃	Camping gaz
🎾	Tennis court	🔋	Battery charging
🚿	Shower	🍼	Baby care
⊙	Electric shaver	🍔	Fast food / takeaway
✂	Hairdryer	U	Stables
✳	Ice-pack facility	♪18	Golf course and number of holes
📞	Public telephone	⚓	Boats for hire
🏪	Shop on site, or within 200 yards	🐟	Fishing
🐕	Dog exercise area	◎	Mini golf
🍖	BBQ area	🌊	Watersports
🍴	Picnic area	⊗	No dogs
♿	disabled access	🚫	no credit cards
☕	Café		

RISELEY SU76

Wellington Country Park ▶▶▶ 77%

RG7 1SP

☎ 0118 932 6444 📠 0118 932 6445

email: info@wellington-country-park.co.uk

www.wellington-country-park.co.uk

Dir: *Signed off A33 between Reading and Basingstoke, 4m S of M4 junct 11*

* 🚐 £15-£18 🚌 £15-£18 ▲ £13-£16

Open: Mar-Nov, Booking advisable peak periods, Last arrival 17.30hrs Last departure 13.00hrs

A peaceful woodland site set within an extensive country park, which comes complete with lakes, nature trails, deer farm and boating. Ideal for M4 travellers. An 80-acre site with 72 touring pitches and 10 hardstandings.

Facilities: Boating, fishing, miniature railway, crazy golf 🄰🄼🄽🄾🄿🄰🄱🄲🄳🄴🄵🄶🄷

Services: 🄰🄱🄲🄳🄴🄵🄶 **Facilities found within 3 miles:** 🄰🄱🄲🄳🄴🄵🄶

Notes: No open fires

GRAFHAM TL12

Old Manor Caravan Park

▶▶▶▶ 80%

Church Road Huntingdon PE28 0BB

☎ 01480 810264 📠 01480 819099

email: camping@old-manor.co.uk

www.old-manor.co.uk

Dir: *Signed off A1, S of Huntingdon at Buckden & from A14, W of Huntingdon at Ellington*

* 🚐 £15-£20 🚌 £15-£20 ▲ £13-£18

Open: Open All Year (rs Nov-Feb on site shop closed), Booking advisable wknds & peak times, Last arrival 21.30hrs Last departure 18.00hrs

A secluded park in gardens surrounding a 17th-century cottage. A 6.5-acre site with 84 touring pitches and 7 hardstandings, with views of the surrounding countryside.

Facilities: 🄰🄱🄲🄳🄴🄵🄶🄷🄸

Services: 🄰🄱🄲🄳🄴🄵🄶 **Facilities found within 3 miles:** 🄰🄱 18 🄲🄳🄴🄵🄶

Notes: Dogs must be kept on leads

BERKSHIRE/CAMBRIDGESHIRE

CHESHIRE/CORNWALL

CODDINGTON SJ45
Manor Wood Country Caravan Park

▶▶▶ 86%

Manor Wood Chester CH3 9EN

☎ 01829 782990 ▤ 01829 782990

email: info@manorwoodcaravans.co.uk

www.cheshire-caravan-sites.co.uk

Dir: *From A534 at Barton, turn opposite Cock O'Barton pub signed Coddington. Left in 100yds. Site 0.5m on left*

* ♥ £14-£16 ♥ £14-£16 ▲ £14-£16

Open: Open All Year (rs Oct-May swimming pool closed), Last arrival 20.30hrs Last departure 11.00hrs

A secluded landscaped park with views towards the Welsh Hills. Offers fully serviced pitches, modern facilities, a heated outdoor pool and tennis courts. Lake fishing with country walks and pubs. An 8-acre site with 45 touring pitches and 38 hardstandings.

Facilities: ⬅🅼♨🅝🌲☉℗✕🐕🐎🅫🕹

Services: ↪🅚🅼🅑🎱🖋 Facilities found within 3 miles: ↯36 ✒ 🅚🅪 **Notes:** 🅐

ASHTON SW53
Boscrege Caravan & Camping Park

▶▶▶ 70%

Helston TR13 9TG

☎ 01736 762231

email: enquiries@caravanparkcornwall.com

www.caravanparkcornwall.com

Dir: *Follow signs from B3202 (Hayle-Helston road) to Godolphin Cross. Right at pub to site*

* ♥ £6.75-£14.25 ♥ £6.75-£14.25 ▲ £6.75-£14.25

Open: Mar-Nov, Booking advisable Jul-Aug, Last arrival 22.00hrs Last departure 11.00hrs

A quiet and bright little touring park divided into small paddocks with hedges, and offering plenty of open spaces for children to play. The family-owned park offers clean toilet facilities. In an Area of Outstanding Natural Beauty at the foot of Tregonning Hill. A 12-acre site with 50 touring pitches and 26 statics.

Facilities: Recreation fields, microwave, nature trail 🚶🅰⬛🅝🌲☉℗✕☉🅫♨🕹🟥

Services: 🅣🅚🅼🅑🎱🖋🍴 Facilities found within 3 miles: ∪↯9🐟✒◎🦺🅚🅪

BLACKWATER   SW74

Chiverton Caravan & Touring Park

▶▶▶ 90%

East Hill TR4 8HS

☎ 01872 560667 📄 01872 560667

email: chivertonpark@btopenworld.com

www.chivertonpark.co.uk

Dir: *Exit A30 at Chiverton rdbt (Little Chef) onto unclass road signed Blackwater (3rd exit). 1st right & park 300mtrs on right*

* ⊕ £12-£17 ⛺ £12-£22 ▲ £7-£17

Open: 3 Mar-3 Nov (rs Mar-May & mid Sep-Nov limited stock kept in shop), Booking advisable mid Jul-Aug, Last arrival 21.00hrs Last departure noon

A small site with a good toilet block and a steam room, sauna and gym. Games room with pool table, and children's outside play equipment. A 4-acre site with 12 touring pitches, 10 hardstandings and 50 statics.

Facilities: Drying lines ♦ 🏔 🏕 ⊙ ☺ ☼ 🕙 🛏 🗞 👫 ⚼ **Services:** 🚾 🚱 📶 **Facilities found within 3 miles:** ∪ ↥ 18 🖉 ⚡ 🏊 🗞 🗞 **Notes:** 🐾

BOLVENTOR   SX17

Colliford Tavern Campsite

▶▶▶▶ 78%

Colliford Lake St Neot PL14 6PZ

☎ 01208 821335 📄 01208 821335

email: info@colliford.com

www.colliford.com

Dir: *Exit A30 1.25m W of Bolventor onto unclass road signed Colliford Lake. Site 0.25m on left*

* ⊕ £10 ⛺ £10 ▲ 10

Open: Etr-Sep, Booking advisable bank hols & Jul-Aug, Last arrival 22.30hrs Last departure 11.00hrs

An oasis on Bodmin Moor, a small site with spacious grassy pitches and very good quality facilities. The park is surrounded by mature trees and is very sheltered on the moor. Fly fishing is available at nearby Colliford Lake. A 3.5-acre site with 40 touring pitches.

Facilities: 🏔 🏕 ⊙ ☺ ☼ 🕙 🛏 👫 ⚼ 👫 ⚼ **Services:** 🍴 🛢 🚱 🝙 🖉 ⚼ **Facilities found within 3 miles:** 🖉 **Notes:** Dogs must be on leads

CORNWALL

CORNWALL

BUDE SS20

Budemeadows Touring Holiday Park ►►►► 86%

EX23 0NA

☎ 01288 361646

email: holiday@budemeadows.com

www.budemeadows.com

Dir: *3m S of Bude on A39. Park entered via layby*

🚐 £8.60-£19.80 ⛺ £8.60-£19.80 ▲ £8.60-£19.80

Open: Open All Year (rs Sep-Spring BH shop, bar & pool closed), Booking advisable Jul-Aug, Last arrival 21.00hrs Last departure 11.00hrs

Budemeadows is set on a gentle sheltered slope in naturally landscaped parkland, surrounded by hedges. A 9-acre site with 144 touring pitches and 24 hardstandings.

Facilities: Table tennis, giant chess, baby changing facility 🍴 🔍 🛆 ⌂ 🎣 🛝 ⊙ 🎮 ✳ 🕐 🈶 🍴 🍻 🎍 ⅙ **Services:** 🍴 🚾 🔌 🚰 🛢 🚮 🛒 **Facilities found within 3 miles:** 🖰 ♨ 18 ⅙ 🖊 ◎ ⅙ 🔲 🈷

BUDE SS20

Wooda Farm Park ►►►►► 84%

Poughill EX23 9HJ

☎ 01288 352069 🖷 01288 355258

email: enquiries@wooda.co.uk

www.wooda.co.uk

Dir: *2m E. From A39 at edge of Stratton follow unclass road signed Coombe Valley/Poughill*

* 🚐 £10-£22 ⛺ £10-£22 ▲ £10-£22

Open: Apr-Oct (rs Apr-May & mid Sep-Oct shop & restaurant hours limited), Booking advisable Jul-Aug, Last arrival 20.00hrs Last departure noon

Attractive park overlooking Bude Bay. Sports hall, tennis court, playground, a bar and restaurant. A 25-acre site with 200 touring pitches, 60 hardstandings and 55 statics.

Facilities: Coarse fishing, clay pigeon shooting, pets corner 🔍 🛆 ⌂ 🎣 🛝 ⊙ 🎮 ✳ 🕐 🈶 🚻 🍴 🍻 🎍 **Services:** 🚾 🍴 🔌 🚰 🛒 🛢 🛒 🚮 🍴 🚰 🛒 **Facilities found within 3 miles:** 🖰 ♨ 18 ⅙ 🖊 ◎ ⅙ 🔲 🈷 **Notes:** Restrictions on certain breeds of dogs

BUDE SS20

Sandymouth Bay Holiday Park 72%

EX23 9HW

☎ 01288 352563 📠 01288 354822

www.dolphinholidays.co.uk

Dir: *Signed off A39 approx 0.5m S of Kilkhampton, 4m N of Bude*

* 🚐 £8.30-£16.80 🚐 £8.30-£16.80 ⛺ £8.30-£16.80

Open: Apr-Oct, Booking advisable Jul & Aug, Last arrival 22.00hrs Last departure 10.00hrs

A friendly holiday park with glorious and extensive sea views. This well kept park boasts many on-site facilities, and an extensive entertainment programme for all ages. A 24-acre site with 100 touring pitches and 158 statics.

Facilities: Sauna, solarium, crazy golf 🎣 🔍 ⛰ 🐾 ☉ 🍴 ☀ ⓢ 🗄 ♿ **Services:** 🚽 🍴 🚰 🔲 🔌 🛢 🗑 ⏚ 🛒 💧 **Facilities found within 3 miles:** ∪ ⚓ 18 ⚓ 🏌 ☇ 🗄 🏧 ⊗

BUDE SS20

Penstowe Caravan & Camping Park ▶▶▶▶ 79%

Stibb Road EX23 9QY

☎ 01288 321601 📠 01288 321601

email:

camping@penstowecaravans.wanadoo.co.uk

www.penstoweleisure.co.uk

Dir: *A39 4m N of Bude, turn left to Sandymouth, site 200yds on right*

Open: Open all year Booking advisable Aug, Last arrival 22.00hrs Last departure 10.00hrs

An all-touring park with quality facilities, about 2 miles from Sandymouth Bay. Visitors can use the adjoining Penstowe Leisure Club. Some of the amenities require a small membership charge. A 6-acre site with 140 touring pitches and 80 hardstandings.

Facilities: Sports facilities, tenpin bowling, green bowls 🎣 🏊 🔍 ⛰ 🐾 ☉ 🍴 ☀ ⓢ 🗄 🏧 📡 ♿ **Services:** 🚽 🍴 🚰 ⚡ 🔌 🛢 🛢 🗑 💧 **Facilities found within 3 miles:** ∪ ⚓ 18 ☇ 🗄 🏧

CORNWALL

BUDE   SS20

Upper Lynstone Caravan Park

►►► 74%

Lynstone EX23 0LP

☎ 01288 352017 🖹 01288 359034

email: reception@upperlynstone.co.uk

www.upperlynstone.co.uk

Dir: *0.75m S of Bude on coastal road to Widemouth Bay*

* 🚐 £8-£15 🚏 £8-£15 ▲ £8-£15

Open: Apr-Oct, Last arrival 22.00hrs Last departure 10.00hrs

Enjoy extensive views over Bude from this quiet family-run park set on sheltered ground. There is a small shop selling camping spares, and a children's playground. A path leads directly to the coastal footpath, and the old Bude Canal is a stroll away. A 6-acre site with 65 touring pitches and 41 statics.

Facilities: Baby changing room 🛆 🏳 ⊙ 🅿 ✻ 🕔 🖻 🛆 🕭 **Services:** 🖫 🖻 🖻 🗑 🛢 🖉 🖴

Facilities found within 3 miles: ∪ ♨ 18 ⊀ 🥅 ◎ ⅙ 🖻 🖻 **Notes:** No groups

CAMELFORD   SX08

Juliot's Well Holiday Park

►►► 73%

PL32 9RF

☎ 01840 213302 🖹 01840 212700

email: juliotswell@breaksincornwall.com

www.juliotswell.com

Dir: *Through Camelford, A39 at Valley Truckle turn right onto B3266, then 1st left signed Lanteglos, site 300yds on right*

Open: Mar-Oct, Booking advisable all year, Last arrival 20.00hrs Last departure 11.00hrs

Set in the wooded grounds of an old manor house, this quiet site enjoys lovely and extensive views across the countryside. A rustic inn on site offers occasional entertainment, and there is plenty to do, both on the park and in the vicinity. A 31-acre site with 60 touring pitches and 16 hardstandings.

Facilities: Putting green 🥀 🔍 🛆 🗄 🏳 ⊙ 🅿 ✻ 🕔 🖻 🛪 🕅 **Services:** 🐂 🛢 🖭 🖻 🖻 🎰

Facilities found within 3 miles: ∪ ♨ 18 🖻 🖻

CARLYON BAY   SX05
Carlyon Bay Caravan & Camping Park ▶▶▶▶ 83%
Bethesda Cypress Avenue PL25 3RE
☎ 01726 812735 📠 01726 815496
email: holidays@carlyonbay.net
www.carlyonbay.net
Dir: *Off A390 W of St Blazey, turn left onto A3092 for Par, right in 0.5m. On private road to Carlyon Bay*

* 🚐 £11-£20 🚐 £11-£20 ▲ £9-£18
Open: Etr-3 Oct (rs Etr-mid May & mid Sep-3 Oct swimming pool, take-away & shop closed), Booking advisable mid Jul-mid Aug, Last arrival 21.00hrs Last departure 11.00hrs
An secluded site set amongst trees. On-site attractions. Close to a sandy beach and the Eden Project is 2m away. A 35-acre site with 180 touring pitches and 6 hardstandings.
Facilities: Children's entertainment in Jul & Aug, crazy golf 🍽🏪Ⓜ🚻🚿♨️🔌🌂☕🍴🔥🛒🏧
🚽🚮 **Services:** 🅃🅿♨🛁🚰🗑🚐🚽🚿
Facilities found within 3 miles: ↻ ⚓ 18
🎣 🦮 ⊚ ⚓ 🗑🏧

COVERACK   SW71
Little Trevothan Caravan & Camping Park ▶▶▶ 74%
Trevothan TR12 6SD
☎ 01326 280260
email: sales@littletrevothan.co.uk
www.littletrevothan.co.uk
Dir: *From A3083 onto B3293 signed Coverack, approx 2m after Goonhilly ESS right at Zoar Garage on unclass road. Across Downs approx 1m then take 3rd left. Site 0.5m on left*

* 🚐 £9.50-£12 🚐 £9.50-£12 ▲ £9.50-£12
Open: Mar-Oct, Booking advisable Aug, Last arrival 21.00hrs Last departure noon
A secluded site near the unspoilt fishing village of Coverack, with a large recreation area. The nearby sandy beach has lots of rock pools for children to play in. A 10.5-acre site with 70 touring pitches and 40 statics.
Facilities: 🏪Ⓜ🚻♨️🔌🌂☕🍴🔥🛒🏧🚮🚽🏧
Services: 🅃🅿♨🛁🚰🚐 **Facilities found within 3 miles:** 🎣 🦮 🗑🏧 **Notes:** Dogs must be kept on a lead & waste picked up 🐕

CORNWALL

CRACKINGTON HAVEN   SX19

Hentervene Holiday Park ►►► 73%

Bude EX23 0LF

☎ 01840 230365

email: contact@hentervene.co.uk

www.hentervene.co.uk

Dir: *Exit A39 approx 10m SW of Bude (1.5m beyond Wainhouse Corner) onto B3263 signed Boscastle & Crackington Haven. 0.75m to Tresparret Posts junct, right signed Hentervene. Site 0.75 on right*

* ⚐ £8-£14 ⛺ £8-£14 ⛺ £8-£14

Open: Mar-Oct (rs Nov-Feb statics only), Booking advisable bank and school hols, Last arrival 21.00hrs Last departure 11.00hrs

Much improved park is set in in an Area of Outstanding Natural Beauty. Pitches are in paddocks bordered by hedges; some are on level terraces. A 4.5-acre site with 43 touring pitches, 9 hardstandings and 24 statics.

Facilities: Caravan storage, baby bathroom, microwave ♦ ⚐ ▢ ▨ ⊙ ℗✻ ⊙ 🖾 🚽 🍽

Services: 🔆 ⚐ 🖾 🛢 ⊘ **Facilities found within 3 miles:** ∪ ℘ ⤓ 🖾 🖾

CRANTOCK   SW76

Trevella Tourist Park ►►►► 80%

Newquay TR8 5EW

☎ 01637 830308 🖨 01637 830155

email: trevellapark@aol.com

www.trevella.co.uk

Dir: *Between Crantock & A3075*

* ⚐ £12.50-£18.40 ⛺ £11.50-£17.40

⛺ £9-£14.90

Open: Etr-Oct, Booking advisable BHs & Jul-Aug

A well established and very well run family site. Set in a rural area close to Newquay, it boasts three teeming fishing lakes for the experienced and novice angler, and a superb outdoor swimming pool and paddling area. All areas neat and clean. A 15-acre site with 313 touring pitches and 53 hardstandings.

Facilities: Crazy golf, badminton ✿ ♦ ⚐ ▢ ▨ ⊙ ℗✻ ⊙ 🖾 🚽 🍽 ♿ **Services:** 🔆 ⊤ ⚐ ⚐ 🖾 🛢 ⊘ 🍴 🏧 **Facilities found within 3 miles:** ∪ ⅃ 18 ⋔ ℘ ◎ ⤓ 🖾 🖾

CRANTOCK   SW76
Crantock Plains Touring Park
▶▶▶ 76%

Newquay TR8 5PH

☎ 01637 830955

www.crantock-plains.co.uk

Dir: *Leave Newquay on A3075, take 3rd right signed to park & Crantock. Park on left in 0.75m on narrow road*

Open: Etr-Oct, Booking advisable Jul-Aug, Last arrival 22.00hrs Last departure noon
A small rural park with pitches on either side of a narrow lane, surrounded by mature trees for shelter. The family-run park has modern toilet facilities appointed to a good standard. A 6-acre site with 60 touring pitches.

Facilities: ◐ ⚠ ◖ ⊙ ⦿ ⋇ ⊘ ▣ ⋔
Services: ◘ ▢ ▮ ⊘ ☎ **Facilities found within 3 miles:** ∪ ↓ 18 ⌁ ⊚ ⩥ ▢ ▣
Notes: ⊛

CRANTOCK   SW76
Higher Moor ▶▶▶ 82%

Treago Road Newquay TR8 5QS

☎ 01637 830928

Dir: *Turn off A3075 (Newquay to Redruth road) for Crantock. Follow brown signs for Treago, site 200mtrs beyond Treago Farm*

Open: Apr-Oct, Booking advisable Jul-Aug, Last arrival 23.00hrs Last departure 11.00hrs
On the edge of the extensive National Trust Cubert Common, this site is one of Cornwall's best kept secrets. It is tucked away from the main tourist areas, and has excellent toilet facilities. There are lovely beaches nearby. A 2-acre site with 22 touring pitches.

Facilities: ⚠ ◖ ⊙ ⋇ ▣ ⋔ ⅋ **Services:** ☎
⊷ **Facilities found within 3 miles:** ∪ ↓
18 ⌁ ⊚ ⩥ ▢ ▣ **Notes:** ⊛

CORNWALL

CORNWALL

EDGCUMBE SW73

Retanna Holiday Park ▶▶▶ 73%

Helston TR13 OEJ

☎ 01326 340643 📄 01326 340643

email: retannaholpark@lineone.net

www.retanna.co.uk

Dir: *100mtrs off A394, signed*

* 🚐 £11-£15 🚙 £11-£15 ⛺ £11-£15

Open: Apr-Sep, Booking advisable Jul & Aug, Last arrival 21.00hrs Last departure noon

A small family-owned and run park in a rural location between Falmouth and Helston. Its sheltered grassy pitches make this an ideal location for visiting the lovely beaches and towns nearby. An 8-acre site with 24 touring pitches, 2 hardstandings and 29 statics.

Facilities: Free use of fridge/freezer in laundry room 🔌 🗛 📁 🦮 ⊙ 🏳 ✳ 🕓 🖨 🛏 🎋 ♿ **Services:** 🇹 🚐 🛢 🍴 🚿 🛒 🚾 **Facilities found within 3 miles:** ∪ ♨ 18 ≒ 🔎 ◎ 🛥 🖫 🖻 **Notes:** No dogs allowed during school holidays

FALMOUTH SW73

Pennance Mill Farm Touring Park

▶▶▶ 74%

Maenporth TR11 5HJ

☎ 01326 317431 📄 01326 317431

www.pennancemill.co.uk

Dir: *From A39 (Truro-Falmouth) follow brown camping signs towards Maenporth Beach*

* 🚐 £4-£5 🚙 £4-£5 ⛺ £4-£5

Open: Etr-Xmas (rs Jan-Etr), Booking advisable Jan-Etr, Last arrival 22.00hrs Last departure 10.00hrs

Set approximately half a mile from the safe, sandy Bay of Maenporth this is a mainly level, grassy park in a rural location sheltered by mature trees and shrubs and divided into three meadows. It has a modern toilet block. A 6-acre site with 75 touring pitches, 8 hardstandings and 4 statics.

Facilities: 🔌 🗛 🕉 🦮 ⊙ 🏳 ✳ 🕓 🖨 🛏 **Services:** ⚡ 🚐 🛢 🍴 🚿 🚾 **Facilities found within 3 miles:** ∪ ♨ 12 ≒ 🔎 ◎ 🛥 🖫 🖻 **Notes:** 😊

GOONHAVERN SW75

Silverbow Park ▶▶▶▶ 80%

Perranwell TR4 9NX

☎ 01872 572347 📄 01872 572347

www.chycor.co.uk/parks/silverbow

Dir: *Adjacent to A3075, 0.5m S of village*

* 🚐 £8-£17 🚐 £8-£17 ▲ £8-£17

Open: May-mid Sep (rs mid Sep-Oct & Etr-mid May swimming pool & shop closed), Booking advisable Jun-Sep, Last arrival 22.00hrs Last departure noon

This park has a quiet garden atmosphere, and appeals to families with young children. The landscaped grounds and good quality toilet facilities - including four family rooms - are maintained to a very high standard. A 14-acre site with 100 touring pitches, 2 hardstandings and 15 statics.

Facilities: Badminton courts, short mat bowls rink 🛒 🔍 🗚 ⌂ ⅏ 🌳 ⊙ 🖭 ※ 🕓 ⓢ 🚻 ☴ 🖭 **Services:** 🔟 🚐 ⊠ 🔒 🗑 🖉 **Facilities found within 3 miles:** ∪ ⌀ 18 🖉 ⓢ ⓢ **Notes:** 🐾

GOONHAVERN SW75

Roseville Holiday Park ▶▶▶ 70%

Truro TR4 9LA

☎ 01872 572448 📄 01872 572448

www.rosevilleholidaypark.co.uk

Dir: *From mini-rdbt in Goonhavern follow B3285 towards Perranporth, site 0.5m on right*

* 🚐 £10-£18 🚐 £10-£18 ▲ £10-£18

Open: Whit-Oct (rs Apr-Jul, Sep-Oct shop closed), Booking advisable Jul-Aug, Last arrival 21.30hrs Last departure 11.00hrs

A family park set in a rural location with sheltered grassy pitches, some gently sloping. The toilet facilities are modern, and there is an outdoor swimming pool complex. 2 miles from the sandy beach at Perranporth. An 8-acre site with 95 touring pitches and 5 statics.

Facilities: Off-licence in shop 🛒 🔍 🗚 ⌂ ⊙ ⅏ ※ ⓢ 🚻 ⅋ **Services:** 🔟 🚐 ⊠ 🔒 🖉 ☴ **Facilities found within 3 miles:** ∪ ⌀ 18 🖉 ⊙ ⅊ ⓢ ⓢ **Notes:** Families only site 🐾

CORNWALL

CORNWALL

HAYLE   SW53
St Ives Bay
Holiday Park 75%

73 Loggans Road Upton Towans TR27 5BH
☎ 01736 752274 🖷 01736 754523
email: stivesbay@btconnect.com
www.stivesbay.co.uk
Dir: *Leave A30 at Hayle then immediate right onto B3301 at mini-rdbts. Park entrance 0.5m on left*
Open: May-1 Oct (rs Etr-1 May & 25 Sep-25 Oct no entertainment, food & bar service), Booking advisable Jan-Mar, Last arrival 23.00hrs Last departure 09.00hrs

Well maintained holiday park on sand dunes adjacent to a long beach. Touring section forms separate locations. Park is geared for families and couples. Large indoor swimming pool and two pubs. Dogs not allowed. A 90-acre site with 240 touring pitches and 250 statics.
Facilities: Crazy golf, video room 🍽 🔦 /Λ
⊡ ♨ 🐾 ⊙ 🅿 ✳ ⌚ 🖳 & **Services:** 🐦 🖳 T
🕿 🗑 🔋 🚿 ⛴ ⚒ **Facilities found within 3 miles:** ∪ ↨ 18 ⋄ 🗑 🗿 ⊗

HAYLE   SW53
Parbola Holiday Park ▶▶▶ 66%

Wall Gwinear TR27 5LE
☎ 01209 831503 🖷 01209 831503
email: bookings@parbola.co.uk
www.parbola.co.uk
Dir: *At Hayle rdbt on A30 take Connor Downs exit. In 1m turn right signed Carnhell Green. In village right to Wall. Site in village on left*
* 🚐 £11-£17.50 ▲ £11-£17.50
Open: Etr-Sep (rs Etr-end of Jun & Sep shop closed, unheated pool), Booking advisable Jul-Aug, Last arrival 21.00hrs Last departure noon

Pitches in woodland and open areas in this park. Handy for touring the area, especially Hayle with its golden sands. A 16.5-acre site with 110 touring pitches and 28 statics.
Facilities: Crazy golf & table tennis 🍽 🔦 /Λ
⊡ 🐾 ⊙ 🅿 ✳ ⌚ 🗑 🖳 & **Services:** T 🔋 🗑
🔋 ⋄ ⛴ **Facilities found within 3 miles:** ∪ ↨ 9 ⋄ ◎ 🗑 🗿 **Notes:** Dogs not allowed Jul-Aug

HAYLE SW53

Treglisson Camping & Caravan Park ►►► 74%

Wheal Alfred Road TR27 5JT

☎ 01736 753141

email: enquiries@treglisson.co.uk

www.treglisson.co.uk

Dir: *4th exit off rdbt on A30 at Hayle. 100mtrs, turn left at 1st mini-rdbt. 1.5km past golf course, site sign on left*

* ⊞ £11-£13.50 ⊟ £11-£13.50

▲ £11-£13.50

Open: Etr-Oct, Booking advisable Jul-Aug, Last arrival 20.00hrs Last departure 11.00hrs

A small secluded site in a wooded meadow. Has a modern toilet block and level grass pitches, and is just 2 miles from the beach at Hayle. A 3-acre site with 30 touring pitches.

Facilities: Tourist information, milk deliveries 🖥 🅰 🄵 ⊙ 🅿 ✻ ⊙ 🚽 🎗 ♿

Services: 🗲 🗑 🛢 **Facilities found within 3 miles:** 🛦 12 🖉 🛶 🗑 🗿 **Notes:** Max 6 people to a pitch, dogs must be on lead at all times 🐕

HOLYWELL BAY SW75

Trevornick Holiday Park 90%

Newquay TR8 5PW

☎ 01637 830531 📄 01637 831000

email: info@trevornick.co.uk

www.trevornick.co.uk

Dir: *3m from Newquay off A3075 towards Redruth. Follow Cubert & Holywell Bay signs*

* ⊞ £10.75-£18.30 ⊟ £10.75-£18.30

▲ £10.75-£18.30

Open: Etr & mid May-mid Sep, Booking advisable Jul-Aug, Last arrival 21.00hrs Last departure 10.00hrs

A seaside holiday complex with entertainment, including children's club and evening cabaret. 15-minute walk to sandy beach. The park has 68 ready-erected tents for hire. A 20-acre site with 593 touring pitches and 6 hardstandings.

Facilities: Fishing, golf course 🖥 🅽 🄵 🄵 ⊙ 🅿 ✻ ⊙ 🖲 🚽 🎗 ♿ **Services:** 🗲 🖬 🗑 🝙 🗑 🗑 🗑 🝙 🛢 🅰 ⊘ 🛒 ♨ **Facilities found within 3 miles:** Ʊ 🛦 18 🛶 🖉 ◎ 🛶 🗑 🗿 **Notes:** Families and couples only

CORNWALL

CORNWALL

HOLYWELL BAY SW75

Holywell Bay Holiday Park 71%

Newquay TR8 5PR

☎ 01637 871111 📄 01637 850818

email: enquiries@parkdeanholidays.co.uk

www.parkdeanholidays.co.uk

Dir: *Leave A30 onto A392, take A3075 signed Redruth, then right in 2m signed Holywell/Cubert. Follow road through Cubert past Trevornick to park on left*

* 🚐 £10-£28 ⇌ £10-£28 ▲ £7-£25

Open: Mar-Oct, Booking advisable High season, Last arrival 21.00hrs Last departure 10.00hrs

Close to lovely beaches, this level grassy park borders on National Trust land. It has an outdoor pool with a waterslide. A 40-acre site with 56 touring pitches and 162 statics.

Facilities: Live family entertainment & children's club 🍴 🅰 🅡 ⊙ ⊕ 📷 🚻 ♿

Services: 🔌 🚽 🚰 📷 🛢 🖊 🚽 🧺 Facilities found within 3 miles: ∪ ♣ 18 ♬ ◎ 🛶 🛢 🏧 ⊗

INDIAN QUEENS SW85

Gnome World Caravan & Camping Site ►►► 70%

Moorland Road TR9 6HN

☎ 01726 860812 📄 01726 860812

Dir: *Signed from slip road at A30 & A39 rdbt in village of Indian Queens - park on old A30, now unclass road*

* 🚐 £7-£9 ⇌ £7-£9 ▲ £7-£9

Open: Open All Year (rs Nov-Mar Statics closed), Booking advisable Jul-Aug, Last arrival 22.00hrs Last departure noon

Set in open countryside, this spacious park is set on level grassy land only 0.5m from the A30 (Cornwall's main artery route), in a central holiday location for touring the county. There are no narrow lanes to negotiate. A 4.5-acre site with 50 touring pitches and 60 statics.

Facilities: Nature trail 🅰 🅡 ⊙ ⊕ 🚻 ♿

Services: 🔌 🛢 🧺 Facilities found within 3 miles: ∪ ♣ 🛢 🏧 **Notes:** Dogs must be kept on leads

KENNACK SANDS SW71
Gwendreath Farm Holiday Park

► ► ► 72%

Ruan Minor Helston TR12 7LZ

☎ 01326 290666

email: tom.gibson@virgin.net

www.tomandlinda.co.uk

Dir: *From A3083 turn left past Culdrose Naval Air Station onto B3293. Right past Goonhilly Earth Station signed Kennack Sands, left in 1m. At end of lane turn right over cattle grid. Right, through Seaview to 2nd reception*

Open: Etr-Oct, Booking advisable all times, Last arrival 21.00hrs Last departure 10.00hrs A grassy park in an elevated position with extensive sea and coastal views, and the beach just a short walk through the woods. Campers can use the bar and takeaway at an adjoining site. A 5-acre site with 10 touring pitches and 21 statics.

Facilities: ⚠ ⏁ ⊙ ⁕ ⏀ ⇥ ≡ ⋒ **Services:** ⌸ ⎃ ⛊ ⌂ ⊘ ≐ **Facilities found within 3 miles:** ∪ ℘ ⍪ �ℱ **Notes:** ⊛

KENNACK SANDS SW71
Chy-Carne Holiday Park ► ► ► 70%

Kuggar Ruan Minor TR12 7LX

☎ 01326 290547

email: enquiries@chy-carne.co.uk

www.chy-carne.co.uk

Dir: *From A3083 turn left on B3293 after Culdrose Naval Air Station. At Goonhilly ESS right onto unclass road signed Kennack Sands. Left in 3m at junct*

* ⌸ £14-£16 ⛺ £14-£16 ▲ £5-£6

Open: Etr-Oct, Booking advisable Aug, Small but spacious park in quiet, sheltered spot, with extensive sea and coastal views from the grassy touring area. A village pub with restaurant is a short walk by footpath from the touring area, and a sandy beach is less than 0.5 miles away. A 6-acre site with 14 touring pitches and 18 statics.

Facilities: ◆ ⚠ ⏁ ⊙ ⁕ ⁕ ⏀ ⛊ ⇥ ⋒ ⛟ **Services:** ⌸ ⎃ ⛊ ⌂ ⊘ ≐ **Facilities found within 3 miles:** ∪ ⌁ 18 ℘ ◎ ⛊

CORNWALL

KILKHAMPTON SS21

Tamar Lake ▶▶ 72%

Upper Tamar Lake Bude

☎ 01288 321712

www.swlakestrust.org.uk

Dir: *From A39 at Kilkhampton onto B3254, left in 0.5m onto unclass road, follow signs approx 4m to site*

Open: 31 Mar-Oct, Booking advisable

A slightly sloping site overlooking the lake and surrounding countryside, with several signed walks. The site benefits from the excellent facilities provided for the watersports centre and coarse anglers, with a rescue launch on the lake when the flags are flying. A good family site, with Bude's beaches and surfing waves only 8m away. A 2-acre site with 36 touring pitches.

Facilities: Watersports centre, canoeing, sailing, windsurfing 🛝 🚿 💨 ☎ 🍖 🪑 ♿ **Services:** ☕ 🍽 👶 🛒 **Facilities found within 3 miles:** 🐎 ⛳ ⛵ 🐟 🏄 [S] **Notes:** Dogs must be kept on a lead

LAND'S END SW32

Sea View Holiday Park ▶▶▶ 85%

Sennen TR19 7AD

☎ 01736 871266 📠 01736 871190

email: bookings@seaview.co.uk

www.seaview.org.uk

Dir: *From Penzance follow A30/Land's End signs to Sennen, through village until First & Last pub, site on left*

* 🚐 £13 🚌 £14 ⛺ £13

Open: Open All Year (rs Sep-Mar coffee shop closed, pool unheated), Booking advisable Jul-Aug, Last arrival 18.30hrs Last departure 10.00hrs

A countryside park with sea views and plenty of facilities. A 11.5-acre site with 180 touring pitches, 6 hardstandings and 95 statics.

Facilities: 🏊 🏓 🛝 📺 🚼 🚿 🔌 💨 ❄ ☎ [S] 🍖 🪑 ♿ **Services:** ☕ 🍽 🍷 [T] ⬇ 🚐 🧺 🛢 🍃 🛒 **Facilities found within 3 miles:** 🐎 ⛳ ⛵ 🐟 🎯 🏄 🧺 [S] 🚫 **Notes:** Family park, dogs only with permission

LANIVET   SW06

Mena Caravan & Camping Site

▶▶▶ 78%

Mena Farm Bodmin PL30 5HW

☎ 01208 831845

email: mena@campsitesincornwall.co.uk

www.campsitesincornwall.co.uk

Dir: *Exit A30 at Innes Downs rdbt onto A391 signed St Austell. 0.5m 1st left, then 0.75m turn right (before bridge) signed Fowey/Lanhydrock. 0.5m to staggered junct & monument stone, sharp right, 0.5m down hill, right into site*

🚐 £8-£12 🚗 £8-£12 ▲ £8-£12

Open: Etr-Sep, Booking advisable Jul-Aug, Last arrival 22.00hrs Last departure noon
Set in a secluded location with hedges for shelter. Grassy site is 4 miles from the Eden Project. Has a small coarse fishing lake. A 4-acre site with 25 touring pitches and 2 statics.

Facilities: ♦ ⋔ ⋒ ⊙ ✳ ♿ 🖛 ⤢ ᕫ **Services:** 🔌 ⏚ 🚽 **Facilities found within 3 miles:** ∪ ⅃ 18 ⌷ 🗄 **Notes:** ⊛

LEEDSTOWN   SW53

Calloose Caravan & Camping Park

▶▶▶ 81%

Hayle TR27 5ET

☎ 01736 850431 📠 01736 850431

email: calloose@hotmail.com

www.calloose.co.uk

Dir: *From Hayle take B3302 to Leedstown, turn left opposite village hall, before entering village. Park 0.5m on left at bottom of hill*

* 🚐 £7-£13 🚗 £7-£13 ▲ £7-£13

Open: Mar-Nov, Xmas & New Year (rs Mar-mid May & late Sep-Nov swimming pool closed), Booking advisable Etr, May bank hols & Jun-Aug, Last arrival 22.00hrs Last departure 11.00hrs
A well equipped leisure park in a remote rural setting. Offers clean facilities. A 12.5-acre site with 120 touring pitches and 17 statics.

Facilities: Crazy golf, skittle alley ⇆ ♦ ⋔ ⬜ ☌ ⋒ ⊙ ✳ ⊛ 🖛 ⤢ ♿ **Services:** 🔌 ⏚ 🚽 ⏚ 🗄 🖋 ⤢ ⚑ **Facilities found within 3 miles:** ⌷ 🗄 🗄

CORNWALL

CORNWALL

LOOE SX25

Tencreek Holiday Park 68%

Polperro Road PL13 2JR

☎ 01503 262447 📠 01503 262760

email: reception@tencreek.co.uk

www.dolphinholidays.co.uk

Dir: *Take A387 1.25m from Looe. Site on left*

* 🚐 £8.90-£13.50 🚌 £8.90-£13.50
▲ £8.90-£13.50

Open: Open All Year Booking advisable Jul & Aug, Last arrival 23.00hrs Last departure 10.00hrs

Set in a rural position with countryside and sea views, this park has family entertainment, indoor and outdoor pools, an adventure playground and a children's club. A 14-acre site with 254 touring pitches and 101 statics.

Facilities: Nightly entertainment, solarium, 45mtr pool flume 🎯🏊‍♀️🏪🏧🏕️🔆🛒🍴🕐🛁🖊️ 🚻♿ **Services:** 💧🚽🚾🔌🍴🗑️♨️🛒🚮 **Facilities found within 3 miles:** ∪⚓18 ⛳🎣◎⛵🏕🕹️🎱 **Notes:** Families & couples only

LOOE SX25

Tregoad Park ▶▶▶ 80%

St Martin's PL13 1PB

☎ 01503 262718 📠 01503 264777

email: tregoadfarmccp@aol.com

www.cornwall-online.co.uk/tregoad

Dir: *Signed with direct access from B3253, or from E on A387 follow B3253 for 1.75m towards Looe. Site on left*

* 🚐 £13.50-£21.50 🚌 £13.50-£21.50
▲ £7.50-£14.50

Open: Etr-Jan (rs Bistro open in high and mid season), Booking advisable Jul & Aug, Last arrival 21.00hrs Last departure 11.00hrs

A terraced park with sea and rural views. Level pitches. There is a bar with meals served in the conservatory. A 55-acre site with 200 touring pitches, 60 hardstandings and 3 statics.

Facilities: Fishing lake, crazy golf 🎯🏊‍♀️🏪 🏧🏕🔆🛒🍴🕐🛁🖊️🚻♿ **Services:** 🍴 🔌🚾🔌🗑️♨️🛒🚮 **Facilities found within 3 miles:** ∪⚓9⛳🎣◎⛵🏕🎱

LOOE   SX25

Talland Caravan Park ►►► 72%

Talland Bay PL13 2JA

☎ 01503 272715 🖹 01503 272224

email: tallandcaravan@btconnect.com

www.tallandcaravanpark.co.uk

Dir: *1m from A387 on unclass road to*
Talland Bay

* 🚐 £9-£16 🚌 £7.50-£14 ▲ £7-£16

Open: Apr-Oct, Booking advisable School
hols, Last arrival 20.00hrs Last departure
noon

Overlooking the sea just 300 yards from
Talland Bay's two beaches, this quiet park
has an elevated touring area with sea views.
Surrounded by unspoilt countryside and with
direct access to the coastal footpath, it is
halfway between Looe and Polperro. A 4-acre
site with 80 touring pitches and 46 statics.

Facilities: 🍴 🛁 🕼 ☉ 🅿 ✳ 🕔 🖄 ⚓ 🚑 ♿
Services: 🍴 🔧 🅣 🕼 🖄 🗑 ⊘ 🚽 🚰 🛒
Facilities found within 3 miles: ⚓ 18 ⚓
🎣 🚴 🗑 🇸

LOSTWITHIEL   SX05

Powderham Castle Tourist Park
►►► 77%

Nr Lostwithiel PL30 5BU

☎ 01208 872277

email: powderhamcastletp@tiscali.co.uk

www.powderhamcastletouristpark.co.uk

Dir: *1.5m SW of Lostwithiel on A390 turn*
right at brown/white sign in 400mtrs

Open: Etr or Apr-Oct, Booking advisable Jul-
Aug, Last arrival 22.00hrs Last departure
11.30hrs

A grassy park set in attractive paddocks with
mature trees. Facilities are being upgraded,
buildings and grounds are well maintained.
This park is ideal for visiting the Eden Project,
the nearby golden beaches and sailing at
Fowey. A 12-acre site with 72 touring pitches,
12 hardstandings and 38 statics.

Facilities: Badminton, soft tennis, putting
green ⚓ 🛁 🕼 ☉ 🅿 ✳ 🕔 ⚓ ♿ **Services:**
🕼 🖄 🗑 ⊘ 🚰 **Facilities found within 3**
miles: ↻ ⚓ 18 ⚓ 🎣 ◎ 🚴 🗑 🇸 **Notes:** 🐾

CORNWALL

CORNWALL

LUXULYAN SX05

Croft Farm Holiday Park ▶▶▶ 75%

Bodmin PL30 5EQ

☎ 01726 850228 📠 01726 850498

email: lynpick@ukonline.co.uk

www.croftfarm.co.uk

Dir: *Leave A30 at Bodmin for A391 towards St Austell. In 7m left at double rdbt onto unclass road towards Luxulyan/Eden Project, continue to T-junct, turn left signed Luxulyan. Park 1m on left. (NB Do not approach any other way as roads are very narrow)*

🚐 £9.60-£13.80 🚍 £9.60-£13.80

⛺ £6.60-£13.80

Open: Etr-Oct, Booking advisable Jul & Aug, Last arrival 18.00hrs Last departure noon

A peaceful 5-acre site with 52 touring pitches, 15 hardstandings and 38 statics.

Facilities: Mother/baby room, info centre, microwave, freezer 🔌 ⚠ 🏕 ⊙ ℗ ✳ 🕐 🛢 🖮

🛏 **Services:** 🆃 🚐 🛢 🛢 🥛 🍴 **Facilities found within 3 miles:** ∪ 🅿 🛢 **Notes:** Dogs must be kept on leads, no smoking in buildings/caravans/cottages

MAWGAN PORTH SW86

Sun Haven Valley Holiday Park

▶▶▶▶ 75%

Newquay TR8 4BQ

☎ 01637 860373 📠 01637 860373

email: sunhaven@hotmail.co.uk

www.sunhavenvalley.co.uk

Dir: *From B3276 in Newquay take Padstow road. Right onto unclass road just after shopping complex. Park in 1.75m*

* 🚐 £10-£17.50 🚍 £10-£17.50

⛺ £10-£17.50

Open: Apr-Oct (rs Oct-Mar chalets only), Booking advisable Jul-Aug, Last arrival 22.00hrs Last departure 10.30hrs

Attractive site with level pitches on the side of a river valley. Offers a TV lounge, games room and adventure playground. A 5-acre site with 118 touring pitches and 36 statics.

Facilities: 🔌 ⚠ 🔲 🏕 ⊙ ℗ ✳ 🕐 🛢 🖮 ♿ **Services:** 🆃 🚐 🛢 🥛 **Facilities found within 3 miles:** ∪ ⚓ 18 🅿 ◎ 🛢 🛢 **Notes:** Families and couples only

MAWGAN PORTH SW86

Trevarrian Holiday Park ▶▶▶ 74%

Newquay Cornwall TR8 4AQ

☎ 01637 860381

email: holiday@trevarrian.co.uk

www.trevarrian.co.uk

Dir: *From A39 at St Columb rdbt turn right onto A3059 towards Newquay. Fork right in approx 2m for St Mawgan onto B3276. Turn right, site on left*

* ⊕ £7.20-£14.20 ⊕ £7.20-£14.20
Å £7.20-£14.20

Open: Etr-Sep, Booking advisable Jun-Aug, Last arrival 22.00hrs Last departure 11.00hrs
A well-established and well-run holiday park overlooking Mawgan Porth beach. This park has a wide range of attractions including a free entertainment programme in peak season. A 7-acre site with 185 touring pitches.

Facilities: Sports field, pitch 'n' putt ⊕ ●
⋒ □ ⊗ ⋔ ⊙ ℗ ※ ⊙ ⑤ **Services:** ☎ ⊟ Ⓣ
⊕ ⑤ ⌸ ∅ ⌸ **Facilities found within 3 miles:** ∪ ⌶ 18 ∜ ℘ ◎ ⑤ ⑤

MEVAGISSEY SW94

Sea View International Caravan & Camping Park ▶▶▶▶▶ 96%

Boswinger PL26 6LL

☎ 01726 843425 ▤ 01726 843358

email: holidays@seaviewinternational.com

www.seaviewinternational.com

Dir: *From St Austell take B3273 signed Mevagissey. Turn right before entering village. Follow brown tourist signs to site*

* ⊕ £6-£27 ⊕ £6-£27 Å £6-£27

Open: Mar-Oct, Booking advisable Jul-Sep, Last arrival 21.00hrs Last departure 11.00hrs
An attractive holiday park overlooking Veryan Bay. Offers an outstanding holiday experience, with luxury family pitches, refurbished shop and takeaway. A 28-acre site with 189 touring pitches, 13 hardstandings and 38 statics.

Facilities: Crazy golf, volleyball, badminton, cycle hire ⊕ ● ⋒ ⊗ ⋔ ⊙ ℗ ※ ⊙ ⑤ ⌸ 声 ⊟ ☶
⊛ **Services:** Ⓣ ⊕ ⊕ ⑤ ∅ ⇔ **Facilities found within 3 miles:** ≑ ℘ ◎ ≑ ⑤ ⑤

Notes: Restrictions on certain dog breeds

CORNWALL

CORNWALL

MULLION SW61

Mullion Holiday Park 74%

Ruan Minor TR12 7LJ

☎ 01326 240428 📠 01326 241141

email: bookings@weststarholidays.co.uk

www.weststarholidays.co.uk

Dir: *A30 onto A39 through Truro towards Falmouth. A394 to Helston, A3083 for The Lizard. Park 7m on left*

* 🚐 £12.50-£30 🚛 £12.50-£30 ▲ £12.50-£30

Open: 21 May-10 Sep (rs 24 Mar-20 May & 11 Sep-Oct no camping or caravans), Booking advisable Jul-Aug & bank holidays, Last arrival 22.00hrs Last departure 10.00hrs Geared mainly for self-catering holidays, this park offers entertainment, and indoor and outdoor pools. A 49-acre site with 150 touring pitches, 8 hardstandings and 347 statics.

Facilities: Adventure playground, scuba diving, football pitch 🍴🍴🔍🏔️🗄️📶☉ 🎦※🕙📱🕇🍴🗑️♿ **Services:** 🛒🎙️🖥️⬆️📵🔋🏧 🔓🗑️🕌 **Facilities found within 3 miles:** ∪⚓9🏌️◎⛵🛢️💲

NEWQUAY SW86

Hendra Holiday Park 80%

TR8 4NY

☎ 01637 875778 📠 01637 879017

email: enquiries@hendra-holidays.com

www.hendra-holidays.com

Dir: *A30 onto A392 signed Newquay. At Quintrell Downs over rdbt, signed Lane, 0.5m on left*

* 🚐 £9.45-£15.48 🚛 £9.45-£15.48 ▲ £9.45-£15.48

Open: Apr-Oct (rs Apr-Spring bank hol outdoor pool closed), Booking advisable Jul-Aug, Last arrival dusk Last departure 10.00hrs 60-acre site with superb facilities. 600 touring pitches, 28 hardstandings and 283 statics.

Facilities: Solarium, fish bar, kids' club, train rides, evening entertainment during high season 🍴🍴🔍🏔️🗄️🍴☉🎦※🕙🛢️🕇🍴 🍴♿ **Services:** 🛒🎙️🖥️⬆️📵🔋🛢️🗑️🕌🕌 🕌 **Facilities found within 3 miles:** ∪⚓ 18🏌️🏌️◎⛵🛢️💲 **Notes:** Families and couples only

NEWQUAY SW86

Newquay Holiday Park 75%

TR8 4HS

☎ 01637 871111 📠 01637 850818

email: enquiries@parkdeanholidays.co.uk

www.parkdeanholidays.co.uk

Dir: *From Bodmin on A30, under low bridge, turn right towards RAF St Mawgan. Take A3059 towards Newquay, site past Treloy Golf Club*

* 🚐 £12-£30 🚙 £10-£28 ⋀ £7-£25

Open: Mar-Oct, Booking advisable at all times, Last arrival 21.00hrs Last departure 10.00hrs

Well-maintained park with indoor and outdoor activities. Three heated outdoor pools and a waterslide. A 60-acre site with 196 touring pitches, 10 hardstandings and 262 statics.

Facilities: Snooker, 9-hole pitch & putt, family entertainment 🛒 🍴 ⋀ ⏹ 🎨 ☉ 🍽 ✳ 🕓 🖂 🚿 🎣 ⛴ & **Services:** 🍴 🍷 ⏹ 🚐 🔋 🛢 🧹 📯 🛒 **Facilities found within 3 miles:** ∪ 🛳 18 ✳ 🖊 🗒 🗒

NEWQUAY SW86

Trencreek Holiday Park ►►►► 75%

Hillcrest Higher Trencreek TR8 4NS

☎ 01637 874210 📠 01637 874210

email: trencreek@btconnect.com

www.trencreekholidaypark.co.uk

Dir: *A392 to Quintrell Downs, turn right towards Newquay, left at 2 mini-rdbts into Trevenson Road to park*

* 🚐 £9.90-£14.10 🚙 £9.90-£14.10 ⋀ £9.90-£14.10

Open: Whit-mid Sep (rs Etr, Apr-May & late Sep swimming pool, cafe & bar closed), Booking advisable Jul-Aug, Last arrival 22.00hrs Last departure noon

A landscaped park with two fishing lakes and licensed clubhouses. A 10-acre site with 194 touring pitches, 8 hardstandings and 6 statics.

Facilities: Free coarse fishing on site 🛒 🎣 ⋀ ⏹ 🎨 ☉ 🍽 ✳ 🕓 🖂 🍴 🚿 🎣 & **Services:** 🍷 🍴 ⏹ 🚐 🔋 🛢 🧹 🛒 📯 **Facilities found within 3 miles:** ∪ 🛳 18 ✳ 🖊 ◎ 🍽 🗒 🗒 🚫

Notes: Families and couples only 🐾

CORNWALL

NEWQUAY SW86
Riverside Holiday Park ►►► 68%
Gwills Lane TR8 4PE
☎ 01637 873617 📄 01637 877051
email: info@riversideholidaypark.co.uk
www.riversideholidaypark.co.uk
Dir: A30 onto A392 signed Newquay. At
Quintrell Downs cross rdbt signed Lane. 2nd
left in 0.5m onto unclass road signed Gwills.
Park in 400yds
* 🚐 £9-£16 🚏 £9-£16 ▲ £9-£16
Open: Mar-Dec, Booking advisable Jul-Aug,
Last arrival 22.00hrs Last departure 10.00hrs
A sheltered valley beside a river is the idyllic
setting for this lightly wooded park. The fairly
simple facilities are being gradually upgraded,
and the park caters for families and couples
only. An 11-acre site with 100 touring pitches
and 65 statics.
Facilities: Fishing 🛶 🔦 🛖 🗂 🗄 🕎 ⊙ 🅿 ✹ ◷
🗄 🛏 **Services:** 🍴 🗂 🛢 🖕 📦 🍴 ⌂ 🍺
Facilities found within 3 miles: ∪ ₺ 18
🏌 🎣 ◎ 🛶 🗄 🗄 **Notes:** Families and couples
only

NEWQUAY SW86
Treloy Touring Park ►►► 79%
TR8 4JN
☎ 01637 872063 📄 01637 872063
email: treloy.tp@btconnect.com
www.treloy.co.uk
Dir: Off A3059 (St Columb Major-Newquay
road)
* 🚐 £8-£13.50 🚏 £8-£13.50 ▲ £8-£13.50
Open: 25 May-15 Sep (rs Apr & Sep pool,
takeaway, shop & bar closed), Booking
advisable Jul-Aug, Last arrival 21.00hrs Last
departure 10.00hrs
Attractive site with countryside views, within
easy reach of beaches. Pitches are set in four
paddocks with mainly level but some slightly
sloping grassy areas. A 12-acre site with 175
touring pitches and 24 hardstandings.
Facilities: Concessionary green fees for
golf, entertainment 🛶 🔦 🛖 🗂 🗄 🕎 ⊙ 🅿 ✹ ◷
🗄 🛏 ♿ **Services:** 🍺 🍴 🗂 🛢 🖕 📦 🍴 ⌂ 🍺
Facilities found within 3 miles: ∪ ₺ 9 🏌
🎣 🛶 🗄 🗄

NEWQUAY SW86

Trethiggey Touring Park ▶▶▶ 75%

Quintrell Downs TR8 4QR

☎ 01637 877672 📠 01637 879706

email: enquiries@trethiggey.co.uk

www.trethiggey.co.uk

Dir: *From A30 take A392 signed Newquay at Quintrell Downs rdbt, turn left onto A3058 past pearl centre to site 0.5m on left*

* 🚐 £9-£13.60 🚛 £9-£13.60 ▲ £9-£13.60

Open: Mar-Dec, Booking advisable Jul-Aug, Last arrival 22.00hrs Last departure 10.30hrs A family-owned park in a rural setting, ideal for touring this part of Cornwall. Pleasantly divided into paddocks with maturing trees and shrubs, and offering coarse fishing and tackle hire. A 15-acre site with 145 touring pitches, 35 hardstandings and 12 statics.

Facilities: Off licence, recreation field, fishing ♦ 🛒 ♀ 🌳 ⊙ 🅿 ✳ ⊙ 📷 ⛏ 🍴 🏪 🗛 ♿

Services: 🐎 📺 ♻ 🚐 🗑 🥖 🍴 🏪

Facilities found within 3 miles: ∪ ↓ 18 ⛳ 🌊 ⊙ 🎣 🗑 🗿

NEWQUAY SW86

Trebellan Park ▶▶▶ 71%

Cubert TR8 5PY

☎ 01637 830522 📠 01637 830277

email: treagofarm@aol.com

www.treagofarm.co.uk

Dir: *4m S of Newquay, turn W off A3075 at Cubert sign. Left in 0.75m onto unclass road*

* 🚐 £13-£17 🚛 £13-£17 ▲ £10-£14

Open: May-Oct, Booking advisable Jul-Aug, Last arrival 21.00hrs Last departure 10.00hrs A terraced grassy rural park within a picturesque valley with views of Cubert Common, and adjacent to the Smuggler's Den, a 16th-century thatched inn. This park has excellent coarse fishing on site. An 8-acre site with 150 touring pitches and 7 statics.

Facilities: ♦ 🛒 ♀ 🌳 ⊙ 🅿 ✳ ⊙ 🗛 ♿

Services: 🐎 🗑 🍴 **Facilities found within 3 miles:** ∪ ↓ 18 ⛳ ⊙ 🌊 🗑 🗿 **Notes:** Families and couples only

CORNWALL

CORNWALL

OTTERHAM   SX19
St Tinney Farm Holidays ▶▶▶ 73%
Cornwall PL32 9TA
☎ 01840 261274
email: info@st-tinney.co.uk
www.st-tinney.co.uk
Dir: *Signed 1m off A39 via unclass road*
signed Otterham
* 🚐 £10 ▲ £10
Open: Etr-Oct (rs Nov-Etr self catering lodges
only), Booking advisable Spring BH & Jul-
Aug, Last arrival 21.00hrs Last departure
10.00hrs
A family-run farm site in a rural area with
nature trails, lakes, valleys and offering
complete seclusion. Visitors are free to walk
around the farmland lakes and lose
themselves in the countryside. A 34-acre site
with 20 touring pitches and 15 statics.
Facilities: Coarse fishing, wi-fi 🛁🔌🏪🛖
⊙🅿☀🕒🚿🚻🚃 **Services:** 🚰🍴🔥🚐🛢
🔒⌀🚮♿ Facilities found within 3
miles: ∪⚓🖉💲

PADSTOW   SW97
Padstow Holiday Park ▶▶ 74%
Cliffdowne PL28 8LB
☎ 01841 532289 📠 01841 532289
email: alex@cliffdowne.freeserve.co.uk
www.padstowholidaypark.co.uk
Dir: *On B3274/A389 into Padstow. Signed*
1.5m before Padstow
* 🚐 £9.50-£13 🚍 £9.50-£13 ▲ £9.50-£13
Open: Mar-Dec, Booking advisable at all
times, Last arrival 17.00hrs Last departure
noon
A mainly static park with some touring pitches
in a small paddock and others in an open
field. This quiet holiday site can be reached
from Padstow (1m away) by a footpath. A
5.5-acre site with 27 touring pitches and 74
statics.
Facilities: 🏔🏪⊙🅿☀🕒🚃 **Services:** 🔲
🚐🛢🍴⌀ Facilities found within 3
miles: ∪⚓18⚓🖉◎⛴🛢🚿⊗ **Notes:**
🐾

PENTEWAN SX04

Penhaven Touring Park ▶▶▶ 67%

St Austell PL26 6DL

☎ 01726 843687 📄 01726 843870

email: enquiries@penhaventouring.co.uk

www.penhaventouring.co.uk

Dir: *S from St Austell on B3273 towards Mevagissey. Site on left 1m after village of London Apprentice*

* 🚐 £7.80-£18.50 🚏 £7.80-£18.50

Å £7.80-£18.50

Open: Apr-Oct, Booking advisable public hols & end Jul-Aug, Last arrival 21.00hrs Last departure 10.00hrs

An open park in a wooded valley with a river running past. The beach at Pentewan, a mile away, can be accessed by a footpath and cycle path along the river bank. A 13-acre site with 105 touring pitches and 12 hardstandings.

Facilities: Off-licence 🍴 🅼 🏳 ☺ 🍴❄ 🕓 🔒 ♨ 🕭 **Services:** 🖵 🖦 🚗 🔋 🍴 🧺 🎣 🏕 🚿 **Facilities found within 3 miles:** ♨ 18 🎣 🎿 ♨ 🔒 🔒

PENTEWAN SX04

Pentewan Sands Holiday Park 78%

St Austell PL26 6BT

☎ 01726 843485 📄 01726 844142

email: info@pentewan.co.uk

www.pentewan.co.uk

Dir: *On B3273 4m S of St Austell*

* 🚐 £9.95-£23.95 🚏 £9.95-£23.95

Å £9.95-£23.95

Open: Apr-Oct (rs Apr-14 May & 15 Sep-Oct some facilities closed), Booking advisable May-Sep, Last arrival 22.00hrs Last departure 10.30hrs

A large holiday park with a wide range of amenities, set on grassy pitches beside a private beach. A club on site offers evening entertainment. A 32-acre site with 500 touring pitches and 120 statics.

Facilities: Cycles, boat launch, water sports, caravan store 🍴 🅼 🏳 🅂 🏳 ☺❄ 🕓 🔒 ♨ **Services:** 🍴 🖷 🖵 🖦 🚗 🔋 🍴 🧺 🏕 🚿 **Facilities found within 3 miles:** ∪ ♨ 18 🎿 ♨ ◎ 🔒 🔒 🔒 ⊗ **Notes:** No jet skis

CORNWALL

CORNWALL

PENTEWAN SX04
Sun Valley Holiday Park

▶▶▶▶▶ 82%

Pentewan Road PL26 6DJ

☎ 01726 843266 🖨 01726 843266

email: reception@sunvalleyholidays.co.uk

www.sunvalleyholidays.co.uk

Dir: *From St Austell take B3273 towards Mevagissey. Park is 2m on right*

Open: Apr (or Etr if earlier)-Oct, Booking advisable May-Sep, Last arrival 22.00hrs Last departure noon

In a picturesque valley amongst woodland, this neat park is kept to an exceptionally high standard. The extensive amenities include tennis courts, indoor swimming pool, licensed clubhouse and restaurant. The sea is 1m away, and can be accessed via a footpath and cycle path along the river bank. A 20-acre site with 22 touring pitches and 75 statics.

Facilities: ☜ ♠ ⚠ ♨ ♩ ⊙ ℗ ✷ ◐ 🗑 ➤ ⊞

Services: 🌢 🍴 ⚕ ♻ 🗑 ⬧ ☷ ⛪

Facilities found within 3 miles: ∪ ♨ 18 ♪ 🗑 🗑

PERRANPORTH SW75
Perranporth Camping & Touring Park ▶▶▶ 69%

Budnick Road TR6 0DB

☎ 01872 572174 🖨 01872 572174

Dir: *0.5m E off B3285*

* 🚐 £4-£5 🚐 £4-£5 ⛺ £4-£5

Open: Whit-Sep (rs Etr-Whit & mid-end Sep shop & club facilities closed), Booking advisable Jul-Aug, Last arrival 23.00hrs Last departure noon

A mainly tenting site with few level pitches, located high above a fine sandy beach which is much-frequented by surfers. The park is attractive to young people, and is set in a lively town on a spectacular part of the coast. A 6-acre site with 120 touring pitches, 4 hardstandings and 9 statics.

Facilities: ☜ ♠ ⚠ ⬚ ♩ ⊙ ℗ ✷ ◐ 🗑 ➤ ⛪

& Services: 🍴 Ⓣ ♻ 🗑 ⬧ ⬧ ☷ ⛪

Facilities found within 3 miles: ∪ ♨ 18 ⫟ ♪ ◎ 🌢 🗑 🗑

PERRANPORTH SW75
Perran Sands Holiday Park 75%

Truro TR6 0AQ

☎ 01872 573742 📠 01872 571158

www.havenholidays.com

Dir: *A30 onto B3285 towards Perranporth. Park on right before descent on hill into Perranporth*

Open: mid Mar-Oct (rs mid Mar-May & Sep-Oct some facilities may be reduced), Booking advisable school hols, Last arrival 22.00hrs Last departure noon

Nestling amid 500 acres of dune grassland, and with a footpath through to the surf and 3 miles of golden sandy beach, this lively park is set in a large village-style complex. It offers a complete range of on-site facilities and entertainment for all the family. A 550-acre site with 335 touring pitches and 395 statics.

Facilities: 🚿 ⬅ ⚠ ⋔ ⊙ ☂ ※ ⊙ 🎁 ⅏ &

Services: 🌿 🗕 ⅏ ∪ ⬚ 🛢 ⊶ 🚮 ♨ **Facilities found within 3 miles:** ∪ ♨ ⅍ ℓ ◎ ⅍ ⬚

PERRANPORTH SW75
Tollgate Farm Caravan & Camping Park ►►► 84%

Budnick Hill TR6 0AD

☎ 01872 572130

email: enquiries@tollgatefarm.co.uk

www.tollgatefarm.co.uk

Dir: *Off A30 onto B3285 to Perranporth. Site on right 1.5m after Goonhavern*

* 🚐 £9.50-£14 �"£9.50-£14 ▲ £9.50-£14

Open: Etr-Oct, Booking advisable Jul-Aug, Last arrival 21.00hrs Last departure 11.00hrs

A quiet site in a rural location with spectacular coastal views. Pitches are divided into four paddocks sheltered by hedges. Children will enjoy the play equipment and pets corner. The 3 miles of sand at Perran Bay are a walk away through the sand dunes. A 10-acre site with 102 touring pitches and 10 hardstandings.

Facilities: ⚠ ⋔ ⊙ ☂ ※ ⊙ 🎁 ⅏ 🚮 ♨ ⅏ &

Services: 🆃 🗕 ⅏ 🛢 ⍼ 🚐 ⊶ 🚮 ♨ **Facilities found within 3 miles:** ∪ ♨ 18 ⅍ ℓ ◎ ⅍ ⬚ ⬚ **Notes:** No large groups

CORNWALL

CORNWALL

POLPERRO SX25

**Killigarth Manor
Holiday Centre** 69%

PL13 2JQ

☎ 01503 272216 📠 01503 272065

email: killigarthmanor@breathemail.net

www.killigarth.co.uk

Dir: *From A38 at Trerulefoot rdbt onto A387, through Looe, over bridge signed Polperro. In 3.5m left past shelter/phone box. Park 400yds*

* 🚐 £8.75-£13.10 🚊 £8.75-£13.10 ▲ £8.75-£13.10

Open: Etr-Oct, Booking advisable 3rd wk Jul-Aug, Last arrival 20.00hrs Last departure noon

Large holiday centre offering a wide variety of leisure activities. A 7-acre site with 202 touring pitches and 147 statics.

Facilities: Amusement arcade, pool table, table tennis 🏕️ ❀ 🅰️ 🖵 🔆 🌂 ⊙ 𝒫 ✳️ ◐ ⑂ ⊣

🞢 ♿ **Services:** 🐷 🛒 🔲 📁 🗃 🗄 ⊘ 🍴 🏺

Facilities found within 3 miles: ∪ ↧ 18 🞢 𝒫 🗄 🗄 🛇

POLZEATH SW97

South Winds Caravan & Camping Park ►►► 74%

Polzeath Road PL27 6QU

☎ 01208 863267 📠 01208 862080

email: info@southwindcampsite.co.uk

www.rockinfo.co.uk

Dir: *Exit B3314 onto unclass road signed Polzeath, park on right just past turn to New Polzeath*

* 🚐 £20-£30 🚊 £20-£30 ▲ £12-£30

Open: Mar-Oct, Booking advisable Jul & Aug & school hols, Last arrival 21.00hrs Last departure 10.30hrs

A peaceful site 0.75m from beach and village. Within walking distance of a golf complex. A 16-acre site with 100 touring pitches.

Facilities: 🅰️ 🔆 ⊙ 𝒫 ✳️ ◐ 🗃 ⑂ 🞢 🞡 ♿

Services: 🐷 🍴 🔲 ⚡ 🗄 🗄 ⊘ 🍴

Facilities found within 3 miles: ∪ ↧ 18 🞢 𝒫 ◎ 🞡 🗄 🗄 **Notes:** No disposable BBQs, no noise 23.00hrs-07.00hrs, dogs on leads at all times, families & couples only

CORNWALL

REDRUTH SW64

Cambrose Touring Park ▶▶▶ 71%

Portreath Road TR16 4HT

☎ 01209 890747

email: cambrosetouringpark@supanet.com

www.cambrosetouringpark.co.uk

Dir: *A30 onto B3300 towards Portreath. Approx 0.75m at 1st rdbt right onto B3300. Take unclass road on right signed Porthtowan. Site 200yds on left*

* 🚐 £8.50-£13.50 🚌 £8.50-£13.50
▲ £8.50-£13.50

Open: Apr-Oct, Booking advisable Jul-Aug, Last arrival 22.00hrs Last departure 11.30hrs
Situated in a rural setting surrounded by trees and shrubs, this park is divided into grassy paddocks. About two miles from the harbour village of Portreath. A 6-acre site with 60 touring pitches.

Facilities: Mini football pitch 🍴 🔥 🏧 📶 ☺ 🅿️❋ ⓦ 🚿 🚻 🔥 **Services:** 🗂 🔌 🔧 🛢 🚮 🧺 🏧 **Facilities found within 3 miles:** ∪ ⚓ 18 🏌 ◎ 🚣 🗿 🗿 **Notes:** 🐾

REDRUTH SW64

Lanyon Holiday Park ▶▶▶ 74%

Loscombe Lane Four Lanes TR16 6LP

☎ 01209 313474

email: jamierielly@btconnect.com

www.lanyonholidaypark.co.uk

Dir: *Signed 0.5m off B2397 on Helston side of Four Lanes village*

Open: Mar-Oct, Booking advisable Jul & Aug, Last arrival 21.00hrs Last departure noon

Small, friendly rural park in an elevated position with fine views to distant St Ives Bay. This family owned and run park is being upgraded in all areas, and is close to a cycling trail. Stithian's Reservoir for fishing, sailing and windsurfing is two miles away. A 14-acre site with 25 touring pitches and 49 statics.

Facilities: Take-away service, all-day games room 🍴 🔥 🏧 🗂 🔧 ☺ 🅿️❋ 🚿 🔥 🚻 🏧 **Services:** 🍴 📶 🔌 🔧 🛢 🧺 🏧 **Facilities found within 3 miles:** ∪ ⚓ 18 🏊 🏌 ◎ 🚣 🗿 🗿

CORNWALL

REJERRAH SW85

Newperran Holiday Park

▶▶▶▶ 82%

Newquay TR8 5QJ

☎ 01872 572407 📠 01872 571254

email: holidays@newperran.co.uk

www.newperran.co.uk

Dir: *4m SE of Newquay & 1m S of Rejerrah on A3075. Or A30 Redruth, turn off B3275 Perranporth, at 1st T-junct turn right onto A3075 towards Newquay, site 300mtrs on left*

* 🚐 £9-£14.90 🚗 £9-£14.90 ⛺ £9-£14.90

Open: Etr-Oct, Booking advisable Jul-Aug, Last arrival midnight Last departure 10.00hrs

A family site in a rural position near several beaches and bays. Pitches are in paddocks on level ground, some screened. Country inn and café. A 25-acre site with 366 touring pitches, 18 hardstandings and 5 statics.

Facilities: Crazy golf, adventure playground & pool 🏊 🔍 ⛺ 🛝 ☺ ⛳ ✳ ☎ [S] 🐕 🍖 ♿

Services: ☕ 🍷 [T] 💬 🧺 🔒 🍃 🛏 🧺

Facilities found within 3 miles: U ⛳ 18 🏄 🎣 ◎ 🚤 🧺 [S]

REJERRAH SW85

Monkey Tree Holiday Park 76%

Scotland Road Newquay TR8 5QR

☎ 01872 572032 📠 01872 573577

email: enquiries@monkeytreeholidaypark.co.uk

www.monkeytreeholidaypark.co.uk

Dir: *Exit A30 onto B3285 to Perranporth, 0.25m right into Scotland Rd, site on left in 1.5m*

* 🚐 £7-£11.90 🚗 £7-£11.90 ⛺ £7-£11.90

Open: Open All Year Booking advisable Jul & Aug, Last arrival 22.00hrs Last departure 10.00hrs

A busy holiday park with plenty of activities and a holiday atmosphere. Close to beaches, it has an outdoor swimming pool, playground, two bars, a restaurant and a takeaway. A 56-acre site with 505 touring pitches.

Facilities: Sauna, solarium, mntn bike hire, football pitch 🏊 🔍 ⛺ 🛝 ☺ ✳ ☎ [S] 🐕 🍖 🪑 ♿

Services: ☕ 🍷 [T] ⚓ 💬 🧺 🔒 🍃 🛏 🧺

Facilities found within 3 miles: U ⛳ 18 🎣 ◎ 🚤 [S]

Notes: Family park

REJERRAH SW85

Perran-Quay Tourist Park ►►► 72%

Hendra Croft Newquay TR8 5QP

☎ 01872 572561 📄 01872 575043

email: rose@perran-quay.co.uk

www.perran-quay.co.uk

Dir: *Direct access off A3075 behind Braefel Inn*

* 🚐 £10-£26 🚍 £10-£24 ⅄ £7-£22

Open: Open All Year (rs winter shop closed), Booking advisable Jul-Aug, Last departure 10.00hrs

A friendly family-run site set in paddocks with mature trees and shrubs for shelter. The park has its own pub, and is close to the sandy beach at Holywell Bay. With its swimming pool and quiet surroundings, it is well liked by families. An 8.5-acre site with 110 touring pitches, 2 hardstandings and 16 statics.

Facilities: 🛶 🗚 🏕 �🅿✻ 🕚 🖻 ⅃ **Services:** 🐟 🖈 🍽 🔲 🖾 🖸

Facilities found within 3 miles: ∪ ⅃ 18 🎣 ◎ 🛥 🖻 🖾

SCORRIER SW74

Wheal Rose Caravan & Camping Park ►►► 78%

Wheal Rose Truro TR16 5DD

☎ 01209 891496

email: les@whealrosecaravanpark.co.uk

www.whealrosecaravanpark.co.uk

Dir: *Exit A30 at Scorrier sign, follow signs to Wheal Rose. Park 0.5m on left, Wheal Rose to Porthtowan road*

* 🚐 £7.50-£13 🚍 £7.50-£13 ⅄ £7.50-£13

Open: Mar-Dec, Booking advisable Aug, Last arrival 21.00hrs Last departure 11.00hrs

A peaceful park in a secluded valley setting, central for beaches and countryside. Bright toilet block. A 6-acre site with 50 touring pitches, 6 hardstandings and 4 statics.

Facilities: 🛶 🗚 🗚 🏕 �◎ 🅿✻ 🕚 🖻 🖾 ⅃

Services: 🔲 🐟 🖸 🖾 🖋 🛶 **Facilities found within 3 miles:** ∪ ⅃ 18 🎣 🖻 🖸 **Notes:** 5mph speed limit, dogs on leads, minimum noise after 23.00hrs, gates locked 23.00hrs 🐾

CORNWALL

CORNWALL

ST AUSTELL SX05

Trencreek Farm Country Holiday Park ►►► 67%

Hewas Water PL26 7JG

☎ 01726 882540 ▤ 01726 883254

email: reception@trencreek.co.uk

www.surfbayholidays.co.uk

Dir: *4m SW of St Austell on A390, fork left onto B3287. Continue for 1m, park is on left*

* ▭ £8.95–£15.50 ⛺ £8.95–£15.50

▲ £7–£13.50

Open: Mar-Oct (rs Mar-May, Sep-Oct various restrictions), Booking advisable Jul-Aug, Last arrival 21.00hrs Last departure noon

A 56-acre rural site, with 184 touring pitches, 18 hardstandings and 37 statics. Organised children's activities in summer holidays.

Facilities: 4 coarse fishing lakes, farm animals ⛵ ♦ ▦ ▢ ⦿ ☼ ⊙ ⊛ 🔥 ☎ 🍴 ♿

Services: 🕯 🛒 ⊤ 🔌 🔥 🏧 ⊘ 🍴 ♨

Facilities found within 3 miles: ∪ ♨ 18

🛶 🔵 ⓢ **Notes:** Under 15s must be accompanied by an adult around and in pool

ST AUSTELL SX05

Trewhiddle Village Holiday Park

►►► 75%

Pentewan Road PL26 7AD

☎ 01726 879420 ▤ 01726 879421

email: dmcclelland@btconnect.com

www.trewhiddle.co.uk

Dir: *Take B3273 from St Austell towards Mevagissey. Site 0.75m from rdbt on right*

* ▭ £9–£18 ⛺ £9–£18 ▲ £9–£18

Open: Open All Year Booking advisable Jul & Aug,

Secluded wooded site with well-kept gardens, lawns and flower beds, set in the grounds of a mature estate. The Trewhiddle Pub is right in the centre of the park. This park has now changed hands, and the owners plan to upgrade the facilities. A 16.5-acre site with 105 touring pitches and 74 statics.

Facilities: Beauty salon & fast tan sunbed ⛵ ♦ ▦ ⦿ ⊙ ⊛ 🔥 ☎ ♨ **Services:** 🕯 🛒 🔌 🏧 🔥 ⊘ ♨ **Facilities found within 3 miles:** ∪ ♨ 18 ✏ ⓢ

ST AUSTELL SX05
River Valley Holiday Park

▶▶▶▶ 83%

London Apprentice PL26 7AP

☎ 01726 73533 📄 01726 73533

email: river.valley@tesco.net

www.cornwall-holidays.co.uk

Dir: *Direct access to park signed on B3273 from St Austell at London Apprentice*

🚐 £10-£25 🚍 £10-£25 ▲ £10-£25

Open: end Mar-end Sep, Booking advisable Jul-Aug, Last arrival 22.00hrs Last departure 11.00hrs

A neat, well-maintained family-run park set in a pleasant river valley. The quality toilet block and attractively landscaped grounds make this a delightful base for a holiday. A 2-acre site with 45 touring pitches and 40 statics.

Facilities: Cycle trail to beach 🏖 🍴 🗛 📶 ☉ 🄿 ✳ 🕙 🖫 🛏 ⅋ **Services:** 🗭 🖥 🛒

Facilities found within 3 miles: ↯ 18 ≷ 𝒫 ≋ 🖥 🖻

ST AUSTELL SX05
Old Kerrow Farm Holiday Park

▶▶▶ 75%

Stenalees PL26 8GD

☎ 01726 851651 📄 01726 852826

email: oldkerrowfarmholidaypark@hotmail.com

www.oldkerrowfarmholidaypark.co.uk

Dir: *Exit A30 at Innis Downs rdbt onto A391 to Bugle. Left at lights onto unclassified road. Site on right approx 1m just after sign for Kerrow Moor*

* 🚐 £10-£19 🚍 £10-£19 ▲ £10-£19

Open: Open All Year Booking advisable at all times, Last departure 14.00hrs

An improving park on a former working farm. The touring area is divided into two paddocks - one for dog owners with an extensive dog walk. Cycle hire; cycle track to the nearby Eden Project. A 20-acre site with 50 touring pitches and 11 hardstandings.

Facilities: 🗛 📶 ☉ 🄿 ✳ 🕙 🖫 🛏 🛒 🍴 ⅋

Services: 🍺 🍴 🗭 📶 🗍 🖥 🗐 ⊘ 🖳 🛒 🛒 🍺

Facilities found within 3 miles: ∪ ↯ 𝒫 🖥 🖻 **Notes:** No noise as peaceful location

CORNWALL

CORNWALL

ST AUSTELL SX05
Court Farm Holidays ►► 75%

St Stephen PL26 7LE

☎ 01726 823684 🖹 01726 823684

email: truscott@ctfarm.freeserve.co.uk

www.courtfarmcornwall.co.uk

Dir: *From St Austell take A3058 towards Newquay. Through St Stephen (pass Peugeot garage). Right at 'St Stephen/Coombe Hay/Langreth/Industrial site' sign. 400yds, site on right*

* ⛽ £10-£15 ⛺ £12.50-£17.50

▲ £8.50-£17.50

Open: Apr-Sep, Booking advisable Jul-mid Sep, Last arrival by dark Last departure 11.00hrs

Set in a peaceful location, this large camping field is handy for Eden Project. Coarse fishing and use of a large telescope . A 4-acre site with 20 touring pitches and 5 hardstandings.
Facilities: Astronomy lectures 𝕄 📶 ⊙⚹ 🛒 ᚛ **Services:** 🚽 🚮 ⚡ **Facilities found within 3 miles:** ∪ ⌕ 18 🅿 🛒 🛒 **Notes:** No noisy behaviour after dark

ST COLUMB MAJOR SW96
Southleigh Manor Naturist Park
►►► 77%

TR9 6HY

☎ 01637 880938 🖹 01637 881108

email: enquiries@southleigh-manor.com

Dir: *Leave A30 at sign to RAF St Mawgan onto A3059. Park 3m on left*

* ⛽ £19-£22.50 ⛺ £19-£22.50

▲ £19-£22.50

Open: Etr-Oct (rs Shop open peak times only), Booking advisable Jun-Aug, Last arrival 20.00hrs Last departure 11.00hrs

A well maintained naturist park in the heart of the Cornish countryside, catering for families and couples only. Seclusion and security are well planned, and the gardens provide a calm setting. A 4-acre site with 50 touring pitches.
Facilities: Sauna, spa bath, pool table, putting green ⚓ 𝕄 📶 ⊙ 📶⚹ ⊙ 🛒 🛒 **Services:** 🍲 🍴 Ⓣ 🚽 🛒 🚮 ⊘ 🍴 **Facilities found within 3 miles:** ∪ ⌕ 9 🅿 🛒 🛒
Notes: Naturist site ⊛

ST ISSEY   SW97

Trewince Farm Holiday Park

►►► 79%

Wadebridge PL27 7RL

☎ 01208 812830 📠 01208 812835

email: holidays@trewincefarm.fsnet.co.uk

Dir: *From Wadebridge on A39 take A389*
signed Padstow. Site 2m on left

* 🚐 £8.60 🚍 £8.60 ▲ £8.60

Open: Etr-Oct, Booking advisable anytime,
Last departure 11.00hrs

Set amongst rolling farmland close to the
coast, this park is part of a working farm, and
set in well landscaped grounds. It offers good
facilities in a comfortable and friendly
atmosphere, and is only three miles from
Padstow. A 6-acre site with 120 touring
pitches and 35 statics.

Facilities: Crazy golf, farm rides in summer,
near Camel Trail 🚣 🔦 ⋒ ⋒ ☉ ⓟ ✳ ◔ 🔥 🚽
🚿 🚻 ♿ **Services:** 🚽 🔋 🔜 🚮 ⌀ 🚑 **Facilities
found within 3 miles:** ∪ 🎣 18 🚤 ℘ 🚇

ST IVES   SW54

Ayr Holiday Park ►►►► 85%

Cornwall TR26 1EJ

☎ 01736 795855 📠 01736 798797

email: recept@ayrholidaypark.co.uk

www.ayrholidaypark.co.uk

Dir: *From A30 follow St Ives 'large vehicles'*
route via B3311 through Halsetown onto
B3306. Park signed towards St Ives town
centre

* 🚐 £13-£24 🚍 £13-£24 ▲ £13-£24

Open: Open All Year Booking advisable Jun-
Aug, Last arrival 22.00hrs Last departure
10.00hrs

This park overlooks St Ives Bay and has a
heated toilet block for winter holidaying.
Stunning views from most pitches. Harbour
and beach are 0.5m away. A 4-acre site with
40 touring pitches and 20 hardstandings.

Facilities: 🔦 ⋒ ⋒ ☉ ⓟ ✳ ◔ 🔥 🚻 ♿
Services: ⊤ ↻ 🚽 🔋 🔜 🚮 ⌀ 🚑 **Facilities
found within 3 miles:** ∪ 🎣 18 🚤 ℘ 🚤
🚇

CORNWALL

CORNWALL

ST IVES   SW54
Polmanter Tourist Park
▶▶▶▶▶ 85%

Halsetown TR26 3LX

☎ 01736 795640 📠 01736 793607

email: reception@polmanter.com

www.polmanter.com

Dir: *Signed off B3311 at Halsetown*

* ⚏ £13.50-£25 ⚏ £13.50-£25 ▲ £11-£20

Open: Whit-10 Sep (rs Mar-Whit & 12 Sep-Oct shop, pool, bar & takeaway food closed), Booking advisable Jul-Aug, Last arrival 21.00hrs Last departure 10.00hrs
Polmanter offers high quality in all areas, from the immaculate toilet blocks to the outdoor swimming pool and hard tennis courts. Pitches are sited in meadows. The port and beaches of St Ives are just 1.5m away. A 20-acre site with 240 touring pitches and 10 hardstandings.

Facilities: Putting, sports field, 7 family shower rooms ⚎ ♠ ⚏ ⚑ ⚐ ⊙ ⚒ ⚘ ◷ ⚐ ⇥
⚒ **Services:** ⦿ ⚒ Ⓣ ⇩ ⚑ ◎ ⊘ ⚒ 🚽 ⚏
Facilities found within 3 miles: ∪ ⚓ 18
⚒ ℘ ◎ ⚒ ◷ ⚏

ST IVES   SW54
Trevalgan Touring Park ▶▶▶ 79%

Trevalgan TR26 3BJ

☎ 01736 796433 📠 01736 798797

email: recept@trevalgantouringpark.co.uk

www.trevalgantouringpark.co.uk

Dir: *From A30 follow holiday route to St Ives.*
B3311 through Halsetown to B3306. Left
towards Land's End. Site signed 0.5m on right

* ⚏ £12-£18 ⚏ £12-£18 ▲ £12-£18

Open: Jun-Aug (rs Apr-May & Sep shop & takeaway closed), Booking advisable mid Jul-Aug, Last arrival 22.00hrs Last departure 10.00hrs

An open park next to a working farm. The park is surrounded by mature hedges, but there are sea views. It has good toilet facilities, family rooms, and a TV lounge and recreation room. A 4.9-acre site with 120 touring pitches.

Facilities: Farm trail, crazy golf ♠ ⚏ ⚐ ⚑
⊙ ⚒ ⚘ ◷ ⚐ ⚒ ⇥ **Services:** ⚒ Ⓣ ⇩ ⚑ ⚏
⚒ ◎ 🚽 ⚏ **Facilities found within 3**
miles: ∪ ⚓ 9 ⚒ ℘ ⚒ ◷ ⚏

ST IVES   SW54

Little Trevarrack Tourist Park

▶▶▶ 82%

Laity Lane Carbis Bay TR26 3HW

☎ 01736 797580

email: littletrevarrack@hotmail.com

www.littletrevarrack.co.uk

Dir: *A30 onto A3074 signed 'Carbis Bay & St Ives'. Left opposite turn to beach. 150yds, over x-rds, site 2nd on right*

🚐 £12-£19.50 🚛 £12-£19.50 ▲ £12-£19.50

Open: Etr-Oct (rs Etr-Whit, mid Sep-Oct games room & swimming pool closed), Booking advisable summer hols, Last arrival 21.30hrs Last departure 10.00hrs

A pleasant grass park set in countryside but close to beaches and amenities. A 20-acre site with 200 touring pitches and 20 statics.

Facilities: Sports area, recycling ⛱ ❀ ⚠ ☂ ☉ ☞☀ ☮ ☇ & **Services:** ☎ ☏ ☒ ☖ ⊘ ⚓

Facilities found within 3 miles: ∪ ♨ 18 ☌ ☌ ◎ ♨ ☖ ☖

ST IVES   SW54

Penderleath Caravan & Camping Park ▶▶▶ 76%

Towednack TR26 3AF

☎ 01736 798403

email: holidays@penderleath.co.uk

www.penderleath.co.uk

Dir: *From A30 take A3074 towards St Ives. Left at 2nd mini-rdbt, approx 3m to T-junct. Left then immediately right. Left at next fork*

* 🚐 £11.50-£22.50 🚛 £11.50-£22.50 ▲ £11.50-£22.50

Open: Etr-Oct, Booking advisable Jul-Aug, Last arrival 21.30hrs Last departure 10.30hrs

Set in a rugged rural location, this tranquil park has views towards St Ives Bay. There is a bar with beer garden, breakfast room and bar meals. A 10-acre site with 75 touring pitches.

Facilities: Takeaway food ❀ ⚠ ☂ ☉ ☞☀ ☇ ☖ & **Services:** ☉ ☎ ☏ ☒ ☖ ⊘ ☱ ☷

Facilities found within 3 miles: ∪ ♨ 18 ☌ ☌ ◎ ♨ ☖ ☖ **Notes:** Dogs must be well behaved & kept on lead ☺

CORNWALL

CORNWALL

ST JUST SW33
[NEAR LAND'S END]
Trevaylor Caravan & Camping Park
▶▶▶ 74%
Botallack Penzance TR19 7PU
☎ 01736 787016
email: bookings@trevaylor.com
www.trevaylor.com
Dir: *On B3306 (St Just -St Ives road), site on right 0.75m from St Just*
* ♠ £7-£11 ♠ £7-£11 ▲ £7-£11
Open: Fri before Etr-Oct, Booking advisable Jul & Aug, Last departure noon
A sheltered grassy site located off the beaten track in a peaceful location at the western tip of Cornwall. The dramatic coastline and the pretty villages nearby are truly unspoilt. Clean, well-maintained facilities and a good shop are offered along with a bar serving bar meals. A 6-acre site with 50 touring pitches.
Facilities: ♠ ⚑ ⚑ ⊙ ⅋ ✱ ⅏ ⅏ ⅏
Services: ⚑ ⚑ ⊺ ⅏ ⅏ ⅏ ⅏ ⅏ ⅏
Facilities found within 3 miles: ⅃ 18 ⅌
⊚ ⅏ ⅏ **Notes:** ⅏

ST JUST SW33
[NEAR LAND'S END]
Roselands Caravan Park ▶▶▶ 75%
Dowran TR19 7RS
☎ 01736 788571
email: camping@roseland84.freeserve.co.uk
www.roselands.co.uk
Dir: *From A30 Penzance bypass turn right for St Just on A3071. 5m, turn left after tin mine chimney at sign, follow signs to park*
* ♠ £9-£11.50 ♠ £9-£11.50 ▲ £7-£9
Open: Etr-Oct, Booking advisable Jun-Sep, Last arrival 21.00hrs Last departure 11.00hrs
A small, friendly park in a sheltered rural setting, an ideal location for a quiet family holiday. The owners are continuing to upgrade the park, and in addition to the attractive little bar there is an indoor games room, children's playground, and good toilet facilities. A 3-acre site with 15 touring pitches and 15 statics.
Facilities: Cycle hire ♠ ⚑ ⚑ ⊙ ⅋ ✱ ⊚ ⅏
⅌ ⅏ **Services:** ⅏ ⚑ ⊺ ⅏ ⅏ ⅏ ⅏ ⅏
Facilities found within 3 miles: ∪ ⅃ 18
⅌ ⅏ ⅏ **Notes:** ⅏

ST JUST-IN-ROSELAND   SW83

Trethem Mill Touring Park

►►► 87%

Nr St Mawes Truro TR2 5JF

☎ 01872 580504 🖹 01872 580968

email: reception@trethem.com

www.trethem.com

Dir: *From Tregony on A3078 to St Mawes.*
2m after Trewithian, follow signs to park

* ⊟ £11-£16 ⇌ £11-£16 ▲ £11-£16

Open: Apr-Oct, Booking advisable Jul-Aug,
Last arrival 21.00hrs Last departure 11.00hrs
A quality park, with upgraded amenities
including a reception, shop, laundry, and
disabled/family room. This carefully-tended
and sheltered park is in a lovely rural setting,
with spacious pitches separated by young
trees and shrubs. The very keen family who
own it are continually looking for ways to
enhance its facilities. An 11-acre site with 84
touring pitches and 15 hardstandings.
Facilities: Information centre ⚠ ↾ ☺ ℘✕
🕲 🖆 ⇥ & **Services:** ⊤ ⅃ ⊕ 🖸 🖻 ⊘ 🛲 ⛽
⚖ ℘ ⚖ 🖸 💲

ST MABYN   SX07

Glenmorris Park ►►► 79%

Longstone Road Bodmin PL30 3BY

☎ 01208 841677 🖹 01208 841514

email: info@glenmorris.co.uk

www.glenmorris.co.uk

Dir: *S of Camelford on A39, left after BP*
garage onto B3266 to Bodmin, 6m to
Longstone, right at x-rds to St Mabyn, site
approx 400mtrs on right

* ⊟ £10.20 ⇌ £10.20 ▲ £10.20

Open: Etr-Oct (rs Etr-mid May & mid Sep-
Nov swimming pool closed), Booking
advisable Jul-Aug (all year for statics), Last
arrival 23.30hrs Last departure 10.30hrs
A very good, mainly level park in a peaceful
rural location, offering a small games room,
heated outdoor pool, and shop. An 11-acre
site with 80 touring pitches and 11 statics.
Facilities: ⚖ ↾ ⚠ ↾ ☺ ℘✕ 🕲 🖆 ⊓ &
Services: ⊤ ⊕ 🖸 🖻 ⊘ **Facilities found**
within 3 miles: ∪ ⅃ 9 ℘ 💲 **Notes:** Quiet
after 22.00hrs

CORNWALL

ST MERRYN   SW87

**Carnevas Holiday Park & Farm
Cottages ▶▶▶▶** 76%

Carnevas Farm PL28 8PN

☎ 01841 520230 📄 01841 520230

email: carnevascampsite@aol.com

www.carnevasholidaypark.co.uk

Dir: *From St Merryn on B3276 towards
Porthcothan Bay. Approx 2m turn right at site
sign onto unclass road opposite Tredrea Inn.
Site 0.25m on right*

* 🚐 £7.50-£14 🚏 £7.50-£14 ▲ £7.50-£14

Open: Apr-Oct (rs Apr-Whit & mid Sep-Oct
shop, bar & restaurant closed), Booking
advisable Jul-Aug

A family-run park on a working farm, divided
into four paddocks on slightly sloping grass.
Licensed bar serving bar meals. An 8-acre
site with 195 touring pitches and 14 statics.

Facilities: 2 family bathrooms 🔦 🗚 🅿 ⊙
🅟✻ ⓒ 🗟 ⊷ 🕭 **Services:** 🕯 ⊷🗐 ⓣ 🖭 🗟 🛒
⊘ 🍴 **Facilities found within 3 miles:** ∪
♨ 18 🄿 ⇲ 🗟 🗟 **Notes:** ☺

ST MERRYN   SW87

**Trevean Caravan & Camping Park
▶▶▶** 74%

Trevean Lane PL28 8PR

☎ 01841 520772 📄 01841 520772

email: trevean.info@virgin.net

Dir: *From St Merryn take B3276 to Newquay
for 1m. Turn left for Rumford. Site 0.25m on
right*

🚐 £8-£12 🚏 £8-£12 ▲ £8-£12

Open: Apr-Oct (rs Shop open Whit-Sep),
Booking advisable mid Jul-Aug, Last arrival
22.00hrs Last departure 11.00hrs

A small working farm site with level grassy
pitches in open countryside. The toilet
facilities are clean and well kept, and there is
a laundry and good children's playground. A
1.5-acre site with 36 touring pitches.

Facilities: 🗚 🅿 ⊙ 🅟✻ ⓒ 🗟 🕭 🕭 🕭
Services: 🖭 🗟 🛒 ⊘ 🍴 🛒 **Facilities found
within 3 miles:** ∪ ♨ 18 ≉ 🄿 ◎ 🗟 🗟
Notes: No teenage groups ☺

ST MERRYN   SW87

Point Curlew Chalet & Touring Park ▶▶▶ 69%

St Merryn PL28 8PY

☎ 01841 520855 📠 01841 521413

email: sales@pointcurlewholidays.co.uk

www.pointcurlewholidays.co.uk

Dir: *Take B3274 towards Padstow. In 3m turn left onto unclass road to St Merryn, follow brown signs to park*

* 🚐 £12-£20 🚍 £12-£20 ▲ £12-£20

Open: Open All Year Booking advisable end Jun-early Sep, Last arrival 24.00hrs Last departure noon

This park is set in a quiet rural spot yet only two miles from seven popular bays. Free entertainment in high season, also children's fun nights, and a quiet bar. A 4.5-acre site with 70 touring pitches and 220 statics.

Facilities: 🔌 ⚠ ❑ ⋒ ⦿ ⊖ ℗ ✳ ① 🛉 🛒 🚻 ♿

Services: 🍴 🍲 ⊡ ⊠ **Facilities found within 3 miles:** ∪ ⚓ 18 ⤴ 🕭 ◎ ⇘ ⊠ ⊠ ⊗

Notes: No pets

ST MERRYN   SW87

Harlyn Sands Holiday Park 76%

Lighthouse Rd Trevose Head PL28 8SQ

☎ 01841 520720 📠 01841 521251

email: harlyn@freenet.co.uk

www.harlynsands.co.uk

Dir: *Exit B3276 in St Merryn centre onto unclassified road towards Harlyn Sands & Trevose Head. Follow brown park signs for approx 1m. (NB Do not turn right to Harlyn Sands)*

* 🚐 £4-£14 🚍 £4-£14 ▲ £4-£14

Open: Etr-Nov, Last arrival 22.00hrs Last departure 10.00hrs

A family park surrounded by seven bays with sandy beaches. Extensive entertainment, and an indoor pool, restaurant, take-away, and over-30s bar. A 21-acre site with 160 touring pitches, 6 hardstandings and 350 statics.

Facilities: Arcade, clubhouse 🍴 🔌 ⚠ ⋒ ℗ ✳ ① 🛉 🚻 ♿ **Services:** 🍲 🍴 🍲 ⊡ ⊠ 🛢 ⊘ ⚱ **Facilities found within 3 miles:** ∪ ⚓ 18 🕭 **Notes:** Families only

CORNWALL

ST MINVER — SW97

Gunvenna Caravan Park ▶▶▶▶ 74%

Wadebridge PL27 6QN

☎ 01208 862405 🖹 01208 869107

Dir: *From A39 N of Wadebridge take B3314 (Port Isaac road), park 4m on right*

Open: Etr-Oct, Booking advisable Jul-Aug, Last arrival 21.00hrs Last departure 11.00hrs

Attractive park with extensive rural views in a quiet country location, yet within three miles of Polzeath. This popular park is family owned and run, and provides good facilities in an ideal position for touring north Cornwall. A 10-acre site with 75 touring pitches, 5 hardstandings and 44 statics.

Facilities: 🏕 🔌 🅰 🏧 🌂 ⊙ 🅿 ✳ 🕘 🛢 🛒 🍴 🏪 ♿ **Services:** 🇹 ⟳ 🕲 🛢 🛢 🌀 **Facilities found within 3 miles:** ∪ ♨ 18 ✦ 🖊 ⬲ 🛢 🛢 **Notes:** 🐕

TORPOINT — SX45

Whitsand Bay Lodge & Touring Park 74%

Millbrook PL10 1JZ

☎ 01752 822597 🖹 01752 823444

email: enquiries@whitsandbayholidays.co.uk

www.whitsandbayholidays.co.uk

Dir: *From Torpoint take A374, turn left at Anthony onto B3247 for 1.25m to T-junct. Turn left, 0.25m then right onto Cliff Rd. Site 2m on left*

* 🚐 £10-£30 🚍 £10-£30 ▲ £10-£30

Open: Open All Year **Open:** Apr-Sep, Booking advisable Jul-Sep, Last arrival 24.00hrs Last departure 10.00hrs

A well equipped park with panoramic views. A 27-acre site with 30 touring pitches, 30 hardstandings and 5 statics.

Facilities: Sauna, sunbed, entertainment, putting, chapel, library 🏕 🔌 🅰 🛖 🏧 🌂 ⊙ 🅿 ✳ 🕘 🛢 🛒 🍴 🏪 ♿ **Services:** 🔌 🇹 ⟳ 🕲 🛢 🛢 🌀 🔜 **Facilities found within 3 miles:** ∪ ♨ 18 ✦ 🖊 ◎ ⬲ 🛢 🛢 **Notes:** Families & couples only

WADEBRIDGE   SW97

Little Bodieve Holiday Park

►►► 72%

Bodieve Road PL27 6EG

☎ 01208 812323

email:
berry@littlebodieveholidaypark.fsnet.co.uk

www.littlebodieve.co.uk

Dir: *From A39 rdbt on Wadebridge by-pass take B3314 signed Rock/Port Isaac, site 0.25m on right*

* ⚐ £8.80-£13.40 ⚐ £8.80-£13.40 ▲ £8.80-£13.40

Open: Apr-Oct (rs early & late season pool, shop & clubhouse closed), Booking advisable Jul-Aug, Last arrival 20.00hrs Last departure 11.00hrs

Rural park close to Camel Estuary. A 20-acre site with 195 touring pitches and 75 statics. **Facilities:** Crazy golf, water shute/splash pool, pets' corner ⚐ ♠ ⋔ ⋔ ⊙ ⦿ ⋇ ☺ ⓢ ⌂ ⛩ ⅋ **Services:** ☎ ⋔ ⊡ ⚐ ⓢ ⋔ ⊘ ⛩ ⅏ **Facilities found within 3 miles:** ∪ ↨ 18 ⅋ ⅏ ⓢ ⓢ **Notes:** Families & couples only

WADEBRIDGE   SW97

The Laurels Holiday Park ►►► 80%

Padstow Road Whitecross PL27 7JQ

☎ 01209 313474

email: jamierielly@btconnect.com

www.thelaurelsholidaypark.co.uk

Dir: *Off A389 (Padstow road) near junct with A39, W of Wadebridge*

* ⚐ £5-£14 ⚐ £5-£14 ▲ £5-£14

Open: Apr/Etr-Oct, Booking advisable Jun-Sep, Last arrival 20.00hrs Last departure 10.00hrs

A very smart and well-equipped park with individual pitches screened by hedges and young shrubs. The dog walk is of great benefit to pet owners, and the Camel cycle trail and Padstow are not far away. A 2.2-acre site with 30 touring pitches.

Facilities: ⋔ ♠ ⊙ ⦿ ⋇ ⋔ ⋔ ⋔ **Services:** ⚐ ⓢ ⛩ **Facilities found within 3 miles:** ∪ ↨ 18 ⅋ ⅋ ⓢ **Notes:** Dogs must be kept on leads ⊜

CORNWALL

CORNWALL

WATERGATE BAY
SW86

Watergate Bay Tourist Park

►►►► 78%

Watergate Bay Newquay TR8 4AD

☎ 01637 860387 📠 01637 860387

email: email@watergatebaytouringpark.co.uk

www.watergatebaytouringpark.co.uk

Dir: *4m N of Newquay on B3276 (coast road)*

* 🚐 £8.50-£13.50 🚍 £8.50-£13.50

🛆 £8.50-£13.50

Open: Mar-Oct (rs Mar-22 May & 13 Sep-Nov restricted bar/café, shop & swimming pool), Booking advisable Jul-Aug, Last arrival 22.00hrs Last departure noon

A well-established park above Watergate Bay, with good toilet facilities, a range of activities and entertainment. A 30-acre site with 171 touring pitches and 14 hardstandings.

Facilities: Entertainment, free minibus to beach. 🛉🔦🗛🏠🕃🅡☉👁🅟☀☉🅢🗮🚻🍴🛆

Services: 🕾🞇🎦🛅♿🛲🅢🛎🖋🛒🚿

Facilities found within 3 miles: 🏌9🐾◎ 🏊🅢🖪

WHITE CROSS
SW85

Summer Lodge Holiday Park

►►► 69%

Newquay TR8 4LW

☎ 01726 860415 📠 01726 861490

email:
summer.lodge@snootyfoxresorts.co.uk

www.snootyfoxresorts.co.uk

Dir: *From Indian Queens on A30 take A392 to Newquay. Site on left at Whitecross in 2.5m*

Open: Mar-Oct (rs Etr-Whit & Sep-Oct shop café closed), Booking advisable Jul-Aug, Last departure 10.00hrs

Small holiday complex offering use of good facilities. This park has a nightly cabaret in the licensed pub, plus other on-site entertainment. A 26-acre site with 100 touring pitches and 118 statics.

Facilities: Crazy golf 🛉🔦🗛🅡☉👁🅟☀☉ 🅢🗮🛆 **Services:** 🕾🞇🎦🛅♿🛲🅢🛎🖋🛒🚿

Facilities found within 3 miles: ∪🐾🖪 🅢⊗

WHITE CROSS SW85

**White Acres
Holiday Park** 78%

Nr Newquay TR8 4LW

☎ 01726 862100 📠 01726 860777

email: enquiries@parkdeanholidays.co.uk

www.parkdeanholidays.co.uk

Dir: *From A30 at Indian Queens take A392
signed Newquay. Site 2m on right*

* 🚐 £13-£33 🚃 £15-£35 ▲ £10-£29

Open: Mar-Oct (rs Nov-Feb), Booking
advisable high season, Last arrival 21.00hrs
Last departure 10.00hrs

A holiday park with upmarket facilities. One of
best coarse fishing centres in the South West;
also a heated indoor pool, sauna, jacuzzi and
gym, coffee bar, restaurant and pub, and clubs
for children. A 167-acre site with 40 touring
pitches, 6 hardstandings and 271 statics.

Facilities: Entertainment, solarium, bowling
🏠🔌♨🏧☺🅿✳🕐🧺🍴🎣🚾 **Services:** 🍺
🍽🛒🚿🛁🕯🚮♿ **Facilities found
within 3 miles:** ∪ 🎣 ◎ 🗄 🗃

WIDEMOUTH BAY SS10

**Widemouth Bay
Caravan Park** 71%

Bude Cornwall EX23 0DF

☎ 01288 361208 & 📠 01271 866791

email: bookings@jfhols.co.uk

www.johnfowlerholidays.com

Dir: *Take Widemouth Bay coastal road off
A39, turn left. Park on left*

* 🚐 £8-£20 🚃 £8-£20 ▲ £6-£18

Open: Mar-Oct, Last departure 10.00hrs

A partly sloping rural site set in countryside
overlooking the sea and one of Cornwall's
finest beaches. Nightly entertainment in high
season with emphasis on children's and
family club programmes. This park is located
less than half a mile from the sandy beaches
of Widemouth Bay. A 58-acre site with 220
touring pitches, 90 hardstandings and 200
statics.

Facilities: 🏠♨🏧☺🅿✳🕐🧺🚾🎣🚾
Services: 🍺🍽🛒🚿🗄♿ **Facilities found
within 3 miles:** ∪ ⛴18 ⛵ 🎣 ◎ 🏊 🗄 🗃

CORNWALL

CORNWALL

WIDEMOUTH BAY SS10
Penhalt Farm Holiday Park

▶▶▶ 71%

Bude EX23 0DG

☎ 01288 361210 ▤ 01288 361210

email: denandjennie@penhaltfarm.fsnet.co.uk

www.holidaybank.co.uk/penhaltfarmholidaypark

Dir: *From Bude take 2nd turn right to Widemouth Bay road off A39, left at end by Widemouth Manor signed Millook onto coastal road. Site 0.75m on left*

* ▭ £7-£14 ➠ £7-£14 Å £6-£12

Open: Etr-Oct, Booking advisable Jul & Aug, Splendid views of the sea and coast can be enjoyed from all pitches on this sloping but partly level site, set on a working farm. One mile away is one of Cornwall's finest beaches, popular with all the family as well as surfers. An 8-acre site with 100 touring pitches.

Facilities: Pool table, netball & football posts ❤ ⚠ ♠ ⦿ ☞※ ◔ ⑤ ☞ & **Services:** ☻ ⚱ ∅ ⛺ **Facilities found within 3 miles:** ∪ ↓9 ≒ ✐ ≋ ⑤

WIDEMOUTH BAY SS10
Cornish Coast Caravan & Camping Park ▶▶▶ 70%

Middle Penlean Poundstock EX23 0EE

☎ 01288 361380

email: enquiries5@cornishcoasts.co.uk

www.cornishcoasts.co.uk

Dir: *5m S of Bude on A39, 0.5m S of Rebel Cinema on right*

* ▭ £8-£10 ➠ £8-£10 Å £8-£10

Open: Apr-Oct, Booking advisable school hols, Last arrival 22.00hrs Last departure 10.30hrs

A quiet family-run park, with terraced pitches and stunning views over the countryside to the sea at Widemouth Bay. Reception is in a 13th-century cottage, and the park is well equipped. A 3.5-acre site with 46 touring pitches, 2 hardstandings and 4 statics.

Facilities: ⚠ ♠ ⦿ ☞※ ⑤ & **Services:** ☻ ☻ ⚱ ∅ ⛺ ⛺ **Facilities found within 3 miles:** ∪ ≒ ✐ ⦿ **Notes:** Quiet after 22.00hrs ⊜

APPLEBY-IN-WESTMORLAND NY62

Wild Rose Park ►►►►► 94%

Ormside CA16 6EJ

☎ 017683 51077 🖨 017683 52551

email: reception@wildrose.co.uk

www.wildrose.co.uk

Dir: *Signed on unclass road to Great Ormside, off B6260*

* 🚐 £15-£25 🚎 £15-£25 ⛺ £15-£25

Open: Open All Year (rs Nov-Mar shop & swimming pool closed), Booking advisable bank & school hols, Last arrival 22.00hrs Last departure noon

Set in the Eden Valley, this park offers superb facilities. A 40-acre site with 240 touring pitches, 140 hardstandings and 273 statics.

Facilities: Tourist Information, pitch and putt 🍴 🔍 ♨ ◻ ⬡ 👁 🅿 ☼ 🕐 🛢 🛒 ↻ 🚻 **Services:** 🛢 🔲 ⚡ 🛢 🖈 **Facilities found within 3 miles:** 🚲 18 🖊 ◎ 🛢 🏬 **Notes:** No unaccompanied teenagers, no dangerous dogs, no group bookings

BARROW-IN-FURNESS SD16

South End Caravan Park ►►► 79%

Walney Island LA14 3YQ

☎ 01229 472823 🖨 01229 472822

email: kath.mulgrew@virgin.net

www.walney-island-caravan-park.co.uk

Dir: *A590 in Barrow follow signs for Walney Island. Turn left after crossing bridge. 4m S*

* 🚐 £10-£20 🚎 £10-£20

Open: Mar-Oct, Booking advisable Jul-Aug, Last arrival 22.00hrs Last departure noon

A friendly family-owned and run park next to the sea and close to a nature reserve, on the southern end of Walney Island. It offers an extensive range of quality amenities including an adult lounge, and high standards of cleanliness and maintenance. A 7-acre site with 50 touring pitches and 100 statics.

Facilities: Bowling green, snooker table 🍴 🔍 ♨ ◻ 👁 ☼ 🕐 🛢 🖈 **Services:** 🍴 ⚡ 🛢 🛒 ↻ 🚻 **Facilities found within 3 miles:** ↻ 🚲 18 🖊 🛢 🏬

CUMBRIA

FLOOKBURGH SD37

Lakeland Leisure Park 77%

Moor Lane LA11 7LT

☎ 01539 558556 📠 01539 558559

www.havenholidays.com

Dir: *On B5277 through Grange-over-Sands to Flookburgh. Left at village square, park 1m*

Open: mid Mar-Oct, Last departure 10.00hrs

A complete leisure park with full range of activities and entertainments, making this flat, grassy site ideal for families. The touring area is quietly situated away from the main amenities, but the swimming pools, all-weather bowling green and evening entertainment are just a short stroll away. A 105-acre site with 95 touring pitches.

Facilities: 🏖 ⛱ ⚠ 🐾 🎣 ⊙ 🅿✕ 🕐 🔥 🛖 🛒
& Services: 🐕 🚽 Ⓣ 🚻 🗑 🛢 🏧 **Facilities found within 3 miles:** ☉ ♨ 18 🎣 ⚓ 🛶 🗑

Notes: Family park, no pets at Etr, May Day, Whitsun or summer hols

GREYSTOKE NY42

Hopkinsons' Whitbarrow Hall Caravan Park ►►► 72%

Berrier CA11 0XB

☎ 01768 483456

Dir: *From M6 junct 40, A66 to Keswick, right in 8m, follow tourist signs to site*

* 🚐 £13.50 🚛 £13.50 **Open:** Mar-Dec, Booking advisable bank hols & for electric hook up, Last arrival 21.00hrs Last departure 13.00hrs

A rural park on the fringe of the Lake District National Park. This family-run park offers plenty of amenities including a small bar and clubhouse, a games room and a tennis court. Good mix of grass pitches and hardstandings, and very clean toilet facilities. An 8-acre site with 81 touring pitches and 167 statics.

Facilities: Table tennis, pool table & video games 🍴 ⚠ 🐾 🎣 ⊙ 🅿✕ 🕐 🗑 🔥 🛖 &
Services: 🚽 🚐 🗑 🏧 **Facilities found within 3 miles:** ☉ ♨ 18 🗑 🗑

KESWICK NY32

Gill Head Farm Caravan & Camping Park ►►►► 76%

Troutbeck CA11 0ST

☎ 017687 79652 ▤ 017687 79130

email: enquiries@gillheadfarm.co.uk

www.gillheadfarm.co.uk

Dir: *From M6 junct 40 take A66, then A5091 towards Troutbeck. Turn right after 100yds, then right again*

* ⊞ £15 ⊟ £15 **Open:** Apr-Oct, Booking advisable bank hols, Last arrival 22.30hrs Last departure noon

A family-run park on a working hill farm with lovely fell views. It has level touring pitches, and a new log cabin dining room that is popular with families. Tent pitches are gently sloping in a separate field. A 5.5-acre site with 42 touring pitches and 17 statics.

Facilities: � icons

Services: ⊞ ▤ ▦ ⊘ **Facilities found within 3 miles:** ∪ ↕ 18 ≑ ℓ ≑ ▦ **Notes:** No fires ⊗

PATTERDALE NY41

Sykeside Camping Park ►►► 78%

Brotherswater Penrith CA11 0NZ

☎ 017684 82239 ▤ 017684 82239

email: info@sykeside.co.uk

www.sykeside.co.uk

Dir: *Direct access off A592 (Windermere to Ullswater road) at foot of Kirkstone Pass*

* ⊞ £16-£22 ⊟ £16-£22 ⋀ £12-£20

Open: Open All Year Booking advisable bank hols & Jul-Aug, Last arrival 22.30hrs Last departure 14.00hrs

A camper's delight, this family-run park is sited at the foot of Kirkstone Pass, under the 2000ft Hartsop Dodd in a spectacular area. The park has mainly grass pitches with a few hardstandings, and for those campers without a tent there is bunkhouse accommodation. A small camper's kitchen and bar serves breakfast and bar meals. A 5-acre site with 86 touring pitches and 5 hardstandings.

Facilities: credit icons

Services: service icons

CUMBRIA

CUMBRIA

POOLEY BRIDGE NY42

Park Foot Caravan & Camping Park ▶▶▶ 76%

Howtown Road CA10 2NA

☎ 017684 86309 ▤ 017684 86041

email: holidays@parkfootullswater.co.uk

www.parkfootullswater.co.uk

Dir: *M6 junct 40, A66 towards Keswick, then A592 to Ullswater. Turn left for Pooley Bridge, right at church, right at x-roads signed Howtown*

* ♠ £14 ⛟ £10 ⛺ £10-£21

Open: Mar-Oct (rs Mar-May, mid Sep-Oct Clubhouse open wknds only), Booking advisable bank hols, Last arrival 22.00hrs Last departure noon

A lively park with outdoor sports facilities, meals, discos and live music. An 18-acre site with 323 touring pitches and 131 statics.

Facilities: Boat launch, pony trekking, pool table, table tennis ♠ ⛺ ⛱ ⛲ ⛳ ⊙ ☞ ✳ ⏱ ⓢ ⋈ ⛾ ♿ **Services:** ☎ ⓘ ⛽ ⑪ ⛘ ⓢ ● ⊘ ⛓ ⚓ **Facilities found within 3 miles:** ∪ ⚲ ⌇ ⛾ ⓢ ⓢ **Notes:** Families and couples only

POOLEY BRIDGE NY42

Waterside House Camp Site

▶▶▶ 84%

Howtown Rd Penrith CA10 2NA

☎ 017684 86332 ▤ 017684 86332

email: enquire@watersidefarm-campsite.co.uk

www.watersidefarm-campsite.co.uk

Dir: *From M6 junct 40 take A66 signed Keswick. After 1m left onto A592 signed Ullswater/Pooley Bridge. Turn left by lake, over bridge. 1st right along Howtown Rd, 2nd site on right*

Open: Mar-Sep, Booking advisable bank hols & wknds, Last departure noon

A farm campsite in a very picturesque location at the quiet end of Ullswater, with no bar or club to spoil the peace. Sea cycles, canoes and rowing boats for hire, with direct lake access for sailing boats.

Facilities: Boat, bike and canoe hire, table tennis ⛺ ☞ ⊙ ☞ ✳ ⏱ ⓢ **Services:** ☎ ⏱ ⓢ ● ⊘ **Facilities found within 3 miles:** ∪ ⚲ ⚲ ⌇ ⓢ ⓢ **Notes:** ☻

POOLEY BRIDGE   NY42

Waterfoot Caravan Park ►►► 83%

Penrith CA11 0JF

☎ 017684 86302 🖹 017684 86728

email: enquiries@waterfootpark.co.uk

www.waterfootpark.co.uk

Dir: *From M6 junct 40 take A66 for 1m, then A592 for 4m, site on right before lake*

🚐 £15-£21.50 ⛺ £15-£21.50 **Open:** Mar-14 Nov, Booking advisable bank & school hols, tel bookings only, Last arrival dusk Last departure noon

A quality touring park with neat pitches in a grassy glade within the wooded grounds of an elegant Georgian mansion. There is a bar and family room. Aira Force waterfall, Dalemain House and Garden, and Pooley Bridge are all close by. A 22-acre site with 34 touring pitches, 32 hardstandings and 146 statics.

Facilities: ◕ ⚠ ㋛ ☺ ℗ ※ ☻ 🗑 ♨ ⛱ 🚰 ᬘ

Services: 🚏 🔲 ♨ 🚽 🛒 ▤ 🖬 🛒 **Facilities found within 3 miles:** ∪ ⏌ 🔎 ⛵ 🗑 🖪

Notes: ☺

SILLOTH   NY15

Stanwix Park Holiday Centre 90%

Greenrow CA7 4HH

☎ 016973 32666 🖹 016973 32555

email: enquiries@stanwix.com

www.stanwix.com

Dir: *1m SW on B5300. From A596 (Wigton bypass), follow signs to Silloth on B5302. In Silloth follow signs to site, 1m on B5300*

* 🚐 £16.80-£20.50 ⛺ £16.80-£20.50

⛺ £16.80-£20.50

Open: Open All Year (rs Nov-Feb ex New Year no entertainment/shop closed), Booking advisable Etr, Spring bank hol, Jul-Aug & New Year, Last arrival 22.00hrs Last departure 11.00hrs A large family-run park, attractively laid out, with lots of amenities. A 4-acre site with 121 touring pitches, 100 hardstandings and 212 statics. **Facilities:** Amusement arcade, gym, kitchen 🍴 🍴 ◕ ⚠ ㋛ 🚿 ᬘ ㋛ ☺ ℗ ※ 🗑 🖪 ᬘ **Services:** ☻ 🚏 🔲 🚽 🚽 🛒 ▤ 🖬 🥤 🏺 **Facilities found within 3 miles:** ↓ 18 🔎 ◎ 🗑 🖪

CUMBRIA

CUMBRIA

ULVERSTON SD27

Bardsea Leisure Park ▶▶▶▶ 80%

Priory Road LA12 9QE

☎ 01229 584712 ▤ 01229 580413

email: reception@bardsealeisure.co.uk

www.bardsealeisure.co.uk

Dir: *Off A5087*

* ⊞ £10-£25 ⊟ £10-£25 ▲ £10-£12.50

Open: Open All Year Booking advisable bank hols & Jul-Aug, Last arrival 21.00hrs Last departure 18.00hrs

Attractively landscaped former quarry, making a quiet and very sheltered site. Many of the generously-sized pitches offer all-weather full facilities, and a luxury toilet block provides plenty of privacy. Set on the southern edge of the town, convenient for both the coast and the Lake District. A 5-acre site with 83 touring pitches, 83 hardstandings and 83 statics.

Facilities: ⋔ ⋒ ⊙ ⒫ �� ⊗ ⓕ ⏁ 丼 ⅋

Services: ⏁ ⊕ ⓢ ▯ ⊘ ▦ ⚌ **Facilities found within 3 miles:** ∪ ⚲ 18 ⌔ ⓢ ⓢ

WATERMILLOCK NY42

The Quiet Site ▶▶▶ 79%

Ullswater CA11 0LS

☎ 01768 486337

email: info@thequietsite.co.uk

www.thequietsite.co.uk

Dir: *M6 junct 40, A592 towards Ullswater. Right at lake junct, then right at Brackenrigg Hotel. Site 1.5m on right*

* ⊞ £14-£25 ⊟ £14-£25 ▲ £10-£25

Open: Feb-Nov, Booking advisable wknds, bank hols & Jul-Aug, Last arrival 22.00hrs Last departure noon

A well-maintained site in a lovely, peaceful location, with good facilities, including a family bathroom and a charming olde-worlde bar. A 6-acre site with 88 touring pitches, 50 hardstandings and 23 statics.

Facilities: Pets corner, pool/darts (for adults), caravan storage ⚑ ⋔ ▢ ⋒ ⊙ ⒫ ⯌ ⊗ ⓕ 丼 ⅋ **Services:** 卌 ⏁ ⋃ ⊕ ⓢ ▯ ⊘ ⚌ ⇛ **Facilities found within 3 miles:** ∪ ⚲ ⌔ ⓢ ⓢ **Notes:** Quiet from 22.00hrs onwards

WINDERMERE   NY32

Limefitt Park ▶▶▶▶▶ 80%

LA23 1PA

☎ 015394 32300

email: enquiries@southlakeland-caravans.co.uk

www.southlakeland-caravans.co.uk/parks/1117/view

Dir: *From Windermere take A592 to Ullswater. Site 2.5m on right*

* 🚐 £13-£20 🚐 £13-£20 ▲ £11-£17

Open: Mar-mid Nov, Booking advisable bank hols & Jul-Aug, Last arrival 22.00hrs Last departure 10.00hrs

An attractive family site with superb facilities and spectacular views in a lovely location in the Lake District National Park. Buildings are well-integrated into the landscape, and the River Troutbeck runs through the grounds. There is direct access to the fells and plenty of walks. A 20-acre site with 72 touring pitches, 72 hardstandings and 91 statics.

Facilities: 🔌 🗛 🖵 📧 ⊙ 🗭 ※ 🕓 🗟 🖪 🎵

Services: 🔌 🖬 🗇 🔥 🗟 🖪 ⌀ 🚽 🕋

Facilities found within 3 miles: ∪ ᴊ 18 ⍩ 🗭 ◎ 🎤 🗟 🖪 ⊗

WINDERMER   SD49

Fallbarrow Park ▶▶▶▶ 83%

Rayrigg Road LA23 3DL

☎ 015394 44422 🗋 015394 88736

email: enquiries@southlakeland-caravans.co.uk

www.southlakeland-caravans.co.uk/parks/1115/view

Dir: *0.5m N of Windermere on A591. At mini-rdbt take road to Bowness Bay & the Lake. Site 1.3m on right*

* 🚐 £17-£24 🚐 £17-£24 **Open:** Mar-mid Nov, Booking advisable bank hols & Jul-Aug, Last arrival 22.00hrs Last departure 10.00hrs

A park set in impressive surroundings just a few minutes' walk from Bowness on the shore of Lake Windermere. There is direct access to the lake through the wooded park. A restaurant with a specialist chef is a popular feature. A 32-acre site with 38 touring pitches and 269 statics.

Facilities: Boat launching 🔌 🗛 🖵 🖪 ⊙ 🗭 ※ 🕓 🗟 🎵 **Services:** 🔌 🖬 🗇 ⍩ 🚽 🗟 🖪 ⌀ 🚽 🕋 **Facilities found within 3 miles:** ∪ ᴊ 18 ⍩ 🗭 ◎ 🎤 🗟 🖪 ⊗ **Notes:** No tents

CUMBRIA

WINDERMERE SD49

Park Cliffe Camping & Caravan
Estate ►►►► 77%

Birks Road Tower Wood LA23 3PG

☎ 01539 531344 📄 01539 531971

email: info@parkcliffe.co.uk

www.parkcliffe.co.uk

Dir: *M6 junct 36 onto A590. Right at Newby Bridge onto A592. 4m right into site. (NB Due to difficult access from main road this is the only advised direction for approaching the site)*

* 🚐 £22 🚌 £22 ▲ £18–£22

Open: Mar-15 Nov, Booking advisable bank hols & Aug, Last arrival 22.00hrs Last departure noon

A lovely hillside park set in secluded fell land. A 25-acre site with 250 touring pitches, 60 hardstandings and 55 statics.

Facilities: Off-licence 🍴 🛖 📶 ⊙ 🖗 ✳ ⏰ 🖨
🚻 🚿 ⚖ **Services:** 🔌 🚽 📵 🕁 🔕 🛢 🗑 ⊘ ⊘ 🍴
🚽 🚰 **Facilities found within 3 miles:** ∪
♨ 18 ⚜ 🖊 ◎ ⚓ 🚲 🗑 **Notes:** No noise
22.30hrs -007.30hrs

WINDERMERE SD38

Hill of Oaks & Blakeholme
►►► 83%

Tower Wood LA12 8NR

☎ 015395 31578 📄 015395 30431

email: enquiries@hillofoaks.co.uk

www.hillofoaks.co.uk

Dir: *M6 junct 36 onto A590 towards Barrow. At rdbt signed Bowness turn right onto A592. Site approx 3m on left*

🚐 £11–£27 🚌 £11–£27 **Open:** Mar-14 Nov, Booking advisable bank hols & school hols, Last departure noon

A secluded, heavily wooded park on the shores of Lake Windermere. Picnic areas, woodland walks and a play area. Excellent serviced pitches, licensed shop and a heated toilet block. Also sailing and canoeing, with private jetties for boat launching. A 31-acre site with 43 touring pitches and 215 statics.

Facilities: 🛖 📶 ⊙ 🖗 ✳ ⏰ 🖨 🚻 🚿 ⚖
Services: 🚽 🕁 📵 🛢 🗑 🚰 **Facilities found within 3 miles:** ∪ ♨ 18 ⚜ 🖊 ◎ ⚓ 🗑 🗑
Notes: 🐾

BUXTON SK07

Lime Tree Park ▶▶▶▶ 77%

Dukes Drive SK17 9RP

☎ 01298 22988 🖹 01298 22988

email: limetreebuxton@dukes50.fsnet.co.uk

www.ukparks.co.uk/limetree

Dir: *1m S of Buxton, between A515 & A6*

* ⬛ £14-£17 ⬛ £14-£17 ▲ £14-£17

Open: Mar-Oct, Booking advisable bank hols & Jul-Aug, Last arrival 21.00hrs Last departure noon

A most attractive and well-designed site, set on the side of a narrow valley in an elevated location. Its backdrop of magnificent old railway viaduct and views over Buxton and the surrounding hills make this a sought-after destination. A 10.5-acre site with 99 touring pitches, 8 hardstandings and 43 statics.

Facilities: ⬛ ⬛ ⬛ ⬛ ⬛ ⊙ ⬛ ☼ ⬛ ⬛ ⬛ ⬛

Services: ⬛ ⬛ ⬛ ⬛ ⬛ ⬛ **Facilities found within 3 miles:** ∪ ⬛ 18 ⬛ ⬛ ⬛ ⬛

MATLOCK SK35

Lickpenny Caravan Site ▶▶▶▶ 74%

Lickpenny Lane Tansley DE4 5GF

☎ 01629 583040 🖹 01629 583040

email: lickpenny@btinternet.com

www.lickpennycaravanpark.co.uk

Dir: *From A615 between Alfreton & Matlock, approx 1m N of Tansley. Turn into Lickpenny Lane at x-rds*

* ⬛ £14.50-£18.50 ⬛ £14.50-£18.50

Open: Open All Year, Last arrival 20.00hrs Last departure noon

A picturesque site in the grounds of an old plant nursery with areas broken up and screened by shrubs, and spectacular views. Pitches, several fully serviced, are spacious, and facilities are to a very good standard. Popular bistro/coffee shop. A 16-acre site with 80 touring pitches and 80 hardstandings.

Facilities: Child bath available ⬛ ⬛ ⊙ ⬛ ⬛ ⬛ ⬛ ⬛ ⬛ **Services:** ⬛ ⬛ ⬛ ⬛ ⬛

Facilities found within 3 miles: ∪ ⬛ 18 ⬛ ⬛ ⬛ ⬛ ⬛

DERBYSHIRE

DERBYSHIRE

RIPLEY SK45

Golden Valley Caravan & Camping Park ►►►► 73%

Coach Road Butterley Park DE5 3QU

☎ 01773 513881

email: enquiries@goldenvalleycaravanpark.co.uk

www.goldenvalleycaravanpark.co.uk

Dir: *M1 junct 26 onto A610 to Codnor. Right at lights, then right onto Alfreton Road, park 1m on left*

* ☎ £15-£20 ☎ £15-£17.50 ▲ £10

Open: Mar-Sep, Last arrival 18.00hrs Last departure noon

A newly created woodland park in the Amber Valley. Fully-serviced pitches are set out in groups in clearings amongst the trees. There is a bar and bistro, fishing lake, wildlife pond, jacuzzi and fitness suite. A 26-acre site with 24 touring pitches and 24 hardstandings.

Facilities: ♠ ⚠ ⛊ ⋒ ☉ ☞ ❋ ⓢ ☜ ☶ ⎅ ⛧ ㊑

Services: ⛲ ⛽ 🆃 ⚡ ⚌ ⛝ 🅿 ⌀ ⛯ ⛩

Facilities found within 3 miles: ひ ⚲ 18 ⓢ ⓢ **Notes:** ⊕

ROWSLEY SK26

Grouse & Claret ►►► 68%

Station Road Matlock DE4 2EB

☎ 01629 733233 📄 01629 735194

Dir: *M1 junct 29. Site on A6, 5m from Matlock & 3m from Bakewell*

☎ £15 ☎ £15 ▲ £7.50

Open: Open All Year Booking advisable wknds, bank hols & peak periods, Last arrival 20.00hrs Last departure noon

A well-designed, purpose-built park at the rear of an eating house on the A6 between Bakewell and Chatsworth, and adjacent to the New Peak Shopping Village. The park comprises a level grassy area running down to the river, and all pitches have hardstandings and electric hook-ups. A 2.5-acre site with 26 touring pitches and 26 hardstandings.

Facilities: ⚠ ⋒ ☉ ☾ ⓢ ⎅ **Services:** ⎙ ⛽ 🅿 ⛩ **Facilities found within 3 miles:** ひ ⚲ 9 ⌀ ⓢ **Notes:** Dogs must be under strict control

ASHBURTON   SX77

River Dart Country Park ►►►► 78%

Holne Park TQ13 7NP

☎ 01364 652511 🖷 01364 652020

email: info@riverdart.co.uk

www.riverdart.co.uk

Dir: *From M5 take A38 towards Plymouth, turn off at Ashburton following brown signs to River Dart Country Park. Site 1m on left*

* ⊕ £9.50-£20 ⇌ £9.50-£20 ▲ £9.50-£17.50

Open: Apr-Sep (rs Etr & Sep no evening facilities or warden cover), Booking advisable Spring bank hol & Jul-Aug, Last arrival 21.00hrs Last departure 11.00hrs

Set in magnificent parkland with exotic trees, close to Dartmoor. Activities include abseiling, caving and canoeing. A 90-acre site with 170 touring pitches and 12 hardstandings.

Facilities: Adventure playground, climbing, canoeing ⬟ ♠ ⋔ ⟁ ⋒ ⊙ ⌖ ⚡ ⏱ ◷ 🖳 🖃 🏕 🎪

🛆 **Services:** 🛎 🗊 🛢 🗦 ⬮ 🛢 🖫 🖉 🗑 ⚱

Facilities found within 3 miles: ∪ ⌕ 18 ⌒ 🖭 🖺

ASHBURTON   SX77

Parkers Farm Holiday Park

►►►► 75%

Higher Mead Farm Devon TQ13 7LJ

☎ 01364 654869 🖷 01364 654004

email: parkersfarm@btconnect.com

www.parkersfarm.co.uk

Dir: *From Exeter on A38, take 2nd left after Plymouth 26m sign, at Alston, signed Woodland-Denbury. From Plymouth on A38 take A383 Newton Abbot exit, turn right across bridge and rejoin A38, then as above.*

* ⊕ £6.50-£16.50 ⇌ £6.50-£16.50 ▲ £6.50

Open: Etr-end Oct, Booking advisable Whitsun & school hols, Last arrival 22.00hrs Last departure 10.00hrs

Part of a working farm, this terraced site offers quality facilities including family rooms with 2 shower cubicles. An 8-acre site with 100 touring pitches and 13 statics.

Facilities: ♠ ⋔ ⋒ ⊙ ⌖ ◷ 🖫 🖃 🏕 🎪 🛆

Services: 🛎 🍴 🗊 🛢 🗦 ⬮ 🛢 🖫 🖉

🏕 ⚱ **Facilities found within 3 miles:** ⌒ 🖭 🖺

DEVON

DEVON

AXMINSTER ST20
Andrewshayes Caravan Park

▶▶▶▶ 76%

Dalwood EX13 7DY

☎ 01404 831225 ▤ 01404 831893

email: enquiries@andrewshayes.co.uk

www.andrewshayes.co.uk

Dir: *On A35, 3m from Axminster. Turn N at Taunton Cross signed Stockland/Dalwood. Site 150mtrs on right*

* ⬛ £10–£20 ⬛ £10–£17 ▲ £10–£17

Open: Mar-Jan (rs Apr-21 May & Oct-Jan shop hrs limited,pool closed Sep-mid May), Booking advisable Spring bank hol & Jul-Aug, Last arrival 22.00hrs Last departure noon
A lively and popular 12-acre site with 150 touring pitches, 105 hardstandings and 80 statics.

Facilities: Licenced bistro from May-Sep ◉ ◉ ⬛ ⬛ ◉ ◉ ◉ ✕ ◉ ⬛ ◉ ◉ **Services:** ◉ ◉ ◉ ◉ ◉ ⬛ ⬛ **Facilities found within 3 miles:** ◉ ◉ ◉ **Notes:** Dogs must be kept on leads

BARNSTAPLE SS53
Tarka Holiday Park ▶▶▶ 79%

Braunton Road Ashford EX31 4AU

☎ 01271 343691 ▤ 01271 326355

email: info@tarkaholidaypark.co.uk

www.tarkaholidaypark.co.uk

Dir: *2m from Barnstaple on A361 towards Chivenor. (NB This is a fast dual-carriageway & care should be taken)*

* ⬛ £6–£14 ⬛ £6–£14 ▲ £6–£14

Open: 22 Jan-1 Jan, Booking advisable all year, Last arrival 22.00hrs Last departure noon
A grass park near the banks of the River Taw, and close to the Tarka cycle trail. Offers a bar with some entertainment, a putting green, a bouncy castle and playground. 5m from sandy beaches. A 10-acre site with 35 touring pitches, 16 hardstandings and 82 statics.

Facilities: Eating area in clubhouse ◉ ◉ ◉ ◉ ✕ ◉ ◉ ◉ **Services:** ◉ ◉ ⬛ ◉ ◉ ◉ **Facilities found within 3 miles:** ◉ ◉ ◉ ◉ ◉ ◉ ◉ ◉

BICKINGTON SX87

The Dartmoor Halfway Inn Caravan Park ►►►► 71%

Newton Abbot TQ12 6JW

☎ 01626 821270 🖹 01626 821820

email: info@dartmoor-halfway-inn.co.uk

www.dartmoor-halfway-inn.co.uk

Dir: *Direct access from A383, 1m from A38 (Exeter-Plymouth road)*

* 🚐 £12.75-£14.75 **Open:** Open All Year Booking advisable high season & bank hols, Last arrival 23.00hrs Last departure 10.00hrs

A well-developed park tucked away on the edge of Dartmoor, beside the River Lemon and adjacent to the Halfway Inn. The neat and compact park has a small toilet block with immaculate facilities, and pitches separated by mature shrubs. An extensive menu at the inn offers reasonably-priced food all day and evening. A 2-acre site with 22 touring pitches.

Facilities: ⚠ ⭐ ⊙ ✳ ⓢ ⇥ 🎠 ⅋ ♿ **Services:** 🍽 🛒 🔌 🛁 **Facilities found within 3 miles:** ∪ ⚓ 18 🎣 🖪 🖻

BRAUNTON SS44

Hidden Valley Park ►►►► 82%

Ilfracombe EX34 8NU

☎ 01271 813837 🖹 01271 814041

email: relax@hiddenvalleypark.com

www.hiddenvalleypark.com

Dir: *Direct access off A361, 8m from Barnstaple & 2m from Mullacott Cross*

Open: Open All Year (rs 15 Nov-15 Mar all weather pitches only), Booking advisable peak season, Last arrival 21.30hrs Last departure 10.00hrs

A delightful, well-appointed family site set in a wooded valley, with superb facilities and a cafe. The park is set in a very rural, natural position not far from the beautiful coastline around Ilfracombe. A 25-acre site with 135 touring pitches and 74 hardstandings.

Facilities: Gardens, woodland walks & lake ⚓ ⚠ ⭐ ⊙ 🅿 ✳ ⓢ ⇥ 🎠 ⅋ ♿ **Services:** 🍴 🍽 🔌 Ⓣ 🔌 🛁 🛒 ⌀ 🛁 **Facilities found within 3 miles:** ∪ ⚓ 18 🎣 🖪 🖻

DEVON

DEVON

BRIDESTOWE SX58

Bridestowe Caravan Park ▶▶▶ 74%

Okehampton EX20 4ER

☎ 01837 861261

email: myoung@myoung.demon.co.uk

www.myoung.demon.co.uk/Index.html

Dir: *Leave A30 at A386/Sourton Cross junct,
follow B3278 signed Bridestowe, turn left in
3m. In village centre, left down unclass road
for 0.5m*

* ⊞ £10-£14 ⇔ £10-£14 ▲ £8-£12

Open: Mar-Dec, Booking advisable summer,
Last arrival 22.30hrs Last departure noon
A small, well-established park in a rural
setting close to Dartmoor National Park. This
mainly static park has a small touring space.
There are many activities to enjoy including
fishing and riding. Part of the National Cycle
Route 27 passes close to this park. A 1-acre
site with 13 touring pitches, 3 hardstandings
and 40 statics.

Facilities: ◣ ⚑ ♦ ⊙✹ 🖻 **Services:** 🖵 🖻
🔒 ⊘ 🍴 Facilities found within 3 miles:
∪ 🔎 🖻 **Notes:** 🐶

BRIDGERULE SS20

**Hedleywood Caravan & Camping
Park ▶▶▶ 78%**

Holsworthy EX22 7ED

☎ 01288 381404 📠 01288 382011

email: alan@hedleywood.co.uk

www.hedleywood.co.uk

Dir: *From B3254 take Widemouth road
(unclass) at the Devon/Cornwall border*

* ⊞ £7-£11.50 ⇔ £7-£11.50 ▲ £7-£11.50

Open: Open All Year (rs Bar/restaurant open
at main hols), Booking advisable public hols
& Jul-Aug,
Set in a very rural location 4 miles from Bude,
this family-owned site has an easy-going
atmosphere. Pitches are in separate paddocks.
A 16.5-acre site with 120 touring pitches, 14
hardstandings and 16 statics.

Facilities: Dog kennels, nature trail ◣ ⚑ ▢
♦ ⊙ ☞✹ ⊙ 🖻 ⨅ 🍴 ▦ & **Services:** 🖳 🕽
▢ ⎘ 🖵 🖻 ⊘ 🍴 🎖 **Facilities found
within 3 miles:** ∪ ♨ 9 🔎 🖻 🖻 **Notes:** 🐶

BRIXHAM SX95

Galmpton Touring Park ▶▶▶ 77%

Greenway Road Brixham TQ5 0EP

☎ 01803 842066

email: galmptontouringpark@hotmail.com

www.galmptontouringpark.co.uk

Dir: *Signed from A3022 (Torbay to Brixham road) at Churston*

* ⛺ £8.70-£15.60 ⛺ £8.70-£15.60

▲ £8.70-£15.60

Open: Etr-Sep, Booking advisable Jul-Aug & bank hols, Last arrival 22.00hrs Last departure 11.00hrs

This excellent location overlooks the River Dart, with outstanding views of the creek and anchorage. Pitches are set on level terraces, and facilities are bright and clean. A 10-acre site with 120 touring pitches.

Facilities: Bathroom for under 5s (charged) ⌂ ⋔ ⊙ ⴲ ⁂ ⓢ ⓖ ⇥ ♿ **Services:** ⊤ ⚑ ⓢ 🔒 ⊘ ⇥ **Facilities found within 3 miles:** ⚘ 18 ⚄ ⚲ ◎ ⚐ ⓢ ⓢ **Notes:** Families & couples only, no dogs during peak season

BUDLEIGH SALTERTON SY08

Pooh Cottage Holiday Park ▶▶ 76%

Bear Lane EX9 7AQ

☎ 01395 442354

email: info@poohcottage.co.uk

www.poohcottage.co.uk

Dir: *M5 junct 30 onto A376 towards Exmouth. Left onto B3179 towards Woodbury & Budleigh Salterton. Left into Knowle on B3178. Through village, at brow of hill take sharp left into Bear Lane (very narrow). Site 200yds*

* ⛺ £10-£18 ⛺ £10-£18 ▲ £10-£18

Open: Open All Year Booking advisable Jul-Aug & bank hols, Last arrival 23.00hrs Last departure 11.00hrs

A rural park with views of the countryside and sea. Lovely play area, and walks, as well as the Buzzard Cycle Way. A 4-acre site with 42 touring pitches, 4 hardstandings and 3 statics.

Facilities: ⚘ ⌂ ⋔ ⁂ ⓢ ⇥ ♿ **Services:** ⚑ ⓢ **Facilities found within 3 miles:** ∪ ⚘ 18 ⚄ ⚲ ◎ ⓢ ⓢ **Notes:** ⊜

DEVON

DEVON

COLYTON SY29

Leacroft Touring Park ►►► 90%

Colyton Hill EX24 6HY

☎ 01297 552823

Dir: *1m from Stafford Cross on A3052 towards Colyton*

* ⊕ £13-£16 ⇔ £13-£16 ▲ £13-£16

Open: Etr-mid Oct, Booking advisable Jul-Aug & Spring bank hol, Last arrival 21.00hrs Last departure 11.00hrs

Located outside the little village of Colyton in the east Devon countryside, the park has distant sea views across Lyme Bay from its slightly elevated position. A wooded area with walks is nearby, and the traffic-free seaside resort of Seaton is about 2.5 miles away. The park is slightly sloping with all pitches well spaced and level. A 10-acre site with 138 touring pitches and 10 hardstandings.

Facilities: Off licence ● ⋒ ⋔ ⊙ ⋔⋇ ⊗ 🅰
⋈ ♨ ♒ ⅙ **Services:** ⊺ ⊗ 🅾 🛢 🗑 ⊘ 🛒
Facilities found within 3 miles: ∪ ⅃ 18
⅛ ♬ ◎ ♨ ⊚ 🅰 **Notes:** ☺

COMBE MARTIN SS54

Stowford Farm Meadows

►►►► 84%

Berry Down EX34 0PW

☎ 01271 882476 🖷 01271 883053

email: enquiries@stowford.co.uk

www.stowford.co.uk

Dir: *M5 junct 27 onto A361 to Barnstaple. Take A39 from town centre towards Lynton, in 1m turn left onto B3230. Right at garage at Lynton Cross onto A3123, site 1.5m on right*

* ⊕ £7-£20 ⇔ £7-£20 ▲ £7-£23

Open: Open All Year (rs Winter pool and bars closed), Booking advisable bank hols & Jul-Aug, Last arrival 20.00hrs Last departure 10.00hrs

This farm park offers a large swimming pool, horse riding and crazy golf. Also a 60-acre nature trail and mini zoo. A 100-acre site with 700 touring pitches and 70 hardstandings.

Facilities: Cycle hire ⊛ ● ⋒ ⋔ ⊙ ⋔⋇ ⊗
🅰 ⋈ ♒ **Services:** ⅌ ⋐ ⊺ ⊗ 🅾 🛢 🗑 ⊘ 🛒 ⊞
Facilities found within 3 miles: ∪ ⅃ 18
♬ ◎ 🅰 🅰

DEVON

CROYDE   SS43
Bay View Farm Caravan & Camping Park ▶▶▶ 75%
EX33 1PN

☎ 01271 890501

www.bayviewfarm.co.uk

Dir: *M5 junct 27 onto A361, through Barnstaple to Braunton, turn left onto B3231. Site at entry to Croyde village*

Open: Mar-Oct, Booking advisable high season, Last arrival 21.30hrs Last departure 11.00hrs

A very busy and popular park close to surfing beaches and rock pools, with a public footpath leading directly to the sea. Set in a stunning location with views out over the Atlantic to Lundy Island, it is just a short stroll from Croyde. Facilities are clean and well maintained, and there is a fish and chip shop on site. No dogs allowed. A 10-acre site with 70 touring pitches and 38 hardstandings.

Facilities: ⋔ ⋒ ⊙ ☞ ✻ ⓒ 🖳 **Services:** 🖳 🛢 💧 🧼 🚜 ⛟ 🕳 **Facilities found within 3 miles:** ∪ ↧ 🥅 🖻 🖻 🛇 **Notes:** ⊛

CROYDE BAY   SS43
Ruda Holiday Park 82%
Braunton EX33 1NY

☎ 01271 890671 📠 01271 890656

email: enquiries@parkdeanholidays.co.uk

www.parkdeanholidays.co.uk

Dir: *M5 junct 27, A361 to Braunton. Left at main lights, follow Croyde signs*

* 🚐 £11-£33 🚖 £11-£33 ⛺ £8-£29

Open: mid Mar-Nov, Booking advisable all times, Last arrival 21.00hrs Last departure 10.00hrs

A spacious park with its own blue flag sandy beach, a surfers' paradise. Set in landscaped grounds, it has a full leisure programme. Cascades tropical adventure pool and a nightclub are popular features. A 220-acre site with 372 touring pitches and 289 statics.

Facilities: Live family entertainment, children's club 📶 ⋒ ⋔ ⊡ ↧ ⌃ ⋒ ⊙ ☞ ✻ ⓒ 🖳 🖻 🖳 ♿ **Services:** 🖳 🛢 🖳 🛢 🍴 🧼 🕳 ⛟ 🚜 **Facilities found within 3 miles:** ∪ ↧ 18 🥅 ⛵ 🖻 🖻 🛇

DEVON

DARTMOUTH SX84

Deer Park Caravan and Camping

►►► 73%

Dartmouth Road Stoke Fleming TQ6 0RF

☎ 01803 770253

email: info@deerparkinn.co.uk

www.deerparkinn.co.uk

Dir: *Direct access from A379 from Dartmouth before Stoke Fleming*

* 🚐 £9-£16 🚙 £9-£16 ⛺ £7.50-£16

Open: mid Mar-mid Nov, Booking advisable Jul-Aug, Bank hols, Last arrival 21.00hrs Last departure 11.00hrs

Set on high ground with extensive sea views over Start Bay, this park is divided into three grassy paddocks. Good food is served next door at the Deer Park Inn, and there is a bus service to local beaches and Dartmouth. A 6-acre site with 160 touring pitches.

Facilities: ⛴ 🔍 /A\ 🚿 ⊙ ✲ ✆ [$] ♿ **Services:** 🍴 🍷 [T] 🔌 🧺 🔒 🛏 🧺 **Facilities found within 3 miles:** U ⛳ 18 ✈ 🎣 ◎ ≋ 🧺 [$] **Notes:** Dogs must be kept on leads

DARTMOUTH SX85

Woodlands Leisure Park

►►►► 92%

Blackawton TQ9 7DQ

☎ 01803 712598 📠 01803 712680

email: fun@woodlandspark.com

www.woodlandspark.com

Dir: *4m from Dartmouth on A3122. From A38 take turn for Totnes & follow brown tourist signs*

* 🚐 £11-£17.50 🚙 £11-£17.50 ⛺ £11-£17.50

Open: Etr-6 Nov, Booking advisable anytime, Last departure 11.00hrs

A woodland park with terraced grass camping area that caters for all the family in a relaxed atmosphere, and boasts the UK's biggest indoor venture zone, water-coasters and rides, and a wildlife park. A 16-acre site with 350 touring pitches and 47 hardstandings.

Facilities: Watercoasters, toboggan run, gliders, falconry centre 🔍 /A\ ▭ 🚿 ⊙ 🔫 ✲ ✆ [$] 🍖 ⛩ ♿ **Services:** ☕ [T] 🔌 🧺 🔒 🍃 🛏 🧺 **Facilities found within 3 miles:** ⛳ 27 🧺 [$] 🚭

DEVON

DAWLISH SX97

Lady's Mile Holiday Park 78%

EX7 0LX

☎ 01626 863411 🖹 01626 888689

email: info@ladysmile.co.uk

www.ladysmile.co.uk

Dir: *1m N of Dawlish on A379*

* 🚐 £11-£22 🚎 £11-£22 ▲ £11-£22

Open: 17 Mar-27 Oct, Booking advisable bank hols & Jul-Aug, Last arrival 20.00hrs Last departure 11.00hrs

A holiday site with all grass touring pitches, two swimming pools with waterslides, a large adventure playground, 9-hole golf course, and a bar with entertainment in high season all add to the enjoyment of a stay here. Facilities are kept clean, and the surrounding beaches are easily accessed. A 16-acre site with 243 touring pitches and 43 statics.

Facilities: 🚿 🛒 🏪 🔥 🎣 ♿ 🚰 ⚡ 🎱 ✗ 🕐 🏧 🔒

♿ **Services:** 🔌 🍴 🛢 🚽 🧺 🗑 🚿 🏪 🚰 🛒

Facilities found within 3 miles: ↻ ⚓ 18

🏸 ⛳ 🏉 ◎ 🏊 🗑 🗑 🗑

DAWLISH SX97

Peppermint Park 78%

Warren Road EX7 0PQ

☎ 01626 863436 🖹 01626 866482

email: info@peppermintpark.co.uk

www.peppermintpark.co.uk

Dir: *From A379 at Dawlish follow signs for Dawlish Warren. Site 1m on left at bottom of hill*

* 🚐 £14-£23 🚎 £14-£23 ▲ £12-£23

Open: Etr-Oct (rs early/late season shop, pool, club closed), Booking advisable Spring bank hol & Jul-Aug, Last arrival 18.00hrs Last departure 11.00hrs

This park has excellent facilities, including club and bar well away from pitches. Heated swimming pool and water chute, and coarse fishing. A 26-acre site with 250 touring pitches, 24 hardstandings and 75 statics.

Facilities: Licensed club, entertainment 🛒

🔥 🎣 ♿ ✗ 🕐 🚰 ⚡ 🏧 **Services:** 🔌 🍴 🛢 🚽 🗑 🗑

🔒 🧺 🚰 **Facilities found within 3 miles:**

↻ ⚓ 18 🏸 ⛳ ◎ 🏊 🗑 🗑 🗑

DEVON

DAWLISH SX97
Cofton Country Holidays Ltd
▶▶▶▶ 77%

Starcross EX6 8RP

☎ 01626 890111 🖨 01626 891572

email: info@coftonholidays.co.uk

www.coftonholidays.co.uk

Dir: *On A379 (Exeter/Dawlish road) 3m from Dawlish*

* 🚐 £12.50-£21 🚙 £12.50-£21 ▲ £12.50-£21

Open: Etr-Oct (rs Etr-Spring bank hol & mid Sep-Oct swimming pool closed), Booking advisable bank hols & Jul-Aug, Last arrival 20.00hrs Last departure 11.00hrs

Set in a rural location surrounded by open grassland. Most pitches overlook the pool or fishing lakes. A 16-acre site with 450 touring pitches, 20 hardstandings and 66 statics.

Facilities: Coarse fishing, pub with family room 🌳 🔍 🔗 🔈 ⊙ ♿️✳ ⏰ 🐕 🐾 ♿

Services: 🔌 🍴 🎱 🚽 🏪 🗑 🛢 🍳 🚮 🛒 🚿

Facilities found within 3 miles: 🎿 18 ⛵

🎣 ◎ 🗼 🏪 **Notes:** Families only

DAWLISH SX97
Golden Sands Holiday Park 74%

Week Lane EX7 0LZ

☎ 01626 863099 🖨 01626 867149

email: info@goldensands.co.uk

www.goldensands.co.uk

Dir: *M5 junct 30 onto A379 signed Dawlish. After 6m pass small harbour at Cockwood, signed on left in 2m*

* 🚐 £10.50-£25 🚙 £10.50-£25

▲ £10.50-£25

Open: Etr-Oct, Booking advisable May-Sep, Last arrival 22.00hrs Last departure 10.00hrs

A holiday centre for all the family, offering a wide range of entertainment. The small touring area is surrounded by mature trees and hedges. There is a licensed club, and heated swimming pools. A 2.5-acre site with 36 touring pitches and 200 statics.

Facilities: 🌊 🌳 🔍 🔗 🔈 ⊙ 🏪 ⏰ 🐕 ♿

Services: 🔌 🍴 🎱 🚽 🛢 🍳 🚿 **Facilities found within 3 miles:** 🎿 18 🎣 ◎ 🗼 🏪 ⊗

Notes: No pets

DAWLISH   SX97

Leadstone Camping ►►► 74%

Warren Road EX7 0NG

☎ 01626 864411 🖹 01626 873833

email: info@leadstonecamping.co.uk

www.leadstonecamping.co.uk

Dir: *M5 junct 30, A379 to Dawlish. Before village turn left on brow of hill, signed Dawlish Warren. Site 0.5m on right*

* 🚐 £14.60-£17 ⛟ £11-£13 ▲ £11-£13

Open: 15 Jun-7 Sep, Booking advisable 14 Jul-27 Aug, Last arrival 22.00hrs Last departure noon

A traditional, mainly level grassy camping park approx 0.5m walk from sands and dunes at Dawlish Warren, an Area of Outstanding Natural Beauty. This mainly tented park has been run by the same friendly family for many years, and is an ideal base for touring. An 8-acre site with 137 touring pitches.

Facilities: ⋔ ⋒ ☉ ⅌ ⊁ ⓢ 🖫 **Services:** 🚐 🖫 🛢 ⌀ 🍴 **Facilities found within 3 miles:** ∪ ⌕ 18 ⌀ ◎ 🖫 🖽 **Notes:** No noise after 23.00hrs

EAST WORLINGTON   SS71

Yeatheridge Farm Caravan Park

►►►► 73%

Crediton EX17 4TN

☎ 01884 860330

email: yeatheridge@talk21.com

www.yeatheridge.co.uk

Dir: *M5 junct 27, A361, at 1st rdbt at Tiverton take B3137 for 9m towards Witheridge. Fork left 1m past Nomansland onto B3042. Site on left in 3.5m. (NB Do not go to East Worlington)*

* 🚐 £7-£13 ⛟ £7-£13 ▲ £7-£13

Open: Etr-Sep, Booking advisable Etr, Spring bank hol & school hols, Last arrival 22.00hrs Last departure 22.00hrs

Gently sloping grass site with good views of distant Dartmoor. Appeals to families with its farm animals, horse riding, and two indoor pools. A 9-acre site with 85 touring pitches.

Facilities: Fishing, pool table 🏊 ⋒ ⋔ ☉ ⅌ ⊁ ⓢ 🖫 🛒 🍴 ♿ **Services:** 🚐 🖫 🍴 🇹 🚐 🛢 ⌀ 🍴 🚽 **Facilities found within 3 miles:** ∪ ⌀ 🖫

DEVON

DEVON

EXMOUTH SY08

Devon Cliffs Holiday Park 84%

Sandy Bay EX8 5BT

☎ 01395 226226 ▤ 01395 223111

www.havenholidays.com

Dir: *M5 junct 30/A376 towards Exmouth, follow brown signs to Sandy Bay*

Open: mid Mar-Oct (rs mid Mar-May & Sep-Oct some facilities may be reduced), Booking advisable school hols, Last arrival 19.00hrs Last departure 10.00hrs

A large and exciting holiday park on a hillside setting close to Exmouth, with spectacular views across Sandy Bay. The all-action park offers a superb entertainment programme for all ages with modern sports and leisure facilities available for everyone, including an internet café. A 163-acre site with 80 touring pitches, 5 hardstandings and 2000 statics.

Facilities: 🖼 🖼 🔧 ⚠ 🐾 ☉ 🍴 ✳ 🕒 🗑 🚻 🎪

🚻 **Services:** 🔧 🍽 🛢 🔌 🗑 🍴 🛢 🚰 🍺

Facilities found within 3 miles: 🚴 18 🎣

🎣 ◎ 🚣 🗑 🗑 **Notes:** Dogs must be on leads

HOLSWORTHY SS30

Noteworthy Caravan and Campsite

► 72%

Noteworthy Bude Road EX22 7JB

☎ 01409 253731

email: jmsb.0603@virgin.net

www.noteworthy-devon.co.uk

Dir: *On A3072 between Holsworthy & Bude. 3m from Holsworthy on right*

* 🚐 £8 🚃 £8 ▲ £8

Open: Open All Year, Booking advisable

A newly established campsite owned by a friendly young couple with their own small children. There are good views from the quiet rural location, and simple toilet facilities. A 5-acre site with 5 touring pitches and 1 static.

Facilities: ⚠ ☉✳ 🕒 🔧 **Services:** 🔧 🚴 18

🎣 🚣 🗑 **Notes:** No open fires 🚭

ILFRACOMBE SS54
Watermouth Cove Holiday Park
▶▶▶ 74%
Berrynarbor EX34 9SJ
☎ 01271 862504
email: info@watermouthcoveholidays.co.uk
www.watermouthcoveholidays.co.uk
Dir: *From M5 junct 27, take A361 to 2nd
rdbt at South Molton, then A399 through
Coombe Martin. Turn left at seafront & site
2m on right*
* ⊞ £10.50-£26 ⇔ £10.50-£26 ▲ £10.50-£23.50
Open: Etr-Oct (rs Etr-Whit & Sep-Nov pool,
takeaway, club & shop limited), Booking
advisable Whit & Jul-Aug, Last arrival
22.00hrs Last departure 11.00hrs
A popular site set amidst trees in meadowland
with access to a private beach with launching
for boats and swimming. A 6-acre site with 90
touring pitches and 10 hardstandings.
Facilities: Coastal headland fishing ⊴ ♦ ⋀
🟡⊙※①🖻⊶🛒🏭🛒 **Services:** 🐤🍴Ⓣ🔌
🖻🛢∅🚮🎣 **Facilities found within 3
miles:** ∪♨18 ⥽ ℓ ◎ 🎣🖻🖻

ILFRACOMBE SS54
Hele Valley Holiday Park
▶▶▶▶ 82%
Hele Bay EX34 9RD
☎ 01271 862460 📄 01271 867926
email: holidays@helevalley.co.uk
www.helevalley.co.uk
Dir: *M5 junct 27 onto A361. Through
Barnstaple & Braunton to Ilfracombe. Then
A399 towards Combe Martin. Follow brown
Hele Valley signs. 400mtrs sharp right, then
to T-junct. Reception on left.*
* ⇔ £12-£22 ▲ £10-£19
Open: May-Sep, Booking advisable at all
times, Last arrival 18.00hrs Last departure
11.00hrs
A 17-acre site in a valley, close to a lovely
beach with 58 touring pitches, 8
hardstandings and 80 statics.
Facilities: Post collection, internet access,
info service ⋀🟡⊙⊝※🖻⊶🛒🏭🛒♿
Services: 🚾🐤🛢∅🎣🚮 **Facilities
found within 3 miles:** ∪♨18 ⥽ ℓ ◎ 🎣
🖻🖻 **Notes:** No groups

DEVON

DEVON

KENTISBEARE ST10
Forest Glade Holiday Park
▶▶▶▶ 76%
Cullompton EX15 2DT
☎ 01404 841381 📄 01404 841593
email: enquiries@forest-glade.co.uk
www.forest-glade.co.uk
Dir: *Tent traffic from A373, signed at Keepers Cottage Inn, 2.5m E of M5 junct 28. Touring caravans via Honiton/Dunkeswell road: phone for access details*
🚐 £12-£16.50 🚉 £12-£16.50 ▲ £9.50-£13
Open: 2 wks before Etr-end Oct (rs low season limited shop hours), Booking advisable school hols, Last arrival 21.00hrs
A quiet, attractive park in a forest clearing. Magnificent hillside walks. A 15-acre site with 80 touring pitches, 40 hardstandings and 57 statics.
Facilities: Adventure play area, paddling/ball pools 🏖🔦🚿🛁👣☉📶☀🕐 📱🚻🛒♿ **Services:** 📺🔌🍴🚽🛢🚿🍽🏪 **Facilities found within 3 miles:** ∪ 🎣 🎖 🛍 **Notes:** Families and couples only

LITTLE TORRINGTON SS41
Smytham Manor ▶▶▶ 84%
EX38 8PU
☎ 01805 622110 📄 01805 625451
email: info@smytham.co.uk
www.smytham.co.uk
Dir: *On A386 (Great Torrington to Okehampton road), 2m S of Great Torrington*
* 🚐 £7.50-£15 🚉 £7.50-£15 ▲ £7.50-£17
Open: Mar-Sep, Booking advisable peak season, Last arrival 21.30hrs Last departure 11.00hrs
This rural retreat is set in landscaped undulating grounds with level terraced touring pitches. There is a new heated toilet block and reception/bar. The famous Tarka Trail Cycle & Walking Track can be accessed directly from this park. A 25-acre site with 45 touring pitches, 13 hardstandings and 94 statics.
Facilities: 🔦🔦🛁👣☉📶🚿☀🕐🛒🚻🛒♿ & **Services:** 📺🚽🔌🛢 **Facilities found within 3 miles:** ⚓18 🎣 ◎🛍

MOLLAND · SS72

Yeo Valley Holiday Park ►►► 74%

South Molton EX36 3NW

☎ 01769 550297 📄 01769 550101

email: info@yeovalleyholidays.com

www.yeovalleyholidays.com

Dir: *From A361 onto B3227 towards Bampton. Follow brown signs for Blackcock Inn. Site opposite*

* 🚐 £9-£13.50 🚐 £9-£13.50 ▲ £9-£13.50

Open: Open All Year (rs Sep-Mar swimming pool closed), Booking advisable Jul-Aug, Last arrival 22.30hrs Last departure 10.00hrs

Set in a beautiful secluded valley on the edge of Exmoor National Park, this family-run park has easy access to both the moors and the north Devon coastline. The park is adjacent to the Blackcock Inn (under same ownership), and has a heated indoor pool. A 7-acre site with 65 touring pitches and 16 hardstandings.

Facilities: Fishing lake & bike hire 🏕 🔍 ⋀ ☐ 🏁 ⊙ 🗚 ⋈ ⏱ 🖪 🏁 **Services:** 🖳 🖷 🖳 🖸 🔒 ⊘ **Facilities found within 3 miles:** ∪ 🗚 🖥

MORTEHOE · SS44

Easewell Farm Holiday Parc & Golf Club ►►► 72%

Woolacombe EX34 7EH

☎ 01271 870343 📄 01271 870089

email: goodtimes@woolacombe.com

www.woolacombe.com

Dir: *Take B3343 to Mortehoe. Turn right at fork, site 2m on right*

* 🚐 £14-£47.50 🚐 £14-£47.50 ▲ £10-£30

Open: Etr-Oct (rs Etr), Booking advisable Jul-Aug, Etr, Whitsun, Last arrival 22.00hrs Last departure 10.00hrs

A clifftop park with full facility pitches for caravans and motorhomes. Indoor bowling and a golf course, and all the facilities of the three other nearby holiday centres within this group. A 17-acre site with 302 touring pitches, 50 hardstandings and 1 static.

Facilities: 9-hole golf on site, indoor bowls, snooker 🏕 🔍 ⋀ 🏁 ⊙ 🗚 🖈 ⊙ 🗚 ⋈ **Services:** 🖳 🖷 🔟 🖳 🖸 🔒 ⊘ 🖆 🛒 **Facilities found within 3 miles:** ∪ 🖟 9 ⅌ 🗚 ◎ 🖢 🖥 🖥

DEVON

DEVON

MORTEHOE SS44
Twitchen House Holiday Parc 74%

Station Road Woolacombe EX34 7ES
☎ 01271 870343 📠 01271 870089
email: goodtimes@woolacombe.com
www.woolacombe.com
Dir: *From Mullacott Cross rdbt take B3343 (Woolacombe road) to Turnpike Cross junct. Take right fork, site 1.5m on left*

* 🚐 £14-£47.50 🚌 £14-£47.50 ▲ £9-£30
Open: Mar-Oct, Booking advisable Etr/Whit & Jul-Aug, Last arrival 24.00hrs Last departure 10.00hrs An attractive park with good leisure facilities. Visitors can use the amenities at three Woolacombe Bay parks, and a bus connects them with the beach. A 45-acre site with 334 touring pitches, 110 hardstandings and 278 statics.
Facilities: Table tennis, sauna, kids' club 🍴 🍴 ♦ ◭ ◻ 🏪 ☺ 🅿 ✕ 🕒 🖐 🖐 🎋 🎋
Services: 🖥 🍴 🔲 🚽 🛁 🛒 ⊘ 🚮 🛒
Facilities found within 3 miles: ∪ ♨ 9 ⚓
🎣 ◎ ⚓ 🖻 🖻

MORTEHOE SS44
Warcombe Farm Caravan & Camping Park ►►► 84%

Station Road EX34 7EJ
☎ 01271 870690 📠 01271 871070
email: info@warcombefarm.co.uk
www.warcombefarm.co.uk
Dir: *N towards Mortehoe from Mullacot Cross rdbt at A361 junct with B3343. Site 2m on right*

* 🚐 £11-£24 🚌 £11-£24 ▲ £9-£19
Open: 15 Mar-Oct, Booking advisable Jul-Aug, Last arrival 10.00hrs Last departure noon
Extensive views from open areas, while other pitches in sheltered paddocks. A 19-acre site with 100 touring pitches and 5 hardstandings.
Facilities: Private fishing ◭ 🏪 ☺ 🅿 ✕ 🖻 🖐 🖥 🎋 ⚓ **Services:** 🔲 🚽 🛒 🛁 🛒 ⊘ 🚮 🛒
Facilities found within 3 miles: ∪ ♨ 18 🎣 ◎ 🖻 🖻 **Notes:** No groups unless booked in advance

MORTEHOE SS44

North Morte Farm Caravan & Camping Park ▶▶▶ 85%

North Morte Road Woolacombe EX34 7EG

☎ 01271 870381 📠 01271 870115

email: info@northmortefarm.co.uk

www.northmortefarm.co.uk

Dir: *From B3343 into Mortehoe, right at post office. Park 500yds on left*

* 🚐 £11-£18.50 🚛 £10-£18.50 ▲ £10-£14

Open: Apr-Sep (rs Oct caravan owners only), Booking advisable school hols, Last arrival 22.30hrs Last departure noon

Set in spectacular coastal countryside close to National Trust land and beach. Mortehoe with its cafés, shops and pubs, is a 5-minute walk away. A 22-acre site with 180 touring pitches, 18 hardstandings and 73 statics.

Facilities: ⚑ 🅟 ⊙ ☔ ✳ ⊙ 🛁 ♨ 🚻 ♿

Services: 🚱 🖥 🛢 ⊘ 🛒 Facilities found within 3 miles: ∪ ♨ 9 ℰ 🖥 ⓢ **Notes:** No large groups, dogs on leads at all times

NEWTON ABBOT SX86

Dornafield ▶▶▶▶▶ 93%

Dornafield Farm Two Mile Oak TQ12 6DD

☎ 01803 812732 📠 01803 812032

email: enquiries@dornafield.com

www.dornafield.com

Dir: *Take A381 (Newton Abbot-Totnes) for 2m. At Two Mile Oak Inn turn right, then left at x-roads in 0.5m to site on right*

* 🚐 £12.50-£21.30 🚛 £13.50-£22.30 ▲ £12.50-£21.30

Open: 17 Mar-5 Jan, Booking advisable bank hols & Jul-Aug, Last arrival 22.00hrs Last departure 11.00hrs

An immaculately kept park in a tranquil wooded valley offering either de-luxe or fully-serviced pitches. The park has two superb, ultra-modern toilet blocks. A 30-acre site with 135 touring pitches and 82 hardstandings.

Facilities: Caravan storage (all year) ♠ ⚑ 🛁 🅟 ⊙ ☔ ✳ ⊙ 🛒 🚻 ♨ ♿ **Services:** 🅣 ↯ 🚱 🖥 🛢 ⊘ 🛒 🏠 **Facilities found within 3 miles:** ♨ 18 ℰ 🖥 ⓢ

DEVON

DEVON

NEWTON ABBOT   SX86

Ross Park ►►►►► 95%

Park Hill Farm Ipplepen TQ12 5TT

☎ 01803 812983 📄 01803 812983

email: enquiries@rossparkcaravanpark.co.uk

www.rossparkcaravanpark.co.uk

Dir: *Off A381, 3m from Newton Abbot towards Totnes, signed opposite 'Power' garage towards 'Woodland'*

* 🚐 £11.50-£19.75 🚙 £11.50-£19.75

▲ £10.50-£18.75

Open: end Feb-1 Jan (rs Nov-Feb & 1st 3wks of Mar restaurant/bar closed (ex Xmas/New Year)), Booking advisable Jul, Aug & BHs, Last arrival 21.00hrs Last departure 10.00hrs

Rural park with superb views. A 26-acre top-class site with 110 secluded touring pitches and 82 hardstandings.

Facilities: Snooker, table tennis, badminton, croquet 🔦 🅰 🏳 🌀 ☉ 🅿 ✳ 🕓 🗟 🛒 🍴 🎠 ⅄

Services: 🖴 🍴 🗑 🔲 ♿ 🐶 🗑 🏧 ⌀ 🧺 🏪

Facilities found within 3 miles: ∪ ⅃ 18 🥅 🗟 🗐 **Notes:** 🐾

PAIGNTON   SX86

Beverley Parks Caravan & Camping Park 85%

Goodrington Road TQ4 7JE

☎ 01803 661979 📄 01803 845427

email: info@beverley-holidays.co.uk

www.beverley-holidays.co.uk

Dir: *On A380/A3022, 2m S of Paignton turn left into Goodrington Road*

* 🚐 £13.75-£34.50 🚙 £13.75-£34.50

▲ £10.25-£28

Open: Feb-Dec, Booking advisable Jun-Sep, Last arrival 22.00hrs Last departure 10.00hrs

A high quality family-run park with extensive views of the bay, and plenty of on-site amenities. A 12-acre site with 175 touring pitches, 36 hardstandings and 189 statics.

Facilities: Table tennis, pool, spa bath, crazy golf, sauna 🎣 🔦 🅰 🌀 ☉ 🅿 ✳ 🕓 🗟 🍴 ⅄ **Services:** 🖴 🍴 🗑 🔲 🐶 🗑 🏧 ⌀ 🏪

Facilities found within 3 miles: ∪ ⅃ 18 🥅 🥏 ◎ 🛶 🗟 🗐 🚫 **Notes:** No pets

PAIGNTON   SX86

Byslades International Touring & Camping Park ▶▶▶ 85%

Totnes Road TQ4 7PY

☎ 01803 555072 📠 01803 555669

email: info@byslades.co.uk

www.byslades.co.uk

Dir: *on A385, between Paignton & Totnes*

* 🚐 £6-£11.50 🚗 £6-£11.50 ▲ £6-£13.50

Open: Whit-Aug BH (rs May & Sep bar & pool closed), Booking advisable Jul-Aug, Last arrival 18.00hrs Last departure 10.00hrs
A well-kept terraced park in beautiful countryside, only 2m from Paignton. It offers a good mix of amenities, including a large heated pool with a toddlers area. A 23-acre site with 190 touring pitches and 40 hardstandings.

Facilities: Crazy golf 🛶 🥤 🔥 🕯 🐾 😊 🗇 ✳
🕐 🗓 🍴 🚻 👶 **Services:** 🛁 🍴 🔱 🚽 🐕 🛢 🛒 ⊘
🚿 🚰 **Facilities found within 3 miles:** 🎣
18 ⚾ 🔗 ⛴ 🗓 🏵 **Notes:** No commercial vehicles, no dogs mid Jul-Aug

PAIGNTON   SX86

Widend Touring Park ▶▶▶▶ 78%

Berry Pomeroy Road Marldon TQ3 1RT

☎ 01803 550116 📠 01803 550116

Dir: *Signed from Torbay ring road*

* 🚐 £6-£13 🚗 £6-£13 ▲ £6-£13

Open: Apr-end Sep (rs Apr-mid May & mid Sep swimming pool & club house closed), Booking advisable Jul-Aug & Whit, Last arrival 21.00hrs Last departure 10.00hrs
A terraced grass park paddocked and screened on high ground overlooking Torbay with views of Dartmoor. Facilities are of a high standard and offer a heated outdoor swimming pool with sunbathing area, a small lounge bar and a well-stocked shop. A 22-acre site with 207 touring pitches and 6 hardstandings.

Facilities: 🛶 🥤 🔥 🕯 😊 ✳ 🕐 🗓 🚻 👶 **Services:** 🍴 🚽 🐕 🛢 🛒 🚿 🚰 🛒 **Facilities found within 3 miles:** ∪ 🎣 18 ⚾ 🔗 🏵 ⛴ 🗓 🏵 **Notes:** No dogs mid Jul-Aug

DEVON

DEVON

PAIGNTON SX86

Whitehill Country Park ▶▶▶ 80%

Stoke Road TQ4 7PF

☎ 01803 782338 📠 01803 782722

email: info@whitehill-park.co.uk

www.whitehill-park.co.uk

* 🚐 £13-£26 🚌 £13-£26 ⛺ £10-£24

Open: 4 Apr-Sep, Booking advisable Jul-Aug, Last arrival 21.00hrs Last departure 10.00hrs

A family-owned and run park set in rolling countryside, with many scenic beaches just a short drive away. This extensive country park covers 40 acres with woodland walks, and plenty of flora and fauna. It offers ideal facilities for an excellent holiday. A 40-acre site with 260 touring pitches and 60 statics.

Facilities: Walking and cycling trails 🏊 🎾 🛝 📺 💨 ☏ 🛍 **Services:** ☕ 🍷 🚐 🧺 🔒 🍃 🛒 **Facilities found within 3 miles:** 🐎 ⛳ 18 🏄 🎣 ◎ ⛵ 🧺 🛍 🚫🐕 **Notes:** No Pets

PLYMOUTH SX55

Riverside Caravan Park ▶▶▶▶ 79%

Longbridge Road PL6 8LL

☎ 01752 344122 📠 01752 344122

email: info@riversidecaravanpark.com

www.riversidecaravanpark.com

Dir: *A38 follow signs at Marsh Mills rdbt, take 3rd exit, then left. 400yds turn right (keep River Plym on right) to park*

Open: Open All Year (rs Oct-Etr bar, restaurant & take-away closed), Booking advisable Jun-Aug, Last arrival 22.00hrs Last departure 10.00hrs

A well-groomed site on the outskirts of Plymouth on the banks of the River Plym, in a quiet location surrounded by woodland. This park is an ideal stopover for the ferries to France and Spain, and makes an excellent base for touring Dartmoor and the coast. An 11-acre site with 293 touring pitches.

Facilities: 🏊 🎾 🛝 📺 🚿 ⊙ 💨 ☏ 🛍 🐕 **Services:** ☕ 🍷 [T] 🚐 🧺 🔒 🍃 🛏 🛒 **Facilities found within 3 miles:** 🐎 ⛳ 18 🏄 🎣 ◎ ⛵ 🧺 🛍

PRINCETOWN SX57

The Plume of Feathers Inn ▶▶ 76%

Plymouth Yelverton PL20 6QQ

☎ 01822 890240

Dir: *Site accessed directly from B3212 rdbt (beside Plume of Feathers Inn) in centre of Princetown*

* ⚐ £6.50 ▲ £6.50

Open: Open All Year Booking advisable all year, Last arrival 23.30hrs Last departure 11.00hrs

Set amidst the rugged beauty of Dartmoor not far from the notorious prison, this campsite boasts new toilet facilities and all the amenities of the inn. The Plume of Feathers is Princetown's oldest building, and serves all day food in an atmospheric setting. The campsite is mainly for tents. A 3-acre site with 85 touring pitches.

Facilities: ⚐ ⚑ ⚒ ⚓ ⚔ ⚕ ⚖ ⚗ **Services:** ⚘ ⚙ ⚚ ⚛ **Facilities found within 3 miles:** ∪ ⚲ 18 ⚴ ⚵ ⚶ ⚷ **Notes:** No caravans

SALCOMBE

Bolberry House Farm Cara Camping Park ▶▶▶ 72%

Bolberry TQ7 3DY

☎ 01548 561251

email: bolberry.house@virgin.net

www.bolberryparks.co.uk

Dir: *At Malborough on A381 turn right signed Hope Cove/Bolberry. Take left fork after village signed Soar/Bolberry. 0.6m right again. Site signed in 0.5m*

* ⚐ £7.50-£11.50 ⚑ £7.50-£11.50 ▲ £7-£11.50

Open: Etr-Oct, Booking advisable Jun-Sep, Last arrival 20.00hrs Last departure 11.00hrs

A very popular park in a peaceful setting on a coastal farm with sea views, fine cliff walks and nearby beaches. Discount in low season for senior citizens. A 6-acre site with 70 touring pitches and 10 statics.

Facilities: Children's play area, play barn ⚐ ⚑ ⚒ ⚓ ⚔ ⚕ ⚖ ⚗ **Services:** ⚘ ⚙ ⚚ ⚛ ⚜ **Facilities found within 3 miles:** ∪ ⚲ 18 ⚴ ⚵ ⚶ ⚷ ⚸ **Notes:** ⚹

DEVON

DEVON

SAMPFORD PEVERELL   SS01

Minnows Touring Park ►►►► 85%

Holbrook Lane EX16 7EN

☎ 01884 821770 🖨 01884 829199

www.ukparks.co.uk/minnows

Dir: *M5 junct 27, A361 signed Tiverton & Barnstaple. In 600yds take 1st slip road, then right over bridge, site ahead*

* 🚐 £11-£19 🚏 £11-£19 ▲ £8-£19

Open: 5 Mar-4 Nov, Booking advisable bank hols & Jun-Sep, Last arrival 20.00hrs Last departure 11.30hrs

A small, well-sheltered park, located amidst fields and mature trees. The toilet facilities are of a high quality, and there is a good laundry. The park has direct gated access to the canal towpath. A 5.5-acre site with 45 touring pitches, 34 hardstandings and 1 static.

Facilities: Tourist information centre 🅰 🏳
☉ 🅿 ⚡ ⊕ ♨ 🛒 🚻 ⅊ ♿ **Services:** 🚽 🚘 🗑 🔋 🛒 ∅
🍴 🛒 **Facilities found within 3 miles:** ♨
18 ⌀ ≋ 🗊 **Notes:** No cycling, no groundsheets on grass

SIDMOUTH   SY19

Oakdown Touring & Holiday Caravan Park ►►►► 81%

Weston EX10 0PH

☎ 01297 680387 🖨 01297 680541

email: enquiries@oakdown.co.uk

www.oakdown.co.uk

Dir: *Off A3052, 2.5m E of junct with A375*

* 🚐 £9.75-£23.75 🚏 £9.75-£23.75
▲ £9.75-£18.25

Open: Apr-Oct, Booking advisable Spring bank hol & Jul-Aug, Last arrival 22.00hrs Last departure 10.30hrs

Friendly park with pitches grouped in paddocks. A 13-acre site with 100 touring pitches, 90 hardstandings and 62 statics.

Facilities: Free use of microwave 🅰 ⛛ 🏳
☉ 🅿 ⚡ ⊕ 🛒 🚻 ♨ ♿ **Services:** 🔋 🚘 🗑 🔋 🛒 ∅ 🍴 🛒 **Facilities found within 3 miles:** ∪ ♨ 9 ≋ ⌀ ◎ ≋ 🗊 🗊 **Notes:** Dogs must be kept on leads & exercised off park, no bikes, no skateboards, no kite flying

STOKENHAM   SX84

Old Cotmore Farm ▶▶▶ 75%

Nr Kingsbridge TQ7 2LR

☎ 01548 580240 📠 01548 580875

email: enquiries@oldcotmorefarm.co.uk

www.oldcotmorefarm.co.uk

Dir: *Leave Kingsbridge on A379 Dartmouth road, passing through Frogmore & Chillington to mini rdbt at Stokenham. Right towards Beesands, site 1m on right*

* 🚐 £9.35-£14.80 🚏 £9.35-£14.80 ▲ £9.35-£14.80

Open: mid Mar-Oct, Booking advisable Jul & Aug, Last arrival 20.00hrs Last departure 11.00hrs

A quiet park in an Area of Outstanding Natural Beauty. Facilities are modern, and beaches are within walking distance. A 3-acre site with 30 touring pitches and 21 hardstandings.

Facilities: 🔦 🚿 🏕 ⊙ 🕊✖ 🕐 🗄 🛒 🚻 🎣 ㊉

Services: 🆃 🚐 🗄 🛢 ⌀ 🚛 **Facilities found within 3 miles:** ∪ 🏇 🥅 🗷 **Notes:** Dogs must be kept on leads

TAVISTOCK   SX47

Woodovis Park ▶▶▶▶ 81%

Gulworthy PL19 8NY

☎ 01822 832968 📠 01822 832948

email: info@woodovis.com

www.woodovis.com

Dir: *A390 from Tavistock signed Callington & Gunnislake. At top of hill turn right at rdbt signed Lamerton & 'Chipshop'. Park 1m on left*

* 🚐 £17-£19 🚏 £17-£19 ▲ £17-£19

Open: Apr-Oct, Booking advisable Jun-Aug, Last arrival 22.00hrs Last departure noon

A well-kept park in a remote woodland setting on the edge of the Tamar Valley. It has lots of on-site facilities. The toilets are excellent, and there is an indoor swimming pool. A 14.5-acre site with 50 touring pitches, 18 hardstandings and 35 statics.

Facilities: Mini-golf, sauna, jacuzzi 🎣 🔦 🛝 🚿 ⊙ 🕊✖ 🕐 🗄 🚻 🎣 ㊉ **Services:** 🆃 ⚡ 🚐 🗄 🛢 ⌀ **Facilities found within 3 miles:** ∪ 🎿 18 🥅 ◎ 🗄 🗷 **Notes:** Dogs must be kept on leads

DEVON

DEVON

TAVISTOCK   SX47

Harford Bridge Holiday Park

▶▶▶ 77%

Peter Tavy PL19 9LS

☎ 01822 810349 🖹 01822 810028

email: enquiry@harfordbridge.co.uk

www.harfordbridge.co.uk

Dir: *2m N of Tavistock, off A386 Okehampton Rd, take Peter Tavy turn, entrance 200yds on right*

* 🚐 £9.50-£12.75 🚏 £9.50-£12.75 ▲ £9.50-£12.75

Open: Open All Year **Open:** end Mar-mid Nov (rs Nov-Mar statics only & 5 hardstanding pitches), Booking advisable Aug, Etr, BHs, Last arrival 21.00hrs Last departure noon

This park is beside the river in the Dartmoor National Park. A 16-acre site with 120 touring pitches, 5 hardstandings and 80 statics.

Facilities: Fly fishing ◉ ⚠ ❑ 🌣 🖍 ⊙ 𝓟 ※ ◐ ⚒ ♨ 🚻 🚮 ♿ **Services:** ⚓ 🚱 🛢 🛒 🥤 **Facilities found within 3 miles:** ∪ ♨ 18 🌶 ◎ ◙ 🖼 **Notes:** No large groups

TAVISTOCK   SX47

Higher Longford Caravan & Camping Park ▶▶▶▶ 88%

Moorshop PL19 9LQ

☎ 01822 613360 🖹 01822 618722

email: stay@higherlongford.co.uk

www.higherlongford.co.uk

Dir: *From A30 to Tavistock take B3357 towards Princetown. 2m on right before hill onto moors*

* 🚐 £13-£15 🚏 £13-£15 ▲ £11-£13

Open: Open All Year Booking advisable Etr, Jun-Oct, Last arrival 22.00hrs Last departure noon

Set in Dartmoor National Park, with views of the moors, this park has mainly sheltered grassy pitches. A 7-acre site with 82 touring pitches, 20 hardstandings and 4 statics.

Facilities: Pool table, campers' lounge, off licence ◉ ⚠ ❑ 🖍 ⊙ 𝓟 ※ ◐ ⚒ 🚻 🚮 🚻 ♿ **Services:** 🖵 🚱 🛢 🛒 🥤 🥤 🚽 **Facilities found within 3 miles:** ∪ ♨ 18 🌶 ◎ ◙ 🖼 **Notes:** Dogs must be kept on leads

TEDBURN ST MARY SX79

Springfield Holiday Park ►►► 72%

Exeter EX6 6EW

☎ 01647 24242 ▤ 01647 24131

email:
enquiries@springfieldholidaypark.co.uk

www.springfieldholidaypark.co.uk

Dir: *M5 junct 31, A30 towards Okehampton,*
exit at 3rd junct, signed to Cheriton Bishop.
Follow brown tourist signs to park

* ⊕ £12-£16 ⊕ £12-£20 ▲ £10-£16

Open: 15 Mar-15 Nov (rs 15 Nov-15 Jan
Static home owners only), Booking advisable
Jul-Aug, Last arrival 22.00hrs Last departure
noon

Set in a rural location with countryside views,
this park continues to be upgraded. It is close
to Dartmoor National Park, as well as village
pubs and stores. A 9-acre site with 48 touring
pitches, 38 hardstandings and 49 statics.

Facilities: Family bathroom ⬡ ♦ ⬠ ⬡ ⊙
⨁ ⊞ ⤧ **Services:** ⊕ ⬓ ▮ ⊘ **Facilities**
found within 3 miles: ⌕ 18 ℘ ⬓ **Notes:**
Dogs must be kept on leads

TORQUAY SX86

Widdicombe Farm Touring Park

►►►► 80%

Marldon TQ3 1ST

☎ 01803 558325 ▤ 01803 559526

email: info@widdicombefarm.co.uk

www.widdicombefarm.co.uk

Dir: *On A380, midway between Torquay &*
Paignton ring road

* ⊕ £7-£18 ⊕ £7-£18 ▲ £7-£18

Open: mid Mar-mid Oct, Booking advisable
Whit & Jul-Aug, Last arrival 21.30hrs Last
departure 11.00hrs

A friendly park on a working farm, with good
facilities. An 8-acre site with 196 touring
pitches, 180 hardstandings and 3 statics.

Facilities: Family bathrooms, BBQ patio,
entertainment ♦ ⬠ ⬡ ⊙ ⨁ ⟊ ⬓ ⬓ ⤧ ⊞ ⤧
⬡ **Services:** ⬓ ⊞ ⬓ ▮ ▭ ⬓ ⬓ ▮ ⊘ ⬓
⬤ ⬢ **Facilities found within 3 miles:** ∪
⌕ 18 ℘ ⊚ ⬓ ⬓ **Notes:** Families & couples
only, 1 family field, adults only fields

DEVON

DEVON

WOOLACOMBE SS44
Golden Coast Holiday Village 76%

Station Road EX34 7HW

☎ 01271 870343 📠 01271 870089

email: goodtimes@woolacombe.com

www.woolacombe.com

Dir: *Follow road to Woolacombe Bay from Mullacott & site is 1.5m on left*

* 🚐 £14-£45 🚎 £14-£45 ▲ £9-£30

Open: Feb-Dec (rs mid Sep-May outdoor pools closed), Booking advisable bank hols & mid Jul-end Aug, Last arrival 24.00hrs Last departure 10.00hrs

A holiday village offering excellent leisure facilities as well as the amenities of the other Woolacombe Bay holiday parks. A 10-acre site with 93 touring pitches, 53 hardstandings and 519 statics.

Facilities: Sauna, solarium, golf, fishing, snooker, cinema 🎿 🍴 🔍 🏕 🏢 🥄 🏹 😊 🌳 💥 🕙 🏧 🍽 🎆 **Services:** 🍺 🎦 🅣 🔌 🛢 🖀 🗑 🚿 🚾 🚐 🛁 **Facilities found within 3 miles:** ∪ 🎣 9 ⛴ 🗺 ◎ 🏊 🔒 🗿 🧑

WOOLACOMBE SS44
Woolacombe Sands Holiday Park 75%

Beach Road EX34 7AF

☎ 01271 870569 📠 01271 870606

email: lifesabeach@woolacombe-sands.co.uk

www.woolacombe-sands.co.uk

Dir: *M5 junct 27, A361 to Barnstaple. Follow Ilfracombe signs, until Mullacott Cross. Turn left onto B3343 to Woolacombe. Site on left*

* 🚐 £9-£25 🚎 £9-£25 ▲ £9-£25

Open: Apr-Oct, Booking advisable 24-31 May & 19 Jul-30 Aug, Last arrival 22.00hrs Last departure 10.00hrs

Set in rolling countryside with grassy terraced pitches. There is a footpath to the beach. Entertainment in high season. A 20-acre site with 200 touring pitches and 80 statics.

Facilities: Kids' club, heated indoor/outdoor swimming pools 🎿 🥄 🔍 🏕 🏹 😊 🌳 💥 🕙 🏧 🚏 ♿ **Services:** 🍺 🎦 🅣 🔌 🛢 🖀 🗑 🚿 🚾 🛁 **Facilities found within 3 miles:** ∪ 🔒 18 🗺 ◎ 🗿 🧑

WOOLACOMBE   SS44

Woolacombe Bay
Holiday Village 77%

Sandy Lane EX34 7AH

☎ 01271 870343 📄 01271 870089

email: goodtimes@woolacombe.com

www.woolacombe.com

Dir: *From Mullacott Cross rdbt take B3343*
(Woolacombe road) to Turnpike Cross junct.
Right towards Mortehoe, site approx 1m on left

* **Å** £10-£30

Open: Mar-Oct (rs Mar-mid May, mid Sep-
Oct no camping), Booking advisable Whit &
summer hols, Last arrival midnight Last
departure 10.00hrs

A well-developed touring section in a holiday
complex. An 8.5-acre site with 180 touring
pitches and 237 statics.

Facilities: Entertainment, kids' club, health
suite 🏊♨🍴🐕♨🚲🛝📷⊙🅿✕🕐🍴🎣🎱

🍺👢 **Services:** 🔌🍴🍷🔋📶🍺🗑📦🚿🛒🚮

Facilities found within 3 miles: ∪↓9⚓
🎿◎⛵🔋🅖🛒

WOOLACOMBE   SS44

Europa Park ►►► 77%

Beach Rd EX34 7AN

☎ 01271 871425 📄 01271 871425

email: europaparkwoolacombe@yahoo.co.uk

Dir: *M5 junct 27, A361 through Barnstaple to*
Mullacott Cross. Left onto B3343 signed
Woolacombe. Site on right at Spa
shop/garage

🚐 £14-£22 🚓 £14-£22 **Å** £14-£22

Open: Open All Year Booking advisable bank
hols & high season, Last arrival 23.00hrs

A lively family-run site handy for the beach at
Woolacombe, and catering well for surfers.
Set in a stunning location high above the bay,
it provides a wide range of accommodation
including surf cabins, and generous touring
pitches. A 16-acre site with 200 touring
pitches, 20 hardstandings and 22 statics.

Facilities: Beer deck, off licence, pub, big
screen TV 🏊♨🍴🚲🛝📷♨⊙✕🕐🅖🍴

Services: 🔌🍴🍷🔋Ⓣ👢🍺🗑📦🚿🛒🚮

Facilities found within 3 miles: ∪↓18
🎿◎⛵🔋🅖🛒

DEVON

DORSET

ALDERHOLT SU11
Hill Cottage Farm Touring Caravan Park ►►►► 81%
Sandleheath Road Fordingbridge SP6 3EG
☎ 01425 650513 📄 01425 652339
Dir: *Take B3078 W of Fordingbridge. Turn off at Alderholt, site 0.25m on left after railway bridge*
* 🚐 £12-£14 🚍 £12-£14 ▲ £10-£12
Open: Mar-Oct, Booking advisable Bank hols & Jul-Aug, Last arrival 19.00hrs Last departure 11.00hrs
Set within extensive grounds this rural, beautifully landscaped park has mainly full facility pitches set in individual hardstanding bays with mature hedges between giving adequate pitch privacy. A modern toilet block is kept immaculately clean, and there's a good range of leisure facilities. In high season there is an area available for tenting.
Facilities: 🔍 🐾 ⊙ 🅿 ✳ 🕐 🚽 🎍
Services: ⚓ 🚐 🖲 🛒 **Facilities found within 3 miles:** ∪ ⚓ 18 🎣 🖲 **Notes:** 🐕

BLANDFORD FORUM ST80
The Inside Park ►►►► 76%
Down House Estate DT11 9AD
☎ 01258 453719 📄 01258 459921
email: inspark@aol.com
http://members.aol.com/inspark/inspark
Dir: *From town, over River Stour, follow Winterborne Stickland signs. Site in 1.5m*
🚐 £11-£18 🚍 £11-£18 ▲ £11-£18
Open: Etr-Oct, Booking advisable bank hols & Jul-Aug, Last arrival 22.00hrs Last departure noon
A well-sheltered and quiet park, 0.5m off a country lane in a wooded valley. Spacious pitches are divided by trees and shrubs, and amenities are housed in an 18th-century coach house and stables. Woodland walks. A 12-acre site with 125 touring pitches.
Facilities: Farm trips (main season), kennels for hire 🔍 🐾 ⊙ 🅿 ✳ 🕐 🖲 🚽 ♿
Services: ▣ 🚐 🖲 🛒 ∅ 🍴 🖱 **Facilities found within 3 miles:** ∪ ⚓ 18 🎣 🖲 🖲

BRIDPORT SY49

Highlands End Holiday Park

▶▶▶▶▶ 84%

Eype DT6 6AR

☎ 01308 422139 🖷 01308 425672

email: holidays@wdlh.co.uk

www.wdlh.co.uk

Dir: *1m W of Bridport on A35, turn south for Eype. Park signed*

* 🚐 £12-£21.50 ⛺ £12-£21.50 ▲ £9-£16

Open: mid Mar-early Nov, Booking advisable public hols & Jul-Aug, Last arrival 22.00hrs Last departure 11.00hrs

A well-screened site with magnificent clifftop views. Pitches are mostly sheltered by hedging and well spaced on hardstandings. A 9-acre site with 195 touring pitches, 45 hardstandings and 160 statics.

Facilities: Gym, steam room, sauna, pitch & putt, tourist info 🏡 🔍 🅰 🛁 🌢 🍴 ⊙ 🅿 ✼ 🕙 🕖 🔔 ⴲ ⴵ **Services:** 🖢 🍴 🚽 ⊥ 🖘 🗄 🖻 ⊘ 🏪 ᇓ

Facilities found within 3 miles: ⚓ 18 🎣 🖻 🖪

BRIDPORT SY49

Freshwater Beach Holiday Park 82%

Burton Bradstock DT6 4PT

☎ 01308 897317 🖷 01308 897336

email: enquiries@freshwaterbeach.co.uk

www.freshwaterbeach.co.uk

Dir: *Take B3157 from Bridport towards Burton Bradstock. Site 1.5m from Crown rdbt on right*

* 🚐 £9-£30 ⛺ £9-£30 ▲ £9-£30

Open: 15 Mar-10 Nov, Booking advisable Jul-Aug, Last arrival 22.00hrs Last departure 10.00hrs

A family holiday centre sheltered by a sandbank and enjoying its own private beach. The park offers a wide variety of leisure and entertainment programmes. A 40-acre site with 500 touring pitches and 250 statics.

Facilities: Large TV, horse riding, internet, entertainment 🌢 🔍 🅰 🍴 ⊙ 🅿 ✼ 🕙 🖻 🔔 ⴵ **Services:** 🖢 🍴 🚽 🗄 🖻 ⊘ 🏪 ᇓ

Facilities found within 3 miles: ∪ ⚓ 18 ⵟ 🎣 ◎ 🖻 🖪 **Notes:** No unaccompanied groups of teenagers

DORSET

BRIDPORT   SY49
West Bay
Holiday Park 79%

West Bay DT6 4HB
☎ 01308 422424 📠 01308 421371
email: enquiries@parkdeanholidays.co.uk
www.parkdeanholidays.co.uk
Dir: *From A35 (Dorchester road), W towards*
Bridport, take 1st exit at 1st rdbt, 2nd exit at
2nd rdbt into West Bay, park on right
* 🚐 £9-£27 �"£11-£30 ▲ £9-£27
Open: 18 Mar-4 Nov (rs 6 Apr-25 May & 14-
19 Sep entertainment restricted), Booking
advisable May-Sep, Last arrival 21.00hrs Last
departure 10.00hrs
Overlooking the pretty little harbour at West
Bay, and close to the shingle beach, this park
offers a full entertainment programme for all
ages. The touring area is terraced. A 6-acre
site with 131 touring pitches and 307 statics.
Facilities: 🎣 🔦 🐾 🛝 ⊙ 🅿 🌂 🕓 🛢 🎮 🛒 ᕑ
Services: 🐾 🍴 🍷 🗜 🛢 🛢 🖋 🍴 🚮 ⚏
Facilities found within 3 miles: ∪ ♨ 18
🎣 🎣 ◎ 🛢 🖭

CHARMOUTH   SY39
Wood Farm Caravan & Camping
Park ▶▶▶▶▶ 84%

Axminster Road DT6 6BT
☎ 01297 560697 📠 01297 561243
email: holidays@woodfarm.co.uk
www.woodfarm.co.uk
Dir: *Park entered directly off A35 rdbt, on*
Axminster side of Charmouth
* 🚐 £12-£24 🚐 £12-£24 ▲ £12-£24
Open: Etr-Oct, Booking advisable school
hols, Last arrival 19.00hrs Last departure
noon
A pleasant, well-established and mature park
overlooking the sea, hills and valleys. The
four camping fields are terraced, each with its
own toilet block. A 13-acre site with 216
touring pitches, 175 hardstandings and 81
statics.
Facilities: Coarse fishing lake 🎣 🔦 🛝 🗖 ♨
🐾 ⊙ 🅿 🌂 🕓 🖭 🚮 ᕑ **Services:** 🗜 🖋 🚐 🛢
🍴 🖋 ⚏ **Facilities found within 3 miles:**
∪ ♨ 18 ♨ 🎣 ◎ 🛢 🖭 **Notes:** No
skateboards, scooters or roller skates

CHARMOUTH SY39
Newlands Caravan & Camping Park ►►►► 85%
Bridport DT6 6RB
☎ 01297 560259 📠 01297 560787
email: enq@newlandsholidays.co.uk
www.newlandsholidays.co.uk
Dir: *4m W of Bridport on A35*
* 🚐 £11-£30 🚍 £11-£30 ▲ £10-£24
Open: Open All Year (rs Nov-Mar restaurant, bar & shop closed), Booking advisable school hols, Last arrival 22.30hrs Last departure 10.00hrs
A smart site with excellent touring facilities. The park offers an entertainment programme for all ages, and boasts an indoor swimming pool with spa and an outdoor pool with water slide. Set on gently sloping ground in hilly countryside. A 23-acre site with 240 touring pitches, 52 hardstandings and 86 statics.
Facilities: 🌣 🏕 🔌 ⚠ 🔲 🦌 🏕 ⊙ 🖉 ✳ 🕓 🛢 🖬
Services: 🐖 🕾 🗍 🔌 🔋 🛢 🛢 🕋 **Facilities found within 3 miles:** ∪ ⎋ 18 ✚ 🖉 ◎ ⎋ 🛢 🛢

CHARMOUTH SY39
Manor Farm Holiday Centre
►►► 78%
Bridport DT6 6QL
☎ 01297 560226
email: enq@manorfarmholidaycentre.co.uk
www.manorfarmholidaycentre.co.uk
Dir: *W on A35 to Charmouth, site 0.75m on right*
* 🚐 £10-£17 🚍 £10-£17 ▲ £10-£17
Open: Open All Year (rs End Oct-mid Mar statics only), Booking advisable high season, Last arrival 20.00hrs Last departure 10.00hrs
Set just a short walk from the safe sand and shingle beach at Charmouth, this family park offers a good range of facilities, including an outdoor swimming pool and an entertainment programme. A 15-acre site with 250 touring pitches, 80 hardstandings and 29 statics.
Facilities: 🌣 🔌 ⚠ 🦌 ⊙ 🖉 ✳ 🕓 🛢 🖬 🌣 ⎅
Services: 🐖 🍴 🗍 🔌 🔋 🛢 🛢 🕋
Facilities found within 3 miles: ∪ ⎋ 18 ✚ 🖉 ◎ ⎋ 🛢 🛢

DORSET

DORSET

CHRISTCHURCH   SZ19
Grove Farm Meadow Holiday Caravan Park ►►►► 88%

Stour Way BH23 2PQ

☎ 01202 483597 📄 01202 483878

email: enquiries@meadowbank-holidays.co.uk

www.meadowbank-holidays.co.uk

Dir: *A31 onto A338 towards Bournemouth. Take 1st exit after 5m then left towards Christchurch on B3073. Right at 1st rdbt into St Catherine's Way/River Way. Stour Way 3rd right, site at end of road*

* 🚐 £7-£26 🚎 £7-£26

Open: Mar-Oct, Booking advisable at all times, Last arrival 21.00hrs Last departure noon Set on the banks of the River Stour, with modern toilet facilities and excellent play equipment. Visitors can choose between pitch sizes. A 2-acre site with 41 touring pitches, 22 hardstandings and 180 statics.

Facilities: Fishing on site 🔍 🏔 🍴 ☺ 🅿 🕐 🖺 🏪 🕭 **Services:** 🚻 🚽 🛁 🛒 🧺

Facilities found within 3 miles: ∪ ♨ 18 ⛴ 🎣 ◎ ⚓ 🛆 🖺 🕭 Ⓝ

HOLTON HEATH   SY99
Sandford Holiday Park 78%

Poole BH16 6JZ

☎ 0870 0667793 📄 01202 625678

email: bookings@weststarholidays.co.uk

www.weststarholidays.co.uk

Dir: *A35 from Poole towards Dorchester, at lights onto A351 towards Wareham. Right at Holton Heath. Park 100yds on left*

* 🚐 £12.50-£28.50 🚎 £12.50-£28.50

▲ £12.50-£28.50

Open: Mar-Nov, Booking advisable Jul-Aug & bank hols, Last arrival 22.00hrs Last departure 10.00hrs

Touring pitches set individually in 20 acres surrounded by woodland. Full range of leisure activities and entertainment. A 64-acre site with 500 touring pitches and 284 statics.

Facilities: Fun factory, bowling, entertainment, crazy golf 🎣 🛶 🔍 🏔 🖵 👤 🕭 ☺✳ 🕐 🅿 🚽 🍴 🏪 🕭 **Services:** 🐩 🍴 🚐 🛒

🛁 🛆 🚰 **Facilities found within 3 miles:** ∪ ♨ 9 ⛴ 🎣 ◎ 🖺 🕭

OWERMOIGNE   SY78

Sandyholme Caravan Park

▶▶▶ 80%

Moreton Road Dorchester DT2 8HZ

☎ 01305 852677 📠 01305 854677

email: smeatons@sandyholme.co.uk

www.sandyholme.co.uk

Dir: *From A352 (Wareham to Dorchester road) turn right to Owermoigne for 1m. Site on left*

* 🚐 £12-£17 🚌 £12-£17 ▲ £9.50-£14.50

Open: Apr-Oct, Booking advisable peak periods, Last arrival 21.30hrs Last departure 10.30hrs

A quiet family-run site in a tree-lined rural setting within easy reach of the coast at Lulworth Cove. The facilities are very good, including a superb toilet block, and good food is available in the lounge/bar. A 6-acre site with 50 touring pitches and 30 statics.

Facilities: Table tennis 🏌 🅰 📮 ⊙ 🅿 ✳ 🕔 🖻 🛪 **Services:** 🐦 🗊 🔳 🗗 🗑 🗎 🖋 🛅 🛓

Facilities found within 3 miles: 🖉 🖻 🖻

Notes: Dogs must be kept on leads

POOLE   SY99

Beacon Hill Touring Park ▶▶▶ 75%

Blandford Road North BH16 6AB

☎ 01202 631631 📠 01202 625749

email: bookings@beaconhilltouringpark.co.uk

www.beaconhilltouringpark.co.uk

Dir: *On A350, 0.25m N of junct with A35, 4m N of Poole*

* 🚐 £11-£21 🚌 £10-£28 ▲ £10-£21

Open: Etr-Sep (rs low & mid season some services closed/restricted opening), Booking advisable Etr, Whit & Jul-Aug, Last arrival 23.00hrs Last departure 11.00hrs

Set in a wooded area with conservation very much in mind. The terraced pitches are informally sited, and there are two large ponds for coarse fishing. A 30-acre site with 170 touring pitches and 10 hardstandings.

Facilities: 🌊 🏌 🅰 📮 �"〰 🅿 ✳ 🕔 🖻 🛪 🛦 **Services:** 🐦 🗊 🔳 🗗 🗑 🗎 🖋 🛅 🛓

Facilities found within 3 miles: ∪ ﹒ 18 ⅄ 🖉 🚣 🖻 🖻 **Notes:** Groups of young people only accepted at management's discretion 🐕

DORSET

POOLE SY99

Rockley Park 78%

Hamworthy BH15 4LZ

☎ 01202 679393 🖹 01202 683159

www.havenholidays.com

Dir: *Take A31 off M27 to Poole centre, then follow signs to park*

Open: mid Mar-Oct (rs mid Mar-May & Sep-Oct some facilities may be reduced), Booking advisable school hols, Last departure 10.00hrs
A complete holiday experience with day and night entertainment, and sports and leisure activities. Water sports are comprehensively covered; also mooring and launching from the park. The touring area provides good quality facilities. A 90-acre site with 71 touring pitches, 68 hardstandings and 1077 statics.

Facilities: Sailing school 🏕 🚿 🛒 ⚙ ⚑ 🎣
☉ 🅿️ ✕ ⏰ 🐕 🛒 🍴 ♿ **Services:** 🔌 🍽 🔌 📶 ⊤
🔧 🗑 🛢 🧺 🚿 **Facilities found within 3 miles:** ≉ ◎ ⛵ 🗑 🖺 **Notes:** dogs not allowed during peak periods or on touring pitches

PORTESHAM SY68

Portesham Dairy Farm Campsite

▶▶▶▶ 78%

Weymouth DT3 4HG

☎ 01305 871297

email: malcolm.doble@btconnect.com

www.porteshamdairyfarm.com

Dir: *From Dorchester on A35 towards Bridport. After 5m left at Winterbourne Abbas, follow Portesham signs. Through village, left at Kings Arms pub, site in 350yds on right*

* 🚐 £8.50-£19 🚗 £8.50-£19 ▲ £7-£17

Open: mid Mar-Oct, Booking advisable at busy times, Last arrival 22.00hrs Last departure 16.00hrs
Located at the edge of the picturesque village of Portesham, this family run park is part of a small working dairy farm. This level park has a local pub where meals are served, and with a garden for children. An 8-acre site with 90 touring pitches and 61 hardstandings.

Facilities: Fully serviced pitches ⚑ 🎣 ☉
🅿️ ✕ ⏰ 🐕 🛒 🍴 **Services:** 🔌 🗑 🛢 🧺 🛢 🚿
✏ 🗑 🖺 **Notes:** ⊕

ST LEONARDS   SU10

Shamba Holiday Park ►►►► 89%

230 Ringwood Road BH24 2SB

☎ 01202 873302 📠 01202 873392

email: enquiries@shambaholidays.co.uk

www.shambaholidays.co.uk

Dir: *Off A31, from Poole turn left into Eastmoors Lane, 100yds past 2nd rdbt from Texaco garage. Park 0.25m on right (just past Woodman Inn)*

* 🚐 £18-£30 🚍 £18-£30 ▲ £18-£30

Open: Mar-Oct (rs low season some facilities only open at wknds), Booking advisable bank hols & Jul-Aug, Last arrival 22.00hrs Last departure 11.00hrs

A 7-acre, well equipped site in pleasant countryside with 150 touring pitches.

Facilities: Phone card top-up facility 🎧 🍴 🔍 📶 📡 ⊙ 🗜 ☀ 🕐 🍴 🚪 & **Services:** 🔌 🚰 🕹 📡 🗑 🍴 🚿 🛒 **Facilities found within 3 miles:** ∪ ₺ 18 🏌 🗑 📷 **Notes:** No large groups, no commercial vehicles

ST LEONARDS   SU10

Oakdene

Forest Park 76%

Ringwood BH24 2RZ

☎ 01590 648331 📠 01590 645610

email: holidays@shorefield.co.uk

www.shorefield.co.uk

Dir: *From E: on A31 left at Hospital sign, park sign under footbridge. From W: on A31 u-turn at rdbt after Texaco garage, left at Hospital sign*

🚐 £7.50-£31 🚍 £7.50-£31 ▲ £7.50-£31

Open: Feb-2 Jan, Booking advisable all times, Last arrival 22.00hrs Last departure 10.00hrs Set in 55 acres of parkland beside Avon Forest, this full-entertainment park offers 'fun and games' for the whole family, and there are both indoor and outdoor pools, and a riding stable on site. A 55-acre site with 81 touring pitches and 350 statics.

Facilities: Woodland walks & crazy golf 🎧 🍴 🔍 📶 📡 ⊙ 🗜 ☀ 🕐 🗑 🚪 🚿 **Services:** 🍴 🍽 🔌 📡 🚰 🗑 🛒 🏪 🛒 **Facilities found within 3 miles:** ∪ ₺ 18 🏌 🗑 📷

DORSET

ST LEONARDS
SU10

Forest Edge Touring Park ▶▶▶ 78%

229 Ringwood Road BH24 2SD

☎ 01590 648331 📠 01590 645610

email: holidays@shorefield.co.uk

www.shorefield.co.uk

Dir: *From E: on A31 over 1st rdbt (Little Chef), pass St Leonards Hotel & left at next rdbt into Boundary Lane, site 100yds on left. From W: on A31 pass Texaco garage & Woodsman Inn, right at rdbt into Boundary Lane*

🚐 £7.50-£28 🚌 £7.50-£28 ▲ £7.50-£28

Open: Feb-Dec (rs mid Jul-Aug pool/bar only open school & summer hols), Booking advisable at all times, Last arrival 21.00hrs Last departure 10.00hrs

A tree-lined park set in grassland with plenty of amenities for all the family. Some pitches may experience traffic noise. A 9-acre site with 192 touring pitches and 7 statics.

Facilities: ☕ 🍴 🄰 🄼 ☉ 🄿 ✳ ◐ 👶

Services: 📶 🅃 🄰 🄾 🄰 🄰 **Facilities found within 3 miles:** ∪ ♨ 🎣 ◎ 🌀 🅾

Notes: 1 dog & car per pitch

SWANAGE
SZ07

Ulwell Cottage Caravan Park

▶▶▶ 79%

Ulwell Cottage Ulwell BH19 3DG

☎ 01929 422823 📠 01929 421500

email: enq@ulwellcottagepark.co.uk

www.ulwellcottagepark.co.uk

Dir: *From Swanage N for 2m on unclass road towards Studland*

🚐 £16-£38 🚌 £16-£38 ▲ £10-£38

Open: Mar-7 Jan (rs Mar-Spring bank hol & mid Sep-early Jan takeaway closed, shop open variable hrs), Booking advisable bank hols & Jul-Aug, Last arrival 22.00hrs Last departure 11.00hrs

Nestling under the Purbeck Hills surrounded by scenic walks, this park offers high quality facilities including an indoor heated pool and a village inn. A 13-acre site with 77 touring pitches, 19 hardstandings and 140 statics.

Facilities: ☕ 🄼 🄺 ◐✳ 👶 🄰 🄰 **Services:** 🍴 📶 🄰 🄾 🄰 🄰 🍽 **Facilities found within 3 miles:** ∪ ♨ 36 🎣 🌀 ◎ 🌀 🅾 🅾

SWANAGE SZ07

Swanage Coastal Park ▶▶▶ 75%

Priestway BH19 2RS

☎ 01590 648331 📄 01590 645610

email: holidays@shorefield.co.uk

www.shorefield.co.uk

Dir: *A351 from Wareham. 1m past 'Welcome to Swanage' sign, right into High St. 1st right into Bell Street Up hill, 1st left into Priests Road, 1st right into Priestway to site*

🚐 £7.50-£20 🚓 £7.50-£20 ▲ £7.50-£20

Open: 24 Mar-Oct, Booking advisable at all times, Last arrival 22.00hrs Last departure 10.00hrs

A spacious site set in stunning countryside with views over Swanage Bay and the Purbeck Hills. The adjacent holiday park offers day membership to its health and fitness club, including bar, indoor swimming pool, gym, sauna, solarium, shop and restaurant. A 15-acre site with 10 touring pitches, 10 hardstandings and 52 statics.

Facilities: 🅰 🅿 🕙 🖐 **Services:** 🖥 🗑 🛉 🖋 🛱 🖥 🖐 **Notes:** Dogs must be kept on leads

THREE LEGGED CROSS SU09

Woolsbridge Manor Farm Caravan Park ▶▶▶ 75%

Wimborne BH21 6RA

☎ 01202 826369 📄 01202 820603

email: woolsbridge@btconnect.com

www.woolsbridgemanorfarmcaravanpark.co.uk

Dir: *2m off A31, 3m W of Ringwood. From Three Legged Cross continue S to Woolsbridge. Site 1.75m on left*

* 🚐 £13.50-£20.50 🚓 £13.50-£20.50 ▲ £13.50-£20.50

Open: Mar-Oct, Booking advisable bank hols & Aug, Last arrival 20.00hrs Last departure 10.30hrs

A small farm site with spacious pitches on a level field. This site is a good base for touring the New Forest, Salisbury and the South coast, and is close to Moors Valley Country Park. A 6.75-acre site with 60 touring pitches.

Facilities: 🅰 🖐 ⊙ 🖋 ✕ 🕙 🖥 🛱 🖐 ♿

Services: 🖽 🖭 🛉 🖋 🖀 **Facilities found within 3 miles:** ∪ 🖐 18 🖋 🖥 🖥

DORSET

DORSET

VERWOOD   SU00

Verwood Camping & Caravanning Club Site ▶▶▶ 75%

Sutton Hill Woodlands BH21 8NQ

☎ 01202 822763

www.campingandcaravanningclub.co.uk

Dir: *Turn left on A354 13m from Salisbury onto B3081, site is 1.5m W of Verwood*

⏦ £17.05-£20.15 ⏦ £17.05-£20.15

▲ £17.05-£20.15

Open: Mar-Oct, Booking advisable bank hols & peak periods, Last arrival 21.00hrs Last departure noon

Set on rising ground between the woodland of the New Forest and the rolling downs of Cranborne Chase and Salisbury Plains. This comfortable site is well kept by very keen wardens. A 12.7-acre site with 150 touring pitches and 18 hardstandings.

Facilities: ➍ ⟡ ⊡ ⟡ ⊙ ⟡ ✻ ⊙ ⟡ ☰ ⟡
Services: �⊡ ⟡ ⊡ ⟡ ⊘ ☰ Facilities found within 3 miles: ⟡ ⊡

WAREHAM   SY89

Wareham Forest Tourist Park

▶▶▶▶ 89%

North Trigon BH20 7NZ

☎ 01929 551393 📠 01929 558321

email: holiday@wareham-forest.co.uk

www.wareham-forest.co.uk

* ⏦ £12.50-£19.75 ⏦ £12.50-£19.75

▲ £10-£18

Open: Open All Year (rs off-peak season limited services), Booking advisable Spring bank hol & Jul-Aug, Last arrival 21.00hrs Last departure 10.30hrs

A woodland park within Wareham Forest. There is a heated outdoor pool, off licence, shop and games room. A 42-acre site with 200 touring pitches and 70 hardstandings.

Facilities: ➍ ➍ ⟡ ⟡ ⊙ ⟡ ✻ ⊙ ⟡ ☰ ☰ ☰
⟡ **Services:** ⊡ ⟡ ⟡ ⊡ ⟡ ⊘ ☰ **Facilities found within 3 miles:** ⟲ ⟡ 18 ⟡ ⟡ ⊡ ⊡
Notes: Couples & families only, no group bookings

WAREHAM SY89

Birchwood Tourist Park ▶▶▶ 82%

Bere Road North Trigon BH20 7PA

☎ 01929 554763 📠 01929 556635

www.birchwoodtouristpark.co.uk

Dir: *From Poole (A351) or Dorchester (A352) on N side of railway line at Wareham, follow road signed Bere Regis (unclassified). 2nd tourist park after 2.25m*

* **Open:** Mar-Oct (rs Nov-Feb some restrictions), Booking advisable bank hols & Jul-Aug, Last arrival 21.00hrs Last departure 11.30hrs

Set in 50 acres of parkland located within Wareham Forest, this site offers direct access for walking, mountain biking, and horse and pony riding. A 25-acre site with 175 touring pitches and 8 hardstandings.

Facilities: Games field, bike hire, pitch & putt, paddling pool 🏓 🛝 🚿 🔌 💨 ❄ ☎ [S] 🐕 🪑 **Services:** [T] ⛽ 🧺 🔒 🍃 📦 🛒 **Facilities found within 3 miles:** 🐴 ⛳ 18 🏄 🎣 [S]

Notes: No generators, no groups on Bank Hols

WEYMOUTH SY67

Littlesea Holiday Park 78%

Lynch Lane DT4 9DT

☎ 01305 774414 📠 01305 760038

www.havenholidays.com

Dir: *A35 onto A354 signed Weymouth. Right at 1st rdbt, 3rd exit at 2nd rdbt towards Chickerell. Left into Lynch Lane after lights. Park at far end of road*

Open: end Mar-end Oct (rs mid Mar-May & Sep-Oct facilities may be reduced), Booking advisable school hols, Last arrival anytime Last departure 10.00hrs

Just 3 miles from Weymouth with its lovely beaches and many attractions, Littlesea has a cheerful family atmosphere and fantastic facilities. The toilet facilities on the touring park are of a good quality. A 75-acre site with 100 touring pitches and 850 statics.

Facilities: 🏊 🌊 🏓 🛝 🚿 🔌 💨 ❄ ☎ [S] 🐕 🍖 🪑 ♿ **Services:** ☕ 🍷 ⛽ 🧺 👶 🛒 **Facilities found within 3 miles:** 🐴 ⛳ 9 🏄 🎣 🎯 🚤 🧺 [S]

DORSET

DORSET

WEYMOUTH   SY67

Sea Barn Farm ►► 72%

Fleet DT3 4ED

☎ 01305 782218 ▤ 01305 775396

email: enquire@seabarnfarm.co.uk

www.seabarnfarm.co.uk

Dir: *From Weymouth take B3157 towards Bridport for 3m. In Chickerell turn left at mini-rdbt towards Fleet. Site 1m on left*

* **Å** £10-£18

Open: 15 Mar-Oct (rs May-Sep pool open), Booking advisable Spring & Aug bank hols & school hols, Last arrival 22.30hrs Last departure noon

A quiet site bordering the Fleet nature reserve, and close to coastal path. Pitches sheltered by hedging, and there is space for games. A 12-acre site with 250 touring pitches and 1 static.

Facilities: Café & fast food available at next door site ⬤ ⒜ ⒭ ⊙☀ ⓒ 🅱 ⛟ ⊞ 🚻 🎍 **Services:** 📞 🆃 🅱 🅾 🗑 ⌀ ⛴ **Facilities found within 3 miles:** ∪ 🅱 **Notes:** Non-family groups by arrangement, dogs must be kept on leads at all times

WEYMOUTH   SY67

West Fleet Holiday Farm ►► 72%

Fleet DT3 4EF

☎ 01305 782218 ▤ 01305 775396

email: enquire@seabarnfarm.co.uk

www.westfleetholidays.co.uk

Dir: *From Weymouth take B3157 towards Bridport for 3m. In Chickerell turn left at mini-rdbt to Fleet, 1m on right*

* **Å** £10-£18

Open: Etr-end Sep (rs May-mid Sep pool open), Booking advisable bank hols & school hols, Last arrival 22.30hrs Last departure noon

A spacious farm site with level and sloping pitches divided into paddocks. A relaxing site with its heated outdoor pool and club house. A 12-acre site with 250 touring pitches.

Facilities: ⬤ ⬤ ⒜ ⒭ ⊙☀ ⓒ 🅱 ⛟ 🚻 🎍 **Services:** ⬤ 🍴 📞 🆃 🅱 🅾 🗑 ⌀ ⛴ ⬤ **Facilities found within 3 miles:** ∪ 🅱 **Notes:** Non-family groups by arrangement, dogs must be on leads at all times & restricted to certain areas

WEYMOUTH SY67

Seaview Holiday Park 68%

Preston DT3 6DZ

☎ 01305 833037 📠 01305 833169

www.havenholidays.com

Dir: *A354 to Weymouth, signs for Preston/Wareham onto A353. Park 3m on right just after Weymouth Bay Holiday Park*

Open: mid Mar-Oct (rs mid Mar-May & Sep-Oct Facilities may be reduced), Booking advisable School hols, Last arrival 22.00hrs Last departure noon

A fun-packed holiday centre for all the family, with plenty of activities and entertainment during the day and evening. Terraced pitches are provided for caravans, and there is a separate field for tents. The park is close to Weymouth and other coastal attractions. A 20-acre site with 96 touring pitches and 259 statics.

Facilities: 🍴 🍴 🐕 🏕 🚻 🛒 🅿️ Services: 🍽️ 🍴 🚿 🔋 🛒

WEYMOUTH SY67

East Fleet Farm Touring Park

▶▶▶▶ 90%

Chickerell DT3 4DW

☎ 01305 785768

email: enquiries@eastfleet.co.uk

www.eastfleet.co.uk

Dir: *On B3157 (Weymouth-Bridport road), 3m from Weymouth*

* 🚐 £8-£17 🚍 £8-£17 ▲ £8-£17

Open: 16 Mar-Oct, Booking advisable peak season, Last arrival 22.00hrs Last departure 10.30hrs

Set on a working organic farm overlooking Fleet Lagoon and Chesil Beach, with a range of amenities and quality new toilet facilities. A family bar serving meals and take-away food is open from Easter. A 21-acre site with 270 touring pitches and 30 hardstandings.

Facilities: 🍴 🏕 🐕 ⊙ 🅿️ 🚿 🛒 🚻 🚾 🏕 🚻 ♿

Services: 🍽️ 🍴 🚿 📶 🔋 🛒 🚮 🍴 🛒 🛒

Facilities found within 3 miles: ∪ ♿ 18 ⚑ ◎ 🎣 🛒 🛒

DORSET

DORSET

WIMBORNE MINSTER SZ09

Wilksworth Farm Caravan Park

►►►►► 85%

Cranborne Road BH21 4HW

☎ 01202 885467 📠 01202 885467

email: rayandwendy@wilksworthfarmcaravanpark.co.uk

www.wilksworthfarmcaravanpark.co.uk

Dir: *1m N of Wimborne on B3078*

🚐 £12-£22 🚗 £12-£22 ⛺ £12-£22

Open: Apr-Oct (rs Apr & Oct no shop or coffee shop), Booking advisable Spring bank hol & Jul-Aug, Last arrival 20.00hrs Last departure 11.00hrs

A popular park set in the grounds of a listed house in rural Dorset. The spacious site has a heated pool, take-away and café, and games room. An 11-acre site with 85 touring pitches, 20 hardstandings and 77 statics.

Facilities: Paddling pool, volley ball, mini football pitch 🏊 ♠ ⛬ 🚿 ⛱ ⊙ 🔌 ✲ ✆ $ 🐕 🍖 ⛩ ♿ **Services:** ☕ [T] ⚓ 🚐 🧺 🔒 🌿 🛏 🛒 **Facilities found within 3 miles:** 🎣 ◎ 🧺 $

WIMBORNE MINSTER SZ09

Merley Court ►►►►► 76%

Merley BH21 3AA

☎ 01590 648331 📠 01590 645610

email: holidays@shorefield.co.uk

www.shorefield.co.uk

Dir: *Site signed on A31, Wimborne by-pass & Poole junct rdbt*

🚐 £10-£33 🚗 £10-£33 ⛺ £10-£33

Open: Feb-7 Jan (rs low season pool closed & bar, shop open limited hrs), Booking advisable bank hols & Jun-Sep, Last arrival 21.00hrs Last departure 11.00hrs

This superb site in a quiet rural position offers sheltered individual pitches. Plenty of amenities for all the family. A 20-acre site with 160 touring pitches and 50 hardstandings.

Facilities: Badminton, mini football, table tennis, crazy golf 🏊 ♠ ⛬ 📺 🚿 ⛱ ⊙ 🔌 ✲ ✆ $ 🐕 ⛩ ♿ **Services:** ☕ 🍷 [T] ⚓ 🚐 🧺 🔒 🌿 🛏 🛒 **Facilities found within 3 miles:** U ⛳ 18 ⛵ 🎣 ◎ 🧺 $ **Notes:** Couples and families only

WIMBORNE MINSTER   SZ09

Springfield Touring Park ►►► 77%

Candys Lane Corfe Mullen BH21 3EF

☎ 01202 881719

Dir: *Turn left off Wimborne by-pass (A31) western end, after Caravan Sales follow brown sign.*

⊞ £12.50-£14.50 ⊟ £12.50-£14.50

▲ £8-£14.50

Open: Apr-Oct, Booking advisable bank hols & Jul-Aug, Last arrival 22.00hrs Last departure 11.00hrs

A small touring park with extensive views over the Stour Valley, with a quiet and friendly atmosphere. The park is maintained immaculately, and has a well-stocked shop. A 3.5-acre site with 45 touring pitches and 18 hardstandings.

Facilities: ⚐ ⚑ ® ⊙ ℗ ✳ ☉ 🖻 ᔕ **Services:** ⚑ 🖻 🛆 🚟 ➡ **Facilities found within 3 miles:** ∪ ⚲ 9 ⚓ ⌀ 🖻 🖻 **Notes:** ⊛

WOOL   SY88

Whitemead Caravan Park

►►►► 77%

East Burton Road BH20 6HG

☎ 01929 462241 🖨 01929 462241

email: whitemeadcp@aol.com

www.whitemeadcaravanpark.co.uk

Dir: *Signed from A352 at level crossing on Wareham side of Wool*

* ⊞ £9.75-£15.50 ⊟ £9.75-£15.50

▲ £7.75-£13.50

Open: mid Mar-Oct, Booking advisable public hols & mid Jul-Aug, Last arrival 22.00hrs Last departure noon

A well laid-out site in the valley of the River Frome, close to the village and surrounded by woodland. A shop and games room enhance the facilities here, and the toilets are heated. A 5-acre site with 95 touring pitches.

Facilities: ⚓ ⚐ ® ⊙ ℗ ✳ ☉ 🖻 ⋈ 🎋 ᔕ **Services:** ⊡ ⚑ 🖻 🛆 ⌀ 🚟 🏛 **Facilities found within 3 miles:** ∪ ⚲ 18 ⌀ 🖻 🖻 **Notes:** ⊛

DORSET

ESSEX/GLOUCESTERSHIRE

MERSEA ISLAND — TM01

Waldegraves Holiday Park 72%

Colchester CO5 8SE

☎ 01206 382898 📠 01206 385359

email: holidays@waldegraves.co.uk

www.waldegraves.co.uk

Dir: *B1025 to Mersea Island across the Strood. Left to East Mersea, 2nd turn on right, follow tourist signs to park*

* 🚐 £17-£25 🚌 £17-£25 🛆 £17-£25

Open: Mar-Nov, Booking advisable all times, Last arrival 22.00hrs Last departure noon

A spacious and pleasant site, located between farmland and its own private beach on the Blackwater Estuary. Plenty of facilities for families. A 25-acre site with 300 touring pitches and 250 statics.

Facilities: Boating, fishing, golf ⌀ ✦ ⚲ ☐ ⌂ ⊙ ☞ ✳ ☯ ⓼ ⊪ ☴ ⧄ & **Services:** ⛟ ⑩ ⌕ Ⓣ ↴ ♨ ⧄ ▤ ⌁ ⌀ ⇃ ⊞ **Facilities found within 3 miles:** ↯ 18 ⌀ ◎ ≽ ⓼ ⓢ **Notes:** No large groups

WINCHCOMBE — SP03

Winchcombe Camping & Caravanning Club Site ▶▶▶ 80%

Brooklands Farm Alderton Tewkesbury GL20 8NX

☎ 01242 620259

www.campingandcaravanningclub.co.uk

Dir: *M5 junct 9 onto A46, straight on at rdbt onto B4077 signed Stow-on-the-Wold. Site 3m on right*

🚐 £18.25-£20.15 🚌 £18.25-£20.15 🛆 £18.25-£20.15

Open: Mar-Jan, Booking advisable BHs & peak periods, Last arrival 21.00hrs Last departure noon

A pleasant rural park with pitches spaced around two attractive lakes. A 20-acre site with 80 touring pitches and 42 hardstandings.

Facilities: Fishing, pool table, table tennis ✦ ⚲ ⌂ ⊙ ☞ ✳ ☯ ☴ ▤ & **Services:** Ⓣ ⌀ ⌁ ⧄ ▤ **Facilities found within 3 miles:** ∪ ⌀ ≽ ⓢ

HAMPSHIRE

FORDINGBRIDGE SU11

Sandy Balls Holiday Centre 88%

Sandy Balls Estate Ltd Godshill SP6 2JY

☎ 01425 653042 📠 01425 653067

email: post@sandy-balls.co.uk

www.sandy-balls.co.uk

Dir: *M27 junct 1 onto B3078/B3079, W 8m to Godshill. Park 0.25m after cattle grid*

* 🚐 £14-£28 🚐 £14-£28 ▲ £14-£28

Open: Open All Year (rs Nov-Feb pitches reduced, no activities), Booking advisable bank & school hols & wknds, Last arrival 21.00hrs Last departure 11.00hrs

Large New Forest holiday complex with good facilities. A 120-acre site with 230 touring pitches, 230 hardstandings and 267 statics.

Facilities: Jacuzzi, sauna, gym, horse riding, bike hire, gift shop 🍴🍟📶🔍🛍️🏕️⊙🅿️✳️🕐 💲🚻♨️🛁🔥⛑️ **Services:** 💬🚽🖥️🆃🔌🚐🛢️🍴 🌀🚰🛒 **Facilities found within 3 miles:** ∪🎣🌿🛥️🛢️🏧 **Notes:** Groups by arrangement, no gazebos

LINWOOD SU10

Red Shoot Camping Park ▶▶▶ 72%

Ringwood BH24 3QT

☎ 01425 473789 📠 01425 471558

email: enquiries@redshoot-campingpark.com

www.redshoot-campingpark.com

Dir: *A31 onto A338 towards Fordingbridge & Salisbury. Right at brown signs for caravan park towards Linwood on unclassified roads, park signed*

Open: Mar-Oct, Last arrival 20.30hrs Last departure 13.00hrs

Sitting behind the Red Shoot Inn in one of the most attractive parts of the New Forest, this park is in an ideal spot for nature lovers, walkers and tourers. Friendly owners, and offers many amenities including a play area. A 3.5-acre site with 130 touring pitches.

Facilities: Mountain bike hire 📶🔍⊙🅿️✳️ 🕐💲♨️ **Services:** 🍴🖥️🆃🚐🛢️🍴🌀🍴

Facilities found within 3 miles: 🎣🛢️💲

HAMPSHIRE

MILFORD ON SEA   SZ29

Lytton Lawn Touring Park ►►► 86%

Lymore Lane SO41 0TX

☎ 01590 648331 📄 01590 645610

email: holidays@shorefield.co.uk

www.shorefield.co.uk

Dir: *From Lymington A337 to Christchurch for 2.5m to Everton. Left onto B3058 to Milford on Sea. After 0.25m left onto Lymore Lane*

🚐 £9.50-£31 🚙 £9.50-£31 ▲ £9.50-£31

Open: Feb-2 Jan (rs Xmas/New year no grass pitches available), Booking advisable at all times, Last arrival 22.00hrs Last departure 10.00hrs

A peaceful well-run park with good facilities, located near the coast. The facilities of a sister park 2.5 miles away are available, including pool and tennis courts. A 5-acre site with 136 touring pitches and 48 hardstandings.

Facilities: Free use of Shorefield Leisure Club ♦ ⚲ ↑ ⊙ ☞ ✳ ③ 🔒 ⊣ ⚹ **Services:** ⊤ 🚐 ⊗ 🔒 ⊘ **Facilities found within 3 miles:** ∪ ⚲ 18 ✒ ⛵ ⓢ ③ **Notes:** Family only park

ROMSEY   SU22

Hill Farm Caravan Park ►►►► 85%

Branches Lane Sherfield English SO51 6FH

☎ 01794 340402 📄 01794 342358

email: gjb@hillfarmpark.com

www.hillfarmpark.com

Dir: *Signed from A27 (Salisbury to Romsey road) in Sherfield English, 4m NW of Romsey & M27 junct 2*

* 🚐 £16-£25 🚙 £16-£25 ▲ £16-£25

Open: Mar-Oct, Booking advisable bank & school hols & wknds, Last arrival 20.00hrs Last departure noon

A small, well-sheltered park. Unisex showers as well as a fully en suite family/disabled room. A 10.5-acre site with 70 touring pitches, 16 hardstandings and 6 statics.

Facilities: 9-hole pitch & putt, goal posts, badminton ⚲ ↑ ⊙ ☞ ✳ ③ ⊣ ⚹ ⚹ **Services:** ⚹ ⊤ ↯ 🚐 🔒 ⊘ ⚹ ⚹ **Facilities found within 3 miles:** ∪ ⚲ 18 ✒ ③ **Notes:** No noise after 23.00hrs, one unit per pitch ⚹

COWES SZ49

Thorness Bay Holiday Park 75%

Thorness PO31 8NJ

☎ 01983 523109 📠 01983 822213

email: holidaysales.thornessbay@park-resorts.com

www.park-resorts.com

Dir: *On A3054 towards Yarmouth, 1st right after BMW garage, signed Thorness Bay*

* 🚐 £6-£27 🚌 £6-£27 ⛺ £3-£24

Open: Apr-1 Nov, Booking advisable Jul-Aug, Last arrival anytime Last departure 10.00hrs. Views of the Solent can be enjoyed from this rural park. A footpath leads directly to the coast, and there is an all-weather sports court. There are 23 serviced pitches with TV boosters. A 148-acre site with 80 touring pitches, 20 hardstandings and 560 statics.

Facilities: Kids' clubs, evening entertainment, water slide 🏊 🎠 ⛹ ⊙ ☎ [$] 🐕 ♿ **Services:** ☕ 🍷 ⚓ 🚐 [🧺] 🔒 🍃 🧺 **Facilities found within 3 miles:** 🐎 🎣 🏄 [🧺] [$]

NEWBRIDGE SZ48

Orchards Holiday Caravan Park

►►►►► 87%

Yarmouth PO41 0TS

☎ 01983 531331 📠 01983 531666

email: info@orchards-holiday-park.co.uk

www.orchards-holiday-park.co.uk

Dir: *4m E of Yarmouth; 6m W of Newport on B3401*

* 🚐 £12.10-£17 🚌 £12.10-£17 ⛺ £12.10-£17

Open: 11 Feb-2 Jan (rs Nov-Jan & Feb-mid Mar shop/takeaway closed/pool closed Sep-May), Booking advisable Etr, Spring BH, Jun-Aug, Oct half term, Last arrival 23.00hrs Last departure 11.00hrs

A really excellent, well-managed park set in a peaceful village location, with downland views. A 15-acre site with 171 touring pitches, 74 hardstandings and 65 statics.

Facilities: Coarse fishing, petanque 🏊 🏊 🎾 🎠 📺 ⛹ ⊙ 🚿 ❄ ☎ [$] 🐕 ♿ **Services:** ☕ [T] 🚐 [🧺] 🔒 🍃 🍴 🧺 **Facilities found within 3 miles:** 🐎 🎣 [🧺] [$]

ISLE OF WIGHT

NEWCHURCH SZ58
Southland Camping Park

▶▶▶▶▶ 88%

Nr Sandown PO36 0LZ

☎ 01983 865385 📄 01983 867663

email: info@southland.co.uk

www.southland.co.uk

Dir: *A3056 towards Sandown. 2nd left after Fighting Cocks pub towards Newchurch. Site 1m on left*

🚐 £10.80-£16.20 🚌 £10.80-£16.20

🛆 £10.80-£16.20

Open: Apr-Sep, Booking advisable Jun-Aug, Last arrival 21.30hrs Last departure 11.00hrs Beautifully maintained site, peacefully located and impressively laid out on the outskirts of the village in the Arreton Valley. Pitches are well screened by lovely trees and shrubs. A 9-acre site with 120 touring pitches.

Facilities: Free wi-fi internet hotspot 🅼 🖎 ⊙ 🄿✕ 🕔 🖻 🚻 🏧 🎋 ₺ **Services:** 🆃 🚽 🚰 🖻 🧺 🛒 **Facilities found within 3 miles:** ∪ ↓ 18 ♣ ℓ ◎ ⇉ 🖻 🖻

SANDOWN SZ58
Adgestone Camping & Caravanning Club Site ▶▶▶▶ 80%

Lower Adgestone Road Nr Sandown PO36 0HL

☎ 01983 403432

www.campingandcaravanningclub.co.uk

Dir: *Turn off A3055 (Sandown/Shanklin road) at Manor House pub, in Lake. Past school & golf course on left, turn right at T-junct, park 200yds on right*

🚐 £18.35-£23.25 🚌 £18.35-£23.25

🛆 £18.35-£23.25

Open: Apr-Oct, Booking advisable bank hols & peak period, Last arrival 21.00hrs Last departure noon

A popular park in a quiet, rural location. The level pitches are imaginatively laid out and there is excellent provision for families. A 22-acre site with 270 touring pitches.

Facilities: Fishing 🎣 🅼 🖎 ⊙ 🄿✕ 🕔 🖻 🚻 🍴 ₺ **Services:** 🆃 🚰 🖻 🛢 🧺 🛒 **Facilities found within 3 miles:** ∪ ↓ ℓ ⇉ 🖻

SHANKLIN   SZ58

Lower Hyde Holiday Park 80%

Landguard Road PO37 7LL

☎ 01983 866131 📠 01983 862532

email: holidaysales.lowerhyde@park-resorts.com

www.park-resorts.com

Dir: *From Fishbourne ferry terminal follow A3055 to Shanklin. Park signed just past lake*

* 🚐 £6-£28 🚎 £6-£28 ▲ £6-£25

Open: 17 Apr-1 Nov, Booking advisable all year, Last arrival anytime Last departure 10.00hrs

A popular holiday park on the outskirts of Shanklin, close to the sandy beaches. Outdoor swimming pool and plenty of organised activities for youngsters of all ages. A 65-acre site with 82 touring pitches and 313 statics.

Facilities: Water flume, evening entertainment, kids' club 🍴 🍷 🏕 🌳 ⛱ 🎣 ✹ 🛝 ✳ ☉ 🗑 🚻 ♿ **Services:** 🔌 🍴 🚐 🛢 🛢 🍴 🚽

Facilities found within 3 miles: ∪ ⚓ 18 ⚘ 🎣 ◎ ⏃ 🗑 💲

SHANKLIN   SZ58

Ninham Country Holidays ►►► 79%

Ninham PO37 7PL

☎ 01983 864243 📠 01983 868881

email: info@ninham.fsnet.co.uk

www.ninham-holiday.co.uk

Dir: *Signed off A3056 (Newport to Sandown road)*

* 🚐 £12-£16 🚎 £12-£16 ▲ £12-£16

Open: May-Sep (rs 1-27 May & 10-30 Sep outdoor pool & launderette closed), Booking advisable Jun-Sep

Enjoying a lofty rural position with fine country views, this delightful, spacious park occupies two separate well-maintained areas in a country park setting near the sea and beach. A 14-acre site with 200 touring pitches and 6 statics.

Facilities: Coarse fishing 🍷 🏕 🌳 ⛱ ☉ 🎣 ✳ ☉ 🗑 🚻 ♿ 🚻 🍴 **Services:** 🔌 🔲 🚐 🛢 🛢 🍴 🚽

🚽 **Facilities found within 3 miles:** ∪ ⚓

18 ⚘ 🎣 ◎ ⏃ 🗑 🗑 ⊗

ISLE OF WIGHT

SHANKLIN SZ58

Landguard Camping Park ▶▶▶ 79%

Landguard Manor Road PO37 7PH

☎ 01983 867028 📠 01983 865988

email: landguard@weltinet.com

www.landguard-camping.co.uk

Dir: *A3056 to Sandown, right after passing Morrisons at Lake into Whitecross Lane. Follow site signs*

* 🚐 £12-£17 🚑 £12-£17 Å £12-£17

Open: Etr-Sep, Booking advisable school hols, Last arrival 20.00hrs Last departure noon

Surrounded by trees in a rural setting, this peaceful and secluded touring park is within walking distance of Shanklin. Facilities are clean and tidy, and the park benefits from a very good outdoor pool. A 7-acre site with 150 touring pitches and 6 hardstandings.

Facilities: 🍴 🗖 🔦 ⊙ ℗ ✻ ⓒ 🖮 ⅙

Services: 🔲 🔧 🖳 🗗 🖥 ∅ 🖴 🏸 🛒 🝙

Facilities found within 3 miles: 🎣 18 ≠ ℗ ◎ 🥂 🖥 🖯 ⊗ **Notes:** Families only

ST HELENS SZ68

Nodes Point Holiday Park 74%

Nodes Road PO33 1YA

☎ 01983 872401 📠 01983 874696

email: gm.nodespoint@park-resorts.com

www.park-resorts.com

Dir: *From Ryde take B3330 signed Seaview/ Puckpool. At junct for Puckpool bear right. 1m past Road Side Inn in Nettlestone, on left*

* 🚐 £6-£28 🚑 £6-£28 Å £3-£25

Open: Apr-Oct (rs Mar park open, no facilities), Booking advisable May-Aug, Last arrival 21.00hrs Last departure 10.00hrs

A well-equipped holiday centre on an elevated position overlooking Bembridge Bay with direct access to the beach. The touring area is mostly sloping with some terraces. Buses pass the main entrance road. A 16-acre site with 145 touring pitches and 195 statics.

Facilities: 🍴 🗖 🔦 ⊙ ℗ ✻ ⓒ 🖮 🝙 🛉 ⅙

Services: 🔧 🍴 🖳 🗗 🖥 ∅ 🖴 🝙 **Facilities found within 3 miles:** ∪ 🎣 18 ≠ ℗ ◎ 🥂 🖥 🖯 **Notes:** Family park

WHITECLIFF BAY   SZ68

Whitecliff Bay Holiday Park 80%

Hillway Road Bembridge PO35 5PL

☎ 01983 872671 🖷 01983 872941

email: holiday@whitecliff-bay.com

www.whitecliff-bay.com

Dir: *1m S of Bembridge, signed off B3395 in village*

* 🚐 £9.20-£15.90 🚎 £9.20-£15.90 ▲ £9.20-£15.90

Open: Mar-Oct, Booking advisable Jul-Aug, Last arrival 21.00hrs Last departure 10.30hrs

A seaside complex on two sites, with tourers and tents on one, and tourers and statics on the other. A 49-acre site with 400 touring pitches, 50 hardstandings and 227 statics.

Facilities: Leisure centre with fun pool, spa bath & sauna 🎣 ⛱ 🍴 🛝 🛖 ⊙ 🅿 🌣 🕐 🐴 ﬨ 🚻 ♿ **Services:** 🕿 🖦 🍽 ⟙ 🚽 🗑 🖥 🛒 🍴 ⚱

Facilities found within 3 miles: ∪ ⚓ 9 ⛷ 🎿 ◎ 🗑 ⓢ ⊗ **Notes:** Adults and families only, no dogs during high season

PETERCHURCH   SO33

Poston Mill Caravan & Camping Park ▶▶▶▶ 87%

Hereford HR2 0SF

☎ 01981 550225 🖷 01981 550000

email: enquiries@poston-mill.co.uk

www.bestparks.co.uk

Dir: *11m SW of Hereford on B4348*

* 🚐 £14-£18 🚎 £14-£18 ▲ £14-£18

Open: Open All Year (rs Nov-Mar limited toilet facilities), Booking advisable bank & summer hols, Last departure noon

Delightfully set in the Golden Valley and surrounded by hills, with beautiful views. This quality park has excellent facilities including sporting amenities. There is also an adjoining restaurant, and a pleasant walk alongside the River Dore. A 33-acre site with 43 touring pitches, 33 hardstandings and 113 statics.

Facilities: 9-hole pitch & putt ⚓ 🛝 🎿 ⊙ 🅿 🌣 🕐 🐴 ﬨ 🚻 ♿ **Services:** 🕿 🖦 🍽 ⟙ 🚽 🖥 🛒 🍴 ⚱ **Facilities found within 3 miles:** 🎿 9 🖋 ◎ 🗑 ⓢ

HEREFORDSHIRE

STANFORD BISHOP   SO65
Boyce Caravan Park ►►► 79%

Bringsty Nr Worcester WR6 5UB

☎ 01886 884248

email: enquiries@boyceholidaypark.co.uk

www.boyceholidaypark.co.uk

Dir: *From B4220 (Malvern road) take sharp turn opposite Herefordshire House pub, then right after 0.25m. Signed Linley Green, then 1st drive on right*

🚐 £12–£13.50 🚎 £12–£13.50 ⛺ £12–£13.50

Open: Feb-Dec, Booking advisable bank hols, wknds & Jun-Aug, Last arrival 18.00hrs Last departure noon

A peaceful park with access allowed onto the 100 acres of farmland. Coarse fishing is also available in the grounds, and there are extensive views over the Malvern and Suckley Hills. Many walks available. A 10-acre site with 15 touring pitches and 150 statics.

Facilities: 🅰 🕭 ⊙ 🕭 ✳ 🕭 🚻 🚾 ♿

Services: 🔌 🔋 🍴 🚽 🛒 📮 🅿️ 💷 **Notes:** Certain dog breeds are not accepted 🚫

SYMONDS YAT [WEST]   SO51
Doward Park Camp Site ►►► 79%

Great Doward HR9 6BP

☎ 01600 890438

email: enquiries@dowardpark.co.uk

www.dowardpark.co.uk

Dir: *2m from A40 between Ross-on-Wye & Monmouth. Take Symonds Yat (West) turn, then Crockers Ash, follow signs to site*

Open: Mar-Oct, Booking advisable wknds, BHs & Jul-Aug, Last arrival 20.00hrs Last departure 11.30hrs

This delightful little park is set in peaceful woodlands on the hillside above the Wye Valley. It is ideal for campers and motor homes but not caravans due to the narrow approach roads. A warm welcome awaits and the facilities are kept spotless. A 1.5-acre site with 25 touring pitches and 8 hardstandings.

Facilities: 🅰 🕭 ⊙ 🕭 ✳ 🕭 ♿ **Services:** 🔌 🍴 🚽 🛒 🅿️ 💷 📮 **Notes:** No caravans or fires, quiet after 22.00hrs, dogs must be on leads

WALTHAM CROSS   TL30

Theobalds Park C&C Club Site

▶▶ 70%

Theobalds Park Bulls Cross Ride EN7 5HS

☎ 01992 620604

www.campingandcaravanningclub.co.uk

Dir: *M25 junct 25. A10 towards London keep in right lane. Right at 1st lights. Right at T-junct, right behind dog kennels. Site towards top of lane on right*

🚐 £12.75-£16.75 🚎 £12.75-£16.75

▲ £12.75-£16.75

Open: Mar-Oct, Booking advisable bank hols & peak periods, Last arrival 21.00hrs Last departure noon

A lovely open site surrounded by mature trees, and set in parkland at Theobalds Hall. The portacabin toilet facilities are freshly painted and extremely clean, and there are two separate glades for tents. A 14-acre site with 90 touring pitches.

Facilities: ◆ ∧ ↑ ⊖❄ ◐ ◂ ▮ **Services:** ⊤ ⊕ ⬛ ■ ⊘ 📆 Facilities found within 3 miles: ∪ ⅃ ◿ ⑂

ASHFORD   TR03

Broad Hembury Caravan & Camping Park ▶▶▶▶ 86%

Steeds Lane Kingsnorth TN26 1NQ

☎ 01233 620859 📄 01233 620918

email: holidays@broadhembury.co.uk

www.broadhembury.co.uk

Dir: *From M20 junct 10 take A2070 then A2042 for 3m. Left at 2nd rdbt signed Kingsnorth, then left at 2nd x-roads in village*

* 🚐 £12-£18 🚎 £12-£18 ▲ £10-£15

Open: Open All Year Booking advisable Jul-Aug & bank hols, Last arrival 23.00hrs Last departure noon

Well-run small family park surrounded by open pasture, with pitches sheltered by mature hedges. A 10-acre site with 60 touring pitches, 24 hardstandings and 25 statics.

Facilities: Football, volleyball & kitchen appliances ◆ ∧ ⊡ ↑ ⊙ ☞❄ ◐ 🗑 📆 ♿

Services: ⊤ ⬛ ⊕ ⬛ ■ ⊘ 📆 ⊷ 📆 **Facilities found within 3 miles:** ∪ ⅃ 18 ◿ ◉ ⬛ ⑂

KENT

BIRCHINGTON TR36
Two Chimneys Caravan Park
▶▶▶ 77%

Shottendane Road CT7 0HD

☎ 01843 841068 & 843157 ▤ 01843 848099

email: info@twochimneys.co.uk

www.twochimneys.co.uk

Dir: *From A28 to Birchington Sq, right into Park Lane (B2048). Left at Manston Road (B2050) then 1st left*

* ⊞ £12-£20 ⊞ £12-£20 ▲ £12-£20

Open: Mar-Oct (rs Mar-May & Sep-Oct shop, bar, pool & takeaway restricted), Booking advisable bank & school hols, Last arrival 22.00hrs Last departure noon

A well-managed site with two pools, a tennis court, play area, and a fully-licensed clubhouse. A 30-acre site with 200 touring pitches, 5 hardstandings and 200 statics.

Facilities: Amusement arcade 🎮 🛆 🕄 ⊙ 🅿✕ Ⓢ 🖧 ⚅ **Services:** 🖿 🔲 🖦 🔟 🛢 ⬛ 🡸 ⚓ **Facilities found within 3 miles:** ∪ 🛆 18 🛝 🥏 ◎ 🛥 🔟 🖸

FOLKESTONE TR23
Little Satmar Holiday Park
▶▶▶ 78%

Winehouse Lane Capel Le Ferne CT18 7JF

☎ 01303 251188 ▤ 01303 251188

email: info@keatfarm.co.uk

www.keatfarm.co.uk/touringparks/littlesatmar.htm

Dir: *Signed off B2011*

Open: Mar-Nov, Booking advisable bank hols & Jul-Aug, Last arrival 23.00hrs Last departure 14.00hrs

A quiet, well-screened site well away from the road and statics, with clean and tidy facilities. A useful base for visiting Dover and Folkestone, and just a short walk from cliff paths with their views of the Channel, and sandy beaches below. A 5-acre site with 60 touring pitches and 80 statics.

Facilities: 🛆 🕄 ⊙ 🅿✕ Ⓢ 🖸 **Services:** 🔲 🖦 🛢 ⬛ 🡸 ⚓ **Facilities found within 3 miles:** ∪ 🛆 18 🥏 🔟 🖸

SANDWICH — TR35

Sandwich Leisure Park ►►►► 81%

Woodnesborough Road CT13 0AA

☎ 01304 612681 ▤ 01304 615252

email: info@sandwichleisurepark.co.uk

www.sandwichleisurepark.co.uk

Dir: *From Sandwich town centre, then follow brown tourist signs*

* ♫ £17-£21 ♫ £17-£21 ▲ £10-£21

Open: Mar-Oct, Booking advisable Etr, Spring bank hol & Jul-Aug, Last arrival 20.00hrs Last departure 11.00hrs

A large site with impressive toilet facilities, including a suite of family rooms, and 18 fully-serviced pitches. The park backs onto farmland. A 15-acre site with 187 touring pitches, 34 hardstandings and 103 statics.

Facilities: ⚲⚲⊙⚲⚲⚲⚲ **Services:** ⚲⚲⚲⚲⚲ **Facilities found within 3 miles:** ⚲ 18 ⚲ ⚲ ⚲ ⚲ ⚲ ⚲ **Notes:** No groups of under 17yrs without adult present, no commercial vehicles

WHITSTABLE — TR16

Seaview Holiday Village ►►► 75%

St John's Road CT5 2RY

☎ 01227 792246 ▤ 01227 792247

email: seaview@cplparks.co.uk

www.cinqueportsleisure.com

Dir: *From A299 take A2990 then B2205 to Swalecliffe, site between Herne Bay & Whitstable*

* ♫ £13-£16.50 **Open:** Mar-Oct (rs Feb & Nov limited facilities), Booking advisable all times, Last arrival 21.30hrs Last departure noon

A pleasant open site on the edge of Whitstable, with a smart, modern toilet block and both super and hardstanding pitches. A 12-acre site with 171 touring pitches, 41 hardstandings and 452 statics.

Facilities: Amusements in games room & adventure trail ⚲⚲⚲⚲⚲⊙⚲⚲⚲⚲⚲ ⚲ **Services:** ⚲⚲⚲⚲⚲⚲⚲⚲⚲⚲ **Facilities found within 3 miles:** ⚲⚲ 18 ⚲⚲⚲⚲⚲⚲

KENT

KENT/LANCASHIRE

WHITSTABLE TR06

Homing Park ▶▶▶▶ 82%

Church Lane Seasalter CT5 4BU

☎ 01227 771777 🖷 01227 273512

email: info@homingpark.co.uk

www.homingpark.co.uk

Dir: *Exit A299 for Whitstable & Canterbury, left at brown camping/caravan sign into Church Lane. Park entrance has 2 large flag poles*

* 🚐 £9.50–£17 ⛺ £9.50–£17 ▲ £7.50–£17

Open: Mar-Oct, Booking advisable Etr, bank hols & Aug, Last arrival 20.00hrs Last departure 11.00hrs

A touring park close to Seasalter Beach. Pool and clubhouse on adjacent park. A 12.6-acre site with 43 touring pitches and 195 statics.

Facilities: Fitness centre 🌳 🖤 🔌 🦶 🏧 ☺ ☀ ✖ ◐ ⏱ ♿ **Services:** 🛒 🚰 🔌 🛢 🔋 🗑 ⊘ 🚽

Facilities found within 3 miles: ∪ ✈ 9 ✏ ≋ 🛄 **Notes:** No commercial vehicles, no tents greater than 8 berth, no unaccompanied groups of under 18s

BLACKPOOL SD33

Marton Mere
Holiday Village 73%

Mythop Road FY4 4XN

☎ 01253 767544 🖷 01253 791544

www.havenholidays.com

Dir: *M55 junct 4, A583 towards Blackpool. Right at Clifton Arms lights, onto Mythop Road. Park 150yds on left*

Open: mid Mar-Oct, Booking advisable school hols, Last departure 10.00hrs

A very attractive holiday centre on the edge of the mere, with plenty of birdlife to be spotted. The on-site entertainment is directed at all ages, and includes a superb show bar. Bus service into Blackpool for those who want to explore. The separate touring area is well equipped with hardstandings and electric pitches, and there are good quality facilities. A 30-acre site with 205 touring pitches.

Facilities: 🌊 🌳 🖤 🔌 🦶 🏧 ☺ ☀ 🔋 🗑 ♿ **Services:** 🍽 🚰 🔌 🛢 🔋 🗑 ⊘ 🚽 **Facilities found within 3 miles:** ∪ ✈ 18 ✏ ◎ ≋ 🛄 🗑 **Notes:** No more than 2 dogs per group

COCKERHAM SD44

Mosswood Caravan Park

▶▶▶▶ 80%

Crimbles Lane LA2 0ES

☎ 01524 791041 📠 01524 792444

email: info@mosswood.co.uk

www.mosswood.co.uk

Dir: *Approx 4m from A6/M6 junct 33, 1m W of Cockerham on A588*

* 🚐 £13-£14 ⛺ £13-£14 ▲ £13-£14

Open: Mar-Oct, Booking advisable bank hols & Jul-Sep, Last arrival 20.00hrs Last departure 16.00hrs

A tree-lined grassy park with sheltered, level pitches, located on peaceful Cockerham Moss. The modern toilet block is attractively clad in stained wood, and the facilities include cubicled washing facilities and a launderette. A 25-acre site with 25 touring pitches, 25 hardstandings and 143 statics.

Facilities: Woodland walks 🏕 🐾 ☉ ⅌ ✳ Ⓛ 🔥 🛒 🔥 ♿ **Services:** 🚽 🔄 🔋 🛢 💧

Facilities found within 3 miles: ∪ ♨ 18 ✐ 🔥

GARSTANG SD44

Claylands Caravan Park ▶▶▶▶ 80%

Cabus PR3 1AJ

☎ 01524 791242 📠 01524 792406

email: alan@claylands.com

www.claylands.com

Dir: *From M6 junct 33 S to Garstang, approx 6m pass Little Chef, signed off A6 into private road on Lancaster side of Garstang*

* 🚐 £15-£17 ⛺ £15-£17 ▲ £15-£17

Open: Mar-4 Jan (rs Jan & Feb holiday park only), Booking advisable bank hols & Jul-Aug, Last arrival 23.00hrs Last departure 14.00hrs

A well-maintained site with lovely river and woodland walks and good views over the River Wyre towards the village of Scorton. Guests can enjoy fishing, and the atmosphere is very relaxed. A 14-acre site with 30 touring pitches, 30 hardstandings and 68 statics.

Facilities: 🏕 🐾 ☉ ✳ Ⓛ 🔋 🔥 🛒 🔥 ♿ **Services:** 🚽 🔄 🍴 🔋 🛢 💧 ⛟ 🚐 ♨

Facilities found within 3 miles: ∪ ♨ 18 ✐ 🔥 🔋

LANCASHIRE

LANCASHIRE

HEYSHAM SD45

Ocean Edge
Leisure Park 74%

Moneyclose Lane LA3 2XA

☎ 01524 855657 🖹 01524 855884

email: enquiries@southlakeland-caravans.co.uk

www.southlakeland-caravans.co.uk

Dir: *From M6 junct 34 follow A683 to Heysham. In Heysham site signed before ferry port*

* 🚐 £14-£16 🚙 £15-£18 ▲ £10-£12

Open: mid Feb-Jan, Booking advisable bank/school hols, Last arrival 22.00hrs Last departure 10.00hrs

An open touring area of a large holiday complex adjacent to the sea, and with sea views. Facilities include a large bar and café, and nightly entertainment including bingo, quizzes, cabaret and singsongs. A 10-acre site with 94 touring pitches and 600 statics.

Facilities: 🈺 🔍 🚿 🎣 ☉ ⓟ ☺ 🍴 🐕 ⅃

Services: 🦺 🍴 🍽 🚽 🗑 💧 🚮 🛁 Facilities found within 3 miles: ∪ ⚓ 18 ✏ 🔍 🗑 🏧

MORECAMBE SD46

Venture Caravan Park ▶▶▶ 76%

Langridge Way Westgate LA4 4TQ

☎ 01524 412986 🖹 01524 422029

email: mark@venturecaravanpark.co.uk

www.venturecaravanpark.co.uk

Dir: *From M6 junct 34 follow Morecambe signs. At rdbt take road towards Westgate & follow park signs. 1st right after fire station*

* 🚐 £10.10-£12.10 🚙 £10.10-£12.10 ▲ £10.10-£12.10

Open: Open All Year. (rs 6 Jan-22 Feb touring vans only, one toilet block open), Booking advisable bank hols & peak periods, Last arrival 22.00hrs Last departure noon

A large park with good modern facilities and close to town centre.

A 17.5-acre site with 56 touring pitches, 40 hardstandings and 304 statics.

Facilities: Amusement arcade, off licence 🈺 🔍 🚿 🎣 ☉ ⓟ ✂ ☺ 🍴 🐕 **Services:** 🍽 🗑 💧 🚮 🚽 🛁 🍴 Facilities found within 3 miles: ⚓ 18 ✏ 🗑 🏧

ORMSKIRK SD40
Abbey Farm Caravan Park

►►►► 78%

Dark Lane L40 5TX

☎ 01695 572686 🖷 01695 572686

email: abbeyfarm@yahoo.com

www.abbeyfarmcaravanpark.co.uk

Dir: *M6 junct 27 onto A5209 to Burscough. 4m left onto B5240. Immediate right into Hobcross Ln. Park 1.5m on right*

* ⚏ £9.60-£14.50 ⚏ £9.60-£14.50 ▲ £5-£12 **Open:** Open All Year Booking advisable public hols & Jul-Aug, Last arrival 22.00hrs Last departure 13.00hrs

This garden-like rural park is sheltered by hedges and trees. There is a superb recreation field for children of all ages, a games room, library and fishing lake. Tents have their own area with BBQ and picnic tables. A 6-acre site with 56 touring pitches and 44 statics.

Facilities: Off-licence, farm walk ♠ ⚏ ♠ ☺ ⚏ ☼ ☺ ☖ ☂ ┰ ⚓ ⚐ & **Services:** ⊞ ⚏ ☒ ☗ ⚏ ☲ **Facilities found within 3 miles:** ∪ ⚿ 18 ⚿ ☒ ☗

ORMSKIRK SD31
Shaw Hall Caravan Park ►►► 77%

Smithy Lane Scarisbrick L40 8HJ

☎ 01704 840298 🖷 01704 840539

email: shawhall@btconnect.com

www.shawhall.co.uk

Dir: *200yds S of canal bridge at Scarisbrick, 0.25m off A570 at Smithy Lane*

* ⚏ £20-£23 ⚏ £20-£23 **Open:** Mar-7 Jan, Booking advisable bank hols & peak periods, Last arrival 20.30hrs

A large, pleasant park with 20 super pitches and good toilets. The clubhouse and bar offer popular cabaret and discos. The park also boasts canal walks from its direct access to the Leeds-Liverpool Canal, a football field, and putting and bowling greens. A 26-acre site with 45 touring pitches, 45 hardstandings and 300 statics.

Facilities: Fishing ⚏ ♠ ☺ ⚏ ☼ ☺ ☖ ┰ ⚐ & **Services:** ⚍ ⚏ ☒ ☗ ⚏ ☲ **Facilities found within 3 miles:** ∪ ⚿ 18 ⚿ ☒ ☗

LANCASHIRE

LANCASHIRE

SILVERDALE — SD47
Holgate's Caravan Park
▶▶▶▶▶ 95%
Middlebarrow Plain Cove Road Nr Carnforth
LA5 0SH
☎ 01524 701508 📠 01524 701580
email: caravan@holgates.co.uk
www.holgates.co.uk
Dir: *M6 junct 35. 5m NW of Carnforth. From Carnforth centre take unclass Silverdale road & follow tourist signs after Warton*
* 🚐 £29.50-£31 �caravan £29.50-£31 ▲ £26.75-£28
Open: 22 Dec-4 Nov, Booking advisable school hols, public hols & wknds, Last arrival 22.00hrs Last departure noon
A superb family holiday park, set in wooded countryside next to the sea, offering a range of amenities. A 10-acre site with 70 touring pitches, 70 hardstandings and 339 statics.
Facilities: Sauna, spa bath, steam room, mini-golf, gym 🏊🔍 🗛 🌡️ 🖙 ⊙ 🅿️❄ 🕓 🛁 ⛐ &
Services: 🛄🍴🛗 T 🚐 🛱 🗑 ⊘ ⛟ **Facilities found within 3 miles:** ∪ ⚓ 18 🎣 🛍️
Notes: No unaccompanied children

THORNTON — SD34
Kneps Farm Holiday Park
▶▶▶▶ 79%
River Road Stanah Blackpool FY5 5LR
☎ 01253 823632 📠 01253 863967
email: enquiries@knepsfarm.co.uk
www.knepsfarm.co.uk
Dir: *Leave A585 at rdbt onto B5412 to Little Thornton. Right at mini-rdbt after school onto Stanah Rd, over 2nd mini-rdbt, leading to River Road*
* 🚐 £15.50-£17 �caravan £15.50-£17 ▲ £13-£17
Open: Mar-mid Nov, Booking advisable at all times, Last arrival 20.00hrs Last departure noon
A quality park adjacent to the River Wyre and the Wyre Estuary Country Park, well placed for Blackpool. The park is quietly located, but there is some noise from a nearby plastics plant. A 10-acre site with 60 touring pitches, 40 hardstandings and 68 statics.
Facilities: 🗛 🌡️ 🖙 ⊙ 🅿️❄ 🕓 🛁 🚻 & **Services:** T 🚐 🛱 🗑 ⊘ 🛒 🚐 **Facilities found within 3 miles:** ⚓ 9 🎣 ◎ 🛶 🛍️

ANCASTER — SK94

Woodland Waters ▶▶▶ 76%

Willoughby Road Grantham NG32 3RT

☎ 01400 230888 📠 01400 230888

email: info@woodlandwaters.co.uk

www.woodlandwaters.co.uk

Dir: *On A153 W of x-roads with B6403*

Open: Open All Year Booking advisable BHs
Last arrival 21.00hrs Last departure noon
Peacefully set around five impressive fishing
lakes, with a few log cabins in a separate area,
a pleasant open park. The access road is
through mature woodland, and there is a very
good heated toilet block, and a pub/club
house with restaurant. A 5-acre site with 62
touring pitches.

Facilities: ◕ ⚲ ⋔ ⦿ ☉ ⏚ ⓢ ⌁ 🛒 ☕ ⛳

Services: ⛽ 🍴 🚐 🛢 ⛴ ♨ 🚿 **Facilities
found within 3 miles:** ∪ ⒔ ℘ ⓢ ⓢ **Notes:**
Dogs must be kept on leads at all times 🐾

CLEETHORPES — TA30

**Thorpe Park
Holiday Centre** 75%

DN35 0PW

☎ 01472 813395 📠 01472 812146

www.havenholidays.com

Dir: *Take unclass road off A180 at
Cleethorpes, signed Humberstone & Holiday
Park*

Open: mid Mar-Oct (rs mid Mar-May & Sep-
Oct some facilities may be reduced), Booking
advisable bank & school hols, Last arrival
anytime Last departure 10.00hrs
A large static site with touring facilities,
including fully-serviced pitches, adjacent to
the beach. This holiday centre offers excellent
recreational and leisure activities. Parts of the
site overlook the sea. A 300-acre site with 110
touring pitches and 64 hardstandings.

Facilities: Pitch and putt, roller ring, fishing
lakes ☎ ⚲ ⋔ ⓝ ⦿ ⓟ ✳ ☉ ⓢ 🛒 ⛳

Services: 🍴 🚐 🛢 ⛴ 🍺 ⓐ ♨ **Facilities
found within 3 miles:** ∪ ⒔ 18 ℘ ⓞ ♨ ⓢ
ⓢ **Notes:** Maximum of 2 dogs per group

LINCOLNSHIRE

LINCOLNSHIRE

MABLETHORPE   TF58
**Golden Sands
Holiday Park** 73%

Quebec Road LN12 1QJ
☎ 01507 477871 ▤ 01507 472066
www.havenholidays.com
Dir: *From centre of Mablethorpe turn left on
seafront road towards north end. Park on left*
Open: mid Mar-Oct, Booking advisable
school hols, Last arrival 22.00hrs Last
departure 10.00hrs
A large, well-equipped seaside holiday park
with separate touring facilities on two sites,
including fully modernised toilets. The first
floor entertainment rooms are only accessible
via stairs (no lifts). A 7-acre site with 195
touring pitches.
Facilities: Mini bowling alley, snooker/pool,
indoor fun palace. 🎢🛶🔍🅿️⛺️➗⊙❄️🕐💲
♿ **Services:** 🛒🍴🔌💩🛁🚿🗑️🚽 **Facilities
found within 3 miles:** ∪🎣18🏌️◎🗑️💲
Notes: Maximum of 2 dogs per group

MABLETHORPE   TF58
Kirkstead Holiday Park ►►► 77%
North Road Trusthorpe LN12 2QD
☎ 01507 441483 ▤ 08700 336723
email: mark@kirkstead.co.uk
www.kirkstead.co.uk
Dir: *From Mablethorpe town centre take A52
S towards Sutton-on-Sea. 1m turn sharp right
at 2 phone boxes into North Rd. Site signed
in 300yds*
* 🚐 £14-£18 �caravan £14-£18 ▲ £10-£18
Open: Mar-Nov, Booking advisable bank hols
& Jul-Aug, Last arrival 22.00hrs Last
departure 15.00hrs
Controlled entry is a security feature of this
pleasant family-run site. The touring area and
good quality toilets are centrally located, and
the grounds are well maintained. A 10-acre
site with 80 touring pitches and 75 statics.
Facilities: Snooker, volleyball, football pitch,
basketball 🔍⛺️🔲🅿️◎⊙❄️🚿🕐🗑️🎣♿
Services: 🛒🍴🔌💩🛁🚿🚽 **Facilities
found within 3 miles:** ∪🎣18🏌️◎🗑️💲
⊗ **Notes:** No pets

LONDON N9   TQ39

**Lee Valley Camping & Caravan
Park ►►►** 84%

Meridian Way Edmonton N9 0AS

☎ 020 8803 6900 ▤ 020 8884 4975

email: leisurecentre@leevalleypark.org.uk

www.leevalleypark.com

Dir: *From M25 junct 25, A10 S, 1st left on
A1055, approx 5m to Leisure Centre. From
A406 (North Circular), N on A1010, left after
0.25m, right (Pickets Lock Lane)*

* ⊕ £6.30 ⊨ £6.30 ▲ £6.30

Booking advisable Jul-Aug, Last arrival
22.00hrs Last departure noon

A pleasant, open site within easy reach of
London yet peacefully located close to two
large reservoirs. A 4.5-acre site with 160
touring pitches and 41 hardstandings.

Facilities: Kitchen, cinema, 18-hole golf
course ⚁ ⚅ ⊙ ⚆ ⚇ ⚈ ⚉ ⛺ 🚻 🔥 &. **Services:**
🔌 🍴 🚿 Ⓣ ⬇ 🚱 🛢 ∅ 🚮 ♨ **Facilities
found within 3 miles:** ⚓ 18 ⚑ ✎ ♨ 🔓 🛍

Notes: No commercial vehicles

SOUTHPORT   SD31

**Willowbank Holiday Home &
Touring Park ►►►** 83%

Coastal Road Ainsdale PR8 3ST

☎ 01704 571566 ▤ 01704 571576

email: info@willowbankcp.co.uk

www.willowbankcp.co.uk

Dir: *From A565 between Formby and
Ainsdale turn at the Woodvale lights onto
coastal road, site 150mtrs on left*

* ⊕ £11-£14 ⊨ £11-£14 ▲ £9.50-£12.50

Open: Mar-10 Jan, Booking advisable bank
hols & special events, Last arrival 21.00hrs
Last departure 16.00hrs

Set in a wooded clearing on a nature reserve
next to the sand dunes, this park is just off the
coastal road to Southport. Toilet facilities are
well equipped. A 6-acre site with 54 touring
pitches, 30 hardstandings and 228 statics.

Facilities: Baby changing facility ⚁ ⚅ ⊙ ⚆
Ⓒ 🚻 🔥 & **Services:** ⬇ 🚱 🛢 🛢 ∅
Facilities found within 3 miles: ∪ ⚓ 18
⚑ ✎ ◎ ♨ 🔓 🛍

NORFOLK

BARNEY
TG03

The Old Brick Kilns ▶▶▶▶ 91%

Little Barney Lane Fakenham NR21 0NL

☎ 01328 878305 📠 01328 878948

email: enquiries@old-brick-kilns.co.uk

www.old-brick-kilns.co.uk

Dir: *From A148 (Fakenham-Cromer) follow brown tourist signs to Barney, then left into Little Barney Lane. Site at end of lane*

* 🚐 £13.50-£23 🚙 £13.50-£23 Å £12.50-£19

Open: Mar-6 Jan (rs low season bar food/takeaway selected nights only), Booking advisable bank hols & Jul-Aug, Last departure noon

A secluded park on two levels with a boating and fishing pool. Excellent toilet facilities, and short dog walk. Due to a narrow access road, no arrivals until after 1pm. A 12.73-acre site with 65 touring pitches and 65 hardstandings.

Facilities: Outdoor draughts, chess, family games, fishing 🔌 🏕 ⛲ 🄽 ⊙ 🅿 ☀ 🕐 💷 📶 🚾 🛒 🛗 **Services:** 🍽 🗑 🛢 ⬆ 🗑 🛒 🛎 🪣 💧 🔥 🗑 💷

BELTON
TG40

Wild Duck Holiday Park 65%

Howards Common Great Yarmouth NR31 9NE

☎ 01493 780268 📠 01493 782308

www.havenholidays.com

Dir: *From A47 towards Gt Yarmouth take A143 towards Beccles. Turn right at Burgh Castle, right at T-junct, left at next T-junct, park 200mtrs on right*

Open: mid Mar-Oct (rs mid Mar-May & Sep-Oct some facilities may be reduced), Booking advisable school hols, Last arrival 22.30hrs Last departure noon

This a large holiday complex with plenty to do for all ages, both indoors and out. This level grassy site is set in a forest with small cleared areas for tourers. Clubs for children and teenagers, and evening shows. A 97-acre site with 130 touring pitches and 365 statics.

Facilities: Sauna & jacuzzi 🏊 🎱 🄽 🎮 🌰 ⊙ 🅿 ☀ 🕐 💷 🚾 🛒 🛗 **Services:** 🍺 🗑 🛢 🛎 🪣 🚮 🛒 ⬆ 💦 **Facilities found within 3 miles:** ⚓ 18 🎣 🪣 ⊚ 🗑 💷

BELTON TG40

Rose Farm Touring & Camping Park ▶▶▶▶ 85%

Stepshort Nr Great Yarmouth NR31 9JS

☎ 01493 780896 📠 01493 780896

www.rosefarmtouringpark.co.uk

Dir: *Follow signs to Belton off A143, right at lane signed Stepshort, site 1st on right*

* 🚐 £10-£16 🚏 £10-£16 ▲ £8-£16

Open: Open All Year Booking advisable Jul-Aug

A former railway line is the setting for this very peaceful site which enjoys rural views and is beautifully presented throughout. The ever-improving toilet facilities are spotlessly clean and inviting to use, and the park is brightened with many flower and herb beds. Customer care is truly exceptional. A 10-acre site with 80 touring pitches and 15 hardstandings.

Facilities: ♦ ⚠ ▢ ⌢ ⊙ ✳ 🛒 🕹 **Services:** 🚐 🖫 🛢 🧴 🖙 Facilities found within 3 miles: ∪ ⚲ 18 ⚓ 🏌 🖫 🖫 **Notes:** 🐾

CLIPPESBY TG41

Clippesby Hall ▶▶▶▶▶ 82%

Clippesby Hall Great Yarmouth NR29 3BL

☎ 01493 367800 📠 01493 367809

email: holidays@clippesby.com

www.clippesby.com

Dir: *From A47 follow tourist signs for The Broads. At Acle rdbt take A1064, after 2m left onto B1152, 0.5m turn left opposite village sign, 400yds on right*

* 🚐 £13-£19.50 🚏 £13-£19.50 ▲ £13-£19.50

Open: Spring BH-30 Oct (rs Etr-23 May no swimming/tennis.Pub/cafe BH wknds), Booking advisable school hols, Last arrival 17.30hrs Last departure 11.00hrs

A lovely country house estate with secluded pitches. A 30-acre site with 100 touring pitches and 9 hardstandings.

Facilities: Bicycle hire & mini golf ♦ ⚲ ⚠ ⚲ ⌢ ⊙ ⌖ ✳ 🕐 🛒 🕹 🕹 **Services:** 🚐 🖫 🛢 🍴 🖫 🖫 🖙 🛢 🧴 🖙 Facilities found within 3 miles: ∪ ⚲ 18 ⚓ 🏌 ⊙ 🖫 🖫 **Notes:** Dogs must be on leads

NORFOLK

CROMER   TG24
Forest Park Caravan Site ▶▶▶ 73%
Northrepps Road NR27 0JR
☎ 01263 513290 🖷 01263 511992
email: info@forest-park.co.uk
www.forest-park.co.uk
Dir: *A140 from Norwich, left at T-junct signed Cromer, right signed Northrepps, right then immediate left, left at T-junct, site on right*
* 🚐 £10-£18 🚃 £10-£18 ⛺ £10-£18
Open: 15 Mar-15 Jan, Booking advisable Etr, Spring bank hol & Jul-Aug, Last arrival 21.00hrs Last departure 11.00hrs
Surrounded by forest, this gently sloping park offers a choice of pitches. Visitors have the use of a heated indoor swimming pool, and a clubhouse with entertainment. An 85-acre site with 344 touring pitches and 372 statics.
Facilities: BMX track, hair salon 🎣 ♦ 🅼 🐾 ☺ 🄿 ✳ ⊕ 🖃 🖵 ﹠ **Services:** 🐥 🍴 🍻 🆃 🔋 🖅 🗑 ∅ 🚿 **Facilities found within 3 miles:** ∪ ⚓ 18 ⚑ ♪ ◎ 🛶 🖥 🗑

CROMER   TG24
Manor Farm Caravan & Campsite
▶▶▶ 66%
East Runton NR27 9PR
☎ 01263 512858
email: manor-farm@ukf.net
www.manorfarmcaravansite.co.uk
Dir: *1m W of Cromer, turn off A148 or A149 at Manor Farm sign*
* 🚐 £10.50-£12 🚃 £10.50-£12
⛺ £10.50-£12
Open: Etr-Sep, Booking advisable bank hols & all season for EHU points, Last arrival 20.30hrs Last departure noon
A family-run site on a working farm enjoying sea views. There are good modern facilities on the caravan-only area, and a well-maintained toilet block on the tenting field. A 17-acre site with 250 touring pitches.
Facilities: 2 dog-free fields 🅼 🐾 ☺ ✳ 🛒 ﹠ **Services:** 🔋 🆃 ∅ 🖅 **Facilities found within 3 miles:** ∪ ⚓ 18 ♪ ◎ 🛶 🖥 🗑
Notes: ☻

GREAT YARMOUTH   TG50

Vauxhall Holiday Park 78%

4 Acle New Road NR30 1TB

☎ 01493 857231 🖹 01493 331122

email: vauxhall.holidays@virgin.net

www.vauxhall-holiday-park.co.uk

Dir: *On A47 approaching Great Yarmouth*

* 🚐 £13-£28 🚏 £13-£28 ▲ £13-£26

Open: Etr, mid May-Sep & Oct half term,
Booking advisable mid Jul-Aug, Last arrival
21.00hrs Last departure 10.00hrs

A very large holiday complex with plenty of
entertainment and access to beach, river,
estuary, lake and the A47. The touring pitches
are laid out in four separate areas, each with
its own amenity block, and all arranged
around the main entertainment. A 40-acre site
with 220 touring pitches and 421 statics.

Facilities: Children's pool, sauna, solarium,
fitness centre 🥤🥤🍴🖥🗀🔾🔈🕭🌞🕓🖏

& **Services:** 🛱🍴🚿🗂🖥🔾🖥🗑🖉🎔🕭

🚮 **Facilities found within 3 miles:** ∪ ♨

18 ♐ 🖉 🎯 ◎ 🎣 🖥 🖏 🕳

HUNSTANTON   TF64

Searles Leisure Resort 80%

South Beach Road PE36 5BB

☎ 01485 534211 🖹 01485 533815

www.searles.co.uk

Dir: *A149 from King's Lynn to Hunstanton.
At rdbt follow signs for South Beach. Straight
on at 2nd rdbt. Site on left*

* 🚐 £11-£33 🚏 £11-£33 ▲ £10-£32

Open: Feb (half term)-New Year (rs Feb-May
& Oct-Dec outdoor pool closed), Booking
advisable bank hols & Jul-Aug, Last arrival
20.45hrs Last departure 11.00hrs

A large seaside holiday complex with plenty
of well-managed facilities, adjacent to the sea
and beach. The tourers have their own areas.
A 50-acre site with 332 touring pitches, 100
hardstandings and 460 statics.

Facilities: Entertainment programme, hire
shop, golf course 🥤🥤🍴🗀🔾🖏🔾◎🎯🌞🕓

🖥🚮🖩🎌& **Services:** 🛱🍴🚿🗂🖥🔾🖥🗑

🖉🎔🚮 **Facilities found within 3 miles:**

∪♨18 ♐ 🖉 ◎ 🎣 🖥 🖏

NORFOLK

SCRATBY   TG51
Scratby Hall Caravan Park
▶▶▶ 77%
Great Yarmouth NR29 3PH
☎ 01493 730283
Dir: *5m N of Great Yarmouth. Exit A149 onto B1159, site signed*
🚐 £5.75-£14 🚃 £5.75-£14 ▲ £5.75-£14
Open: Spring bank hol-mid Sep (rs Etr-Spring bank hol & mid Sep-Oct reduced hours & shop closed), Booking advisable Spring bank hol wk & Jul-Aug, Last arrival 22.00hrs Last departure noon
A neatly-maintained site with a popular children's play area, well-equipped shop and outdoor swimming pool with sun terrace. The toilets are kept spotlessly clean, and the beach and the Norfolk Broads are close by. A 5-acre site with 108 touring pitches.
Facilities: Food preparation room. ♦ ⚠ ♠ ☉ Ⓟ✳ ⓈⒷ & **Services:** ▯ ☻ ⓢ 🛢 🚽 ⊘ ⇌
Facilities found within 3 miles: ∪ ≰ 18 ⇵ 𝒫 ⓢ Ⓢ **Notes:** No commercial vehicles ⊛

ST JOHN'S FEN END   TF51
Virginia Lake Caravan Park
▶▶▶▶ 73%
Smeeth Road PE14 8JF
☎ 01945 430332
email: louise@virginialake.co.uk
www.virginialake.co.uk
Dir: *From A47 E of Wisbech follow tourist signs to Terrington St John. Park on left*
* 🚐 £15-£20 🚃 £15-£20 ▲ £10-£20
Open: Open All Year Booking advisable bank hols, Last arrival 23.00hrs Last departure noon
A well-established park beside a fishing lake with good facilities for anglers and tourers. A clubhouse serves meals. A 5-acre site with 100 touring pitches and 20 hardstandings.
Facilities: Pool tables, large screen TV ⚠ ♠ ☉ Ⓟ✳ Ⓢ 🅱 ♥ ☷ 🛒 ⏚ & **Services:** ☻ ⓣ 🛢 ▯ 🚽 ⊘ 🛢 🚽 ⊘ ⇌ ▥ **Facilities found within 3 miles:** ∪ ≰ 18 𝒫 ⓢ Ⓢ **Notes:** ⊛

TRIMINGHAM TG23

Woodland Leisure Park ►►► 70%

Norwich NR11 8AL

☎ 01263 579208 📠 01263 576477

email: info@woodland-park.co.uk

www.woodland-park.co.uk

Dir: *4m SE on B1159 coast road*

* 🚐 £15-£18 🚙 £15-£18

Open: Mar-Dec, Booking advisable public hols & Jul-Aug, Last arrival 23.00hrs Last departure noon

A secluded woodland site in an open enclosure, close to the sea but well sheltered from the winds by tall trees. Facilities include two bars, a restaurant, an indoor swimming pool, bowling green and sauna, and entertainment is provided in the clubhouse. A 55-acre site with 55 touring pitches and 230 statics.

Facilities: 🏊 🔍 ⛺ ⛲ 🚿 ⊙ 🚰 ✻ ✆ [$] ⛩ ♿

Services: ☕ 🍴 🍷 🚐 🔒 🛏 🧺 **Facilities found within 3 miles:** U ⛳ 18 🖊 [⊡] [$]

BAMBURGH NU13

Glororum Caravan Park ►►► 70%

Glororum Farm NE69 7AW

☎ 01668 214457 📠 01688 214622

email: info@glororum-caravanpark.co.uk

www.glororum-caravanpark.co.uk

Dir: *Exit A1 at junct with B1341 (Purdy's Lodge). In 3.5m left onto unclass road. Site 300yds on left*

* 🚐 £15-£16 🚙 £15-£16 ⛺ £15-£16

Open: Apr-Oct, Booking advisable school & bank hols, Last arrival 22.00hrs Last departure noon

A pleasantly situated site where tourers have their own well-established facilities. The open countryside setting affords good views of Bamburgh Castle and surrounding farmland. A 6-acre site with 100 touring pitches and 150 statics.

Facilities: ⛺ ⛲ 🚿 ⊙ 🚰 ✻ ✆ [$] 🐕 ⛩

Services: [T] 🚐 [⊡] 🔒 🍃 🛏 **Facilities found within 3 miles:** U ⛳ 18 ✈ 🖊 ◎ 🌊 [⊡] [$]

NORFOLK/NORTHUMBERLAND

NORTHUMBERLAND

BAMBURGH NU13

Waren Caravan Park ▶▶▶▶ 74%

Waren Mill NE70 7EE

☎ 01668 214366 ▤ 01668 214224

email: waren@meadowhead.co.uk

www.meadowhead.co.uk

Dir: *2m E of town. From A1 onto B1342*
signed Bamburgh. Take unclass road past
Waren Mill, signed Budle

⊡ £11-£19.50 ⊟ £11-£19.50 ▲ £11-£23

Open: Apr-Oct (rs Nov-Feb Bar, shop &
restaurant closed), Booking advisable Spring
bank hol & Jul-Aug, Last arrival 20.00hrs
Last departure noon

Attractive site with footpath to the beach. The
park offers excellent facilities including family
bathrooms. A 4-acre site with 180 touring
pitches, 24 hardstandings and 300 statics.

Facilities: 100 acres of private heathland ⚊
⬤ 𝕸 𝕽 ⊙ 𝐏 ✻ ⊙ 🛢 🖈 🏬 𝄞 ❺ **Services:**
🕈 🍲 🔌 🔟 ⚗ ⊡ 🛢 ⊘ ⛟ 🕳 **Facilities**
found within 3 miles: ∪ ⅃ 18 🗲 ◉ 🛢

BELLINGHAM NY88

Brown Rigg Caravan & Camping
Park ▶▶▶▶ 77%

NE48 2JY

☎ 01434 220175

email: enquiries@northumberlandcaravanparks.com

www.northumberlandcaravanparks.com

Dir: *From A69 take A68 N. Then B6318 to*
Chollerford & B6320 to Bellingham. Pass
Forestry Commission land, site 0.5m S of
Bellingham

* ⊡ £12.40-£16.40 ⊟ £12.40-£16.40
▲ £9.90-£16.40

Open: 31 Mar-Oct, Booking advisable at all
times, Last arrival 20.00hrs Last departure
noon

This is a quiet park set in a pleasant rural
location with trees and views. A 5-acre site
with 70 touring pitches and 15 hardstandings.

Facilities: ⬤ 𝕸 𝕽 ⊙ 𝐏 ✻ ⊙ 🛢 🖈 🏬
Services: 🔟 ⊡ 🛢 ⊘ ⛟ **Facilities found**
within 3 miles: ∪ ⅃ 18 🗲 🛢 🛢 **Notes:**
Dogs on leads, no groups, quiet policy
23.00hrs-07.30hrs

NORTHUMBERLAND

BERWICK-UPON-TWEED   NT95
Ord House Country Park

▶▶▶▶▶ 80%

East Ord TD15 2NS

☎ 01289 305288 📠 01289 330832

email: enquiries@ordhouse.co.uk

www.ordhouse.co.uk

Dir: *On A1, Berwick bypass, turn off at 2nd rdbt at East Ord, follow 'Caravan' signs*

* 🚐 £12.50-£18.50 ⇌ £12.50-£18.50

⛺ £7.50-£18.50

Open: Open All Year Booking advisable bank hols & Jul-Aug, Last arrival 23.00hrs Last departure noon

A very well run park set in the grounds of an 18th-century country house. Touring pitches are marked and well spaced. Modern toilet facilities. A 42-acre site with 79 touring pitches, 46 hardstandings and 255 statics.

Facilities: Crazy golf, table tennis, giant draughts ⚙🏪⊙🌳✳⊛🏧🍴🏕🔥

Services: 🍽🔌🗑♿🚰❄🍺🛒🍴

Facilities found within 3 miles: ⚓18 🎣 🏌️⊙🗑🏧

BERWICK-UPON-TWEED   NT95
Haggerston Castle 74%

Beal TD15 2PA

☎ 01289 381333 📠 01289 381433

www.havenholidays.com

Dir: *On A1, 7m S of Berwick-upon-Tweed, site signed*

Open: mid Mar-Oct (rs mid Mar-May & Sep-Oct some facilities may be reduced), Booking advisable school hols, Last arrival anytime Last departure 10.00hrs

A large holiday centre with a well equipped touring park, offering comprehensive holiday activities. The entertainment complex contains amusements for the whole family, and there are several bars, an adventure playground, boating on the lake, a children's club, a 9-hole golf course, tennis courts, and various eating outlets. A 7-acre site with 150 touring pitches, 150 hardstandings and 1200 statics.

Facilities: 📶🛜⚓⚙🏊🏪⊙🌳✳⊛🏧🍴 🏕🔥♿ **Services:** 🍷🍽🔌🗑⊡🏧🛒🍴🚿🍴 🍺🍴 **Facilities found within 3 miles:** ∪ ⚓9🎣🗑🏧

NORTHUMBERLAND

HEXHAM   NY96
Causey Hill Caravan Park Limited
▶▶▶ 70%
Causey Hill NE46 2JN
☎ 01434 602834 📠 01434 609086
email: causeyhillcp@aol.com
www.causeyhill.co.uk
Dir: *Take B6306 from Hexham, 1st right to Whitley Chapel. Right for Hexham Racecourse, right again for site*
* 🚐 £14-£18 🚌 £14-£18 ▲ £12-£15
Open: Mar-Oct, Booking advisable public hols & May-Sep, Last departure noon
A well-maintained site on sloping ground, with plenty of terracing to create level pitches. The site is screened by trees, and a reception area/shop/disabled facility provides a quality amenity. A 6-acre site with 35 touring pitches, 20 hardstandings and 105 statics.
Facilities: 🅐 🏕 ⊙ 🅟 ※ 🕒 🗑 📬 🎾 🍴 🛒 ♿
Services: 🅣 🅟 🛢 🔥 ⌀ Facilities found within 3 miles: ∪ ↓ 18 ⇞ ☌ 🅢 **Notes:** 😊

HEXHAM   NY96
Hexham Racecourse Caravan Site
▶▶▶ 65%
Hexham Racecourse NE46 3NN
☎ 01434 606847 📠 01434 605814
email: hexrace@aol.com
Dir: *From Hexham take B6305 signed Allendale/Alston. Left in 3m signed to racecourse. Site 1.5m on right*
* 🚐 £12 ▲ £9
Open: May-Sep, Booking advisable wknds & bank hols for electric hook-up, Last arrival 20.00hrs Last departure noon
A part-level and part-sloping grassy site situated on a racecourse overlooking Hexhamshire Moors. The facilities are functional and well-maintained. A 4-acre site with 40 touring pitches.
Facilities: 🌢 🅐 🏕 ⊙ 🅟 ※ 🕒 🎾 🍴
Services: 🅟 🛢 🔥 ⌀ 🛒 Facilities found within 3 miles: ∪ ↓ 18 ⇞ ☌ ◎ 🛢 🅢
Notes: 😊

ROTHBURY NU00

Coquetdale Caravan Park ►►► 76%

Whitton NE65 7RU

☎ 01669 620549

email:
enquiries@coquetdalecaravanpark.co.uk

www.coquetdalecaravanpark.co.uk

Dir: *0.5m SW of Rothbury towards Newtown*

* ☐ £12-£15 ☐ £12-£15

Open: Etr-Oct, Booking advisable at all times, Last arrival 21.00hrs Last departure 14.00hrs A very pleasant mainly static site in a lovely location beside the River Coquet, with good open views of moorland and the Simonside Hills. Tourers are on the site's upper area with their own purpose-built toilet facilities. An ideal place for relaxing and touring. A 13-acre site with 30 touring pitches and 160 statics.

Facilities: Adventure playground for older children/adults ⚠ ☐ ⊙ ☐ ☐ **Services:** ☐ ☐ ⊘ ☐ 18 ⌿ ☐ **Notes:** Families & couples only ☐

RADCLIFFE ON TRENT SK63

Thornton's Holt Camping Park
►►► 71%

Stragglethorpe Road Stragglethorpe NG12 2JZ

☎ 0115 933 2125 ☐ 0115 933 3318

email: camping@thorntons-holt.co.uk

www.thorntons-holt.co.uk

Dir: *Take A52, 3m E of Nottingham. Turn S at lights towards Cropwell Bishop. Park 0.5m on left. Or A46 SE of Nottingham. N at lights. Park 2.5m on right*

* ☐ £10-£15 ☐ £10-£15 ▲ £10-£15

Open: Open All Year (rs 2 Nov-24 Mar no pool, shop or games room), Booking advisable bank hols & wknds mid May-Oct, Last arrival 21.00hrs Last departure 13.00hrs A 13-acre site with 155 touring pitches and 35 hardstandings. Pub and restaurant nearby.

Facilities: ☐ ☐ ⚠ ☐ ☐ ⊙ ☐ ☐ ☐ ☐ ☐ ☐ ☐ **Services:** ☐ ☐ ☐ ☐ ⊘ ☐ **Facilities found within 3 miles:** ∪ ☐ 18 ⌿ ☐ ☐ ☐ **Notes:** noise curfew 22.00hrs

NOTTINGHAMSHIRE/OXFORDSHIRE

TEVERSAL
SK46

Teversal Camping & Caravanning Club Site ▶▶▶▶ 92%

Silverhill Lane NG17 3JJ

☎ 01623 551838

www.campingandcaravanningclub.co.uk

Dir: M1 junct 28 onto A38 towards ·Mansfield. Left at lights onto B6027. At top of hill straight over at lights & left at Peacock Hotel. Right onto B6014, left at Craven Arms, site on left

🚐 £18.25-£20.15 🚙 £18.25-£20.15 ▲ £18.25-£20.15

Open: Open All Year Booking advisable bank hols, Last arrival 21.00hrs Last departure noon

A top notch park in a rural former mining area. A 6-acre site with 126 touring pitches, 96 hardstandings and 1 static.

Facilities: 🅰 🏕 ☉ ⊙ ✿ ✕ ⓒ ⓢ ⓑ **Services:** 🖵 ⬆ 🚐 ⓢ ⓪ ⊘ 🛒 **Facilities found within 3 miles:** ∪ ⚓ 18 ℓ ⓢ

BANBURY
SP44

Barnstones Caravan & Camping Site ▶▶▶▶ 80%

Great Bourton OX17 1QU

☎ 01295 750289

Dir: Take A423 from Banbury signed Southam. In 3m turn right signed Gt Bourton/Cropredy, site 100yds on right, (3m N of M40 junct 11)

* 🚐 £8.50-£10.50 🚙 £8.50-£10.50 ▲ £6-£8

Open: Open All Year Booking advisable public hols

Popular, neatly laid-out site with plenty of hardstandings, some fully serviced pitches, and a smart up-to-date toilet block. Well run by personable owner. A 3-acre site with 49 touring pitches and 44 hardstandings.

Facilities: 🅰 🏕 ☉ ⊙ ✕ ⓒ ✿ 🎪 ☰ 🛒 ⓑ **Services:** 🚐 ⓢ 🛒 ⓪ ⊘ 🛒 🛒 **Facilities found within 3 miles:** ∪ ⚓ 18 ✿ ℓ ◎ 🛶 ⓢ ⓢ

Notes: ☺

BLETCHINGDON SP51

Diamond Farm Caravan & Camping Park ▶▶▶ 84%

Islip Road OX5 3DR

☎ 01869 350909

email: warden@diamondpark.co.uk

www.diamondpark.co.uk

Dir: *From M40 junct 9 onto A34 S for 3m, then B4027 to Bletchingdon. Site 1m on left*

Open: Mar-Nov, Booking advisable bank hols & Jul-Sep, Last arrival 22.00hrs Last departure noon

A well-run, quiet rural site in good level surroundings, and ideal for touring the Cotswolds. Situated seven miles north of Oxford in the heart of the Thames Valley. This popular park has excellent facilities, and offers a heated outdoor swimming pool and a games room for children. A 3-acre site with 37 touring pitches and 13 hardstandings.

Facilities: ⊸ ♦ ⋀ ⋔ ⊙ ℘ ✳ ◐ ⓢ

Services: 🗓 🗓 ⊖ ⓢ 🍴 ⊘ 🍴 ↥ 18 ℘ ⓢ ⓢ

Notes: ☻

BLETCHINGDON SP41

Greenhill Leisure Park ▶▶▶ 72%

Greenhill Farm Station Road Oxford OX5 3BQ

☎ 01869 351600 ▤ 01869 350918

email: info@greenhill-leisure-park.co.uk

www.greenhill-leisure-park.co.uk

Dir: *M40 junct 9, A34 south for 3m. Take B4027 to Bletchingdon. Site 0.5m after village on left*

⊟ £9-£11 ⊟ £9-£11 ▲ £9-£11

Open: Open All Year (rs Oct-Mar Shop closed), Booking advisable Bank hols & Jul-Aug, Last arrival 22.00hrs Last departure noon

An all-year round park set in open countryside near Bletchingdon. Fishing is available in the nearby river, and the park has its own farm shop. A 7-acre site with 36 touring pitches and 25 hardstandings.

Facilities: Pets' corner ♦ ⋀ ⋔ ⊙ ℘ ✳ ⓢ ⋈ ⊟ ⅋ **Services:** 🗓 ⊖ ⓢ ⓢ ⊘ ↥

Facilities found within 3 miles: ↥ 18 ℘ ⓢ **Notes:** ☻

OXFORDSHIRE

OXFORDSHIRE

CHARLBURY SP32

Cotswold View Touring park

▶▶▶▶ 80%

Enstone Road OX7 3JH

☎ 01608 810314 📄 01608 811891

email: bookings@gfwiddows.f9.co.uk

www.cotswoldview.co.uk

Dir: *Signed from A44 on to B4022*

* 🚐 £10-£13 🚃 £10-£13 ⛺ £10-£13

Open: Etr or Apr-Oct, Booking advisable bank hols, Last arrival 21.00hrs Last departure noon

A good Cotswold site, well screened and with attractive views. The toilet facilities include fully-equipped family rooms and bathrooms, and there are spacious, sheltered pitches, some with hardstandings. A 10-acre site with 125 touring pitches.

Facilities: Off licence, cycle hire, skittle alley 🍴 ⛰ ⚡ 🐾 ☺ 🅿✻ 🕒 🚿 ⛽ 🚾 ♿ **Services:** 🚽 🚐 🥘 🛢 🧺 🍽 ⛽ **Facilities found within 3 miles:** 🎣 🛍 🏧

HENLEY-ON-THAMES SU78

Swiss Farm International Camping

▶▶▶ 73%

Marlow Road RG9 2HY

☎ 01491 573419

email: enquiries@swissfarmcamping.co.uk

www.swissfarmcamping.co.uk

Dir: *On A4155, N of Henley, next left after rugby club, towards Marlow*

* 🚐 £12-£16 🚃 £12-£16 ⛺ £10-£14

Open: Mar-Oct, Booking advisable all year, Last arrival 21.00hrs Last departure noon

A conveniently-located site within a few minutes walk of Henley. Visitors are invited to fish in the park's well-stocked lake, which is set in a secluded wooded area. A 6-acre site with 165 touring pitches, 12 hardstandings and 6 statics.

Facilities: Fishing lake 🍴 ⛰ ⚡ 🐾 ☺ 🅿✻ 🕒 🚾 🍴 ♿ **Services:** 🚽 🚾 🚐 🥘 🛢 🧺 **Facilities found within 3 miles:** ⛳ ⚓ 18 🚣 🎣 🏧 **Notes:** No groups, max 1 dog per booking

OXFORDSHIRE/RUTLAND

STANDLAKE SP30

Lincoln Farm Park ▶▶▶▶▶ 93%

High Street OX29 7RH

☎ 01865 300239 📠 01865 300127

email: lincolnfarmpark@btconnect.com

www.lincolnfarmpark.co.uk

Dir: *In village off A415 between Abingdon & Witney, 5m SE of Witney*

* 🚐 £14-£20 🚌 £14-£20 🛆 £13-£18

Open: Feb-Nov, Booking advisable bank hols, Jul-Aug & most wknds, Last arrival 21.00hrs Last departure noon

An attractively landscaped park in a quiet village setting, with superb facilities. Family rooms, fully-serviced pitches, two indoor pools and a fully-equipped gym are part of the amenities. A 9-acre site with 90 touring pitches, 75 hardstandings and 19 statics.

Facilities: Indoor leisure centre, putting green, outdoor chess 🏊 🅰 🌂 ⊙ 🅿 ※ 🕒 🖪 🍴 📺 ♿ **Services:** 🚽 🕁 🚮 🛢 🗑 🧺 ⛽

Facilities found within 3 miles: ∪ 🚵 18 ≒ 🏌 ⅏ 🖈 **Notes:** No gazebos

GREETHAM SK92

Rutland Caravan & Camping

▶▶▶ 83%

Oakham LE15 7NX

☎ 01572 813520 📠 01572 812616

email: info@rutlandcaravanandcamping.co.uk

www.rutlandcaravanandcamping.co.uk

Dir: *From A1 onto B668 towards Greetham. Before Greetham turn right at x-rds, then 2nd left to site*

* 🚐 £11.50-£14.50 🚌 £11.50-£14.50 🛆 £9.50-£12.50

Open: Open All Year Booking advisable bank hols

A pretty caravan park surrounded by well-planted banks. The site is close to the Viking Way and other footpath networks, and good for visiting Rutland Water. A 5-acre site with 60 touring pitches and 14 hardstandings.

Facilities: 🔌 🅰 🌂 ⊙ 🅿 ※ 🛏 🍴 ♿

Services: 🕁 🚮 🛢 🗑 🧺 ⛽ **Facilities found within 3 miles:** ∪ 🚵 36 ≒ 🏌 ◎ 🖈 🖪

texts too big.

SHROPSHIRE

BRIDGNORTH SO79
Stanmore Hall Touring Park
▶▶▶▶ 91%

Stourbridge Road WV15 6DT
☎ 01746 761761 🖪 01746 768069
email: stanmore@morris-leisure
Dir: *2m E of Bridgnorth on A458*
* 🚐 £15.10–£20.30 ⛺ £15.10–£20.30
▲ £15.10–£20.30

Open: Open All Year Booking advisable
school & bank hols & Jul-Aug, Last arrival
20.00hrs Last departure noon
An excellent park offering outstanding
facilities. Pitches, many fully serviced, are
arranged around the lake in Stanmore Hall,
home of the Midland Motor Museum. Handy
for touring Ironbridge and the Severn Valley
Railway. A 12.5-acre site with 131 touring
pitches and 44 hardstandings.
Facilities: ⚠🅟☉🅟✗⊙🗟🖈🛏&
Services: 🔲↯🚽🗟🔋∅🌡🛒 **Facilities
found within 3 miles:** ∪↟18🌣🖉🗟🗟
Notes: Max of 2 dogs

SHREWSBURY SJ41
Oxon Hall Touring Park ▶▶▶▶ 91%

Welshpool Road SY3 5FB
☎ 01743 340868 🖪 01743 340869
email: oxon@morris-leisure.co.uk
www.morris-leisure.co.uk
Dir: *Leave A5 ring road at junct with A458.*
Park shares entrance with 'Oxon Park & Ride'
* 🚐 £15.60–£18.60 ⛺ £15.60–£18.60

Open: Open All Year Booking advisable high
season, Last arrival 21.00hrs
A delightful park with quality facilities, and a
choice of grass and fully-serviced pitches. An
adults-only section is very popular with those
wanting a peaceful holiday, and there is an
inviting patio area next to reception and the
shop, overlooking a small lake. A 15-acre site
with 124 touring pitches, 72 hardstandings
and 42 statics.
Facilities: ⚠🅟☉🅟⊙🗟🖈🛏&
Services: 🔲↯🚽🗟🔋∅🛒 **Facilities
found within 3 miles:** ∪↟18🖉🗟🗟

1 3/4 hrs.

1 3/4 hrs.

WEM
SJ54

Lower Lacon Caravan Park

▶▶▶ 75%

Shrewsbury SY4 5RP

☎ 01939 232376 🖷 01939 233606

email: info@llcp.co.uk

www.llcp.co.uk

Dir: *Take A49 to B5065. Site 3m on the right*

* ➡ £15-£21 ➡ £15-£21 ▲ £15-£21

Open: Open All Year (rs Nov-Mar club wknds only, toilets closed if frosty), Booking advisable public hols & Jul-Aug, Last arrival 20.00hrs Last departure 16.00hrs

A large, spacious park with lively club facilities and an entertainments barn. The park is particularly suitable for families, with an outdoor swimming pool and farm animals. A 48-acre site with 270 touring pitches, 30 hardstandings and 50 statics.

Facilities: Crazy golf ➹ ➤ 𝔸 ⌂ ⌐ ↑ ⊙ ℗ ✲ ⊙ ⓢ ↬ ◁ **Services:** ☎ ⅋ 🗊 🔟 ♨ ☵ ▯ ⊘ 🎬 **⚼ Facilities found within 3 miles:** ⌖ 18 ℘ ◻ ⓢ

WENTNOR
SO39

The Green Caravan Park ▶▶▶ 73%

Bishop's Castle SY9 5EF

☎ 01588 650605

email: info@greencaravanpark.co.uk

www.greencaravanpark.co.uk

Dir: *1m NE of Bishop's Castle on A489. Turn right at brown tourist sign*

* ➡ £10 ➡ £10 ▲ £10

Open: Etr-Oct, Booking advisable bank hols & wknds, Last arrival 21.00hrs Last departure 13.00hrs

A pleasant site in a peaceful setting convenient for visiting Ludlow or Shrewsbury. The grassy pitches are mainly level. A 15-acre site with 140 touring pitches, 4 hardstandings and 20 statics.

Facilities: 𝔸 ⌐ ⊙ ℗ ✲ ⓢ ↬ **Services:** ☎ ⅋ 🔟 ♨ ☵ ▯ ⊘ 🎬 **Facilities found within 3 miles:** ∪ ℘ ⓢ **Notes:** Dogs must be kept on leads at all times

SHROPSHIRE

SOMERSET

BATH ST76

Newton Mill Caravan and Camping Park ►►►► 85%

Newton Road BA2 9JF

☎ 01225 333909

email: newtonmill@hotmail.com

www.campinginbath.co.uk

Dir: *From Bath W on A4 to A39 rdbt, immediate left, site 1m on left*

* 🚐 £17.50-£19.50 🚌 £17.50-£19.50 ⛺ £13-£17

Open: Open All Year Booking advisable public hols & Jul-Aug, Last arrival 21.00hrs Last departure noon

An attractive park set in a valley, surrounded by woodland. Excellent toilet facilities, and a restaurant and bar. A 42-acre site with 195 touring pitches and 85 hardstandings.

Facilities: Fishing & satellite TV hook ups. 🔍 ⛺ 🚿 ⊙ ✳ ✆ [$] 🐕 ♿ **Services:** 🍺 🍷 [T] ⚓ 🚐 🗄 🔒 🍃 🛒 **Facilities found within 3 miles:** U ⛳ 9 ✈ 🗄 [$]

BAWDRIP ST34

The Fairways International Touring C & C Park ►►► 70%

Bath Road Bridgwater TA7 8PP

☎ 01278 685569 📠 01278 685569

email: fairwaysint@btinternet.com

www.fairwaysint.btinternet.com.uk

Dir: *A39 onto B3141, 100yds on right*

🚐 £9-£16.50 🚌 £9-£16.50 ⛺ £6

Open: Mar-mid Nov, Booking advisable Etr, Mayday, Whitsun, summer hols & Nov, Last arrival 22.00hrs Last departure 22.00hrs

This family orientated site is well positioned for visiting the many attractions in the area including Burnham-on-Sea, Weston-Super-Mare and Glastonbury. The park also makes a convenient overnight stop off the M5. A 5.75-acre site with 200 touring pitches.

Facilities: Accessory centre 🔍 ⛺ 🚿 ⊙ ✳ ✆ [$] 🐕 🪑 ♿ **Services:** [T] 🚐 🗄 🔒 🍃 🛒 **Facilities found within 3 miles:** 🗄 [$]

BREAN ST25

**Warren Farm
Holiday Centre** 81%

Brean Sands Burnham-on-Sea TA8 2RP

☎ 01278 751227

email: enquiries@warren-farm.co.uk

www.warren-farm.co.uk

Dir: *M5 junct 22 onto B3140 through
Burnham-on-Sea to Berrow and Brean. Centre
1.5m past Brean Leisure Park*

* ☎ £6-£13 ☎ £6-£13 ▲ £6-£13

Open: Apr-Oct, Booking advisable BH's &
school hols, Last arrival 20.00hrs Last
departure noon

A holiday park close to the beach, divided into
several fields. Has a bar and restaurant, and
entertainment for all the family. A 100-acre
site with 575 touring pitches and 800 statics.

Facilities: Fishing lake & ponds, indoor
play area, farm walk ◕ ⚠ ▭ ↟ ⊙ ☞ ⚒ ⊙ ⛱
♯ ♬ ♿ **Services:** ♨ ☵ ♨ ⊤ ⚡ ⚑ ◔ ▣
⌀ ⛟ ⚱ **Facilities found within 3 miles:**
∪ ♨ 18 ✐ ⛻ **Notes:** No commerical vehicles

BRIDGWATER ST24

**Mill Farm Caravan & Camping
Park** ▶▶▶▶ 70%

Fiddington TA5 1JQ

☎ 01278 732286

Dir: *From Bridgwater take A39 W, turn left at
Cannington rdbt for 2m, then right just
beyond Apple Inn towards Fiddington and
follow camping signs*

* ☎ £10-£16 ☎ £10-£16 ▲ £10-£16

Open: Open All Year Booking advisable peak
periods, Last arrival 23.00hrs Last departure
10.00hrs

A mature site with plenty to interest all the
family. A waterfall, stream and safe boating
pool are popular features. The park is divided
into three caravan areas and a large space for
tents, each with its own facilities. A 6-acre site
with 125 touring pitches.

Facilities: Canoeing, pool table,
trampolines, entertainment ⌂ ◕ ◕ ⚠ ▭ ↟
⊙ ☞ ⚒ ⊙ ⛱ ♯ ♬ ♿ **Services:** ♨ ⊤ ▣ ⚑ ◔
⚱ ⌀ ⛱ ⚱ **Facilities found within 3
miles:** ♨ 8 ✐ ◎

SOMERSET

SOMERSET

BURNHAM-ON-SEA — ST34

Burnham-on-Sea Holiday Village 78%

Marine Drive TA8 1LA

☎ 01278 783391 📠 01278 793776

www.havenholidays.com

Dir: *On A38 to Highbridge, cross rail bridge, turn right to Burnham-on-Sea. 1m, left into Marine Parade, follow signs to site on left*

Open: mid Mar-Oct (rs mid Mar-May & Sep-Oct Facilities may be reduced), Booking advisable Jul-Aug, Last arrival anytime Last departure 10.00hrs

A large family-orientated holiday village complex with a separate touring park containing 43 super pitches. The coarse fishing lake is very popular, and the seafront at Burnham is only 0.5m away. A 76-acre site with 75 touring pitches and 75 statics.

Facilities: 🏪 🍴 ⚓ 🏕 🏠 🚿 🛁 🅿 🚻 🛒 ♿

Services: 🔌 🍴 🚐 ♿ 🚗 📮 🛢 🚽 ⛲ **Facilities found within 3 miles:** 🎣 🐾 ⊗

BURTLE — ST34

Orchard Camping ► 71%

Ye Olde Burtle Inn Catcott Road TA7 8NG

☎ 01278 722269 📠 01278 722269

email: chris@theburtleinn.co.uk

www.theburtleinn.co.uk

Dir: *From M5 junct 23 onto A39, approx 4m turn left onto unclass road to Burtle, site by pub in village centre*

* ▲ £10.50-£11.50

Open: Open All Year Booking advisable bank hols & peak season, Last arrival anytime

A simple campsite set in an orchard at the rear of a lovely 17th-century family inn in the heart of the Somerset Levels. The restaurant offers meals; breakfast can be pre-ordered. A shower and disabled toilet are available to campers outside pub opening hours. A 0.75-acre site with 30 touring pitches.

Facilities: Bicycle & tent hire, sleeping bags & equipment ⚓ 🏕 🚿 ⊙ 🅿 ✳ ⊗ 🚻 🛒 ♿

Services: 🔌 🍴 🚐 🛒 ⛲ **Facilities found within 3 miles:** ∪ 🐾 🛢

CHARD ST30

Alpine Grove Touring Park

►►► 84%

Forton TA20 4HD

☎ 01460 63479 🖹 01460 63479

email: stay@alpinegrovetouringpark.com

www.alpinegrovetouringpark.com

Dir: *Turn off A30 between Chard & Crewkerne towards Cricket St Thomas, follow signs. Park 2m on right*

🚐 £6-£16 🚙 £6-£16 ▲ £6-£16

Open: 1 wk before Etr-Sep, Booking advisable bank hols & Jul-Aug, Last arrival 21.00hrs Last departure 11.00hrs

A warm welcome awaits at this quiet wooded park with both hardstandings and grass pitches. Log cabins are also available for hire. An 8.5-acre site with 40 touring pitches and 15 hardstandings.

Facilities: Dog-sitting service 🐾 🖻 🅟 ☺ 📡✳☉🅂♨🎖🎪🅟🛆 & **Services:** 🅣🔁🅟🛢🔒 ⊘🍴 **Facilities found within 3 miles:** ∪ 🎣18 ⚲ 🅑🅢 **Notes:** Dogs must be kept on leads ⊜

CHEDDAR ST45

Broadway House Holiday Caravan & Camping Park ►►►►► 70%

Axbridge Road BS27 3DB

☎ 01934 742610 🖹 01934 744950

email: info@broadwayhouse.uk.com

Dir: *From M5 junct 22 follow signs to Cheddar Gorge & Caves (8m). Park midway between Cheddar & Axbridge on A371*

* 🚐 £12-£22 🚙 £10-£18 ▲ £10-£20

Open: Mar-mid Nov (rs Mar-end May & Oct-Nov bar & pool closed, limited shop hours), Booking advisable bank hols & end Jul-Aug, Last arrival 23.00hrs Last departure noon

A family park with an exceptional range of activities. A 30-acre site with 200 touring pitches, 60 hardstandings and 37 statics.

Facilities: Table tennis, crazy golf, bike hire, BMX track 🐾 🖻 🅟 🖻 ☉ 🅟✳☉🅂♨🎖🎪 🅟 & **Services:** 🅣🔁🅣🛆🔁🅟🛢⊘🍴🏧 **Facilities found within 3 miles:** 🎣18 ⚲ ◎🅑🅢 **Notes:** Children to be supervised at all times

SOMERSET

CROWCOMBE ST13

Quantock Orchard Caravan Park

►►►► 82%

Taunton TA4 4AW

☎ 01984 618618 📠 01984 618618

email: qocp@flaxpool.freeserve.co.uk

www.flaxpool.freeserve.co.uk

Dir: *Site set back from A358*

Open: Open All Year Booking advisable bank hols & Jul-Aug, Last arrival 22.00hrs Last departure noon

An attractive, quiet site with wonderful views, sitting at the western foot of the Quantocks. The park is laid out in an old orchard and the quality facilities are very well maintained. There is a fitness complex and swimming pool. Ideal for visiting Exmoor National Park, and the nearby West Somerset Steam Railway. A 3.5-acre site with 75 touring pitches.

Facilities: Gym & leisure suite, off-licence on site 🏊 🎾 🎠 📺 🚿 🔌 💇 ❄ 📞 🛍 🍖 ♿ **Services:** [T] ⛽ 🧼 🔒 🍃 🔋 **Facilities found within 3 miles:** 🐴 ⛳ 18 🎣 🧼

DULVERTON SS92

Wimbleball Lake ►►► 71%

TA22 9NU

☎ 01398 371257

email: cvallance@swlakestrust.org.uk

www.swlakestrust.org.uk

Dir: *From A396 (Tiverton-Minehead road) take B3222 signed Dulverton Services, follow signs to Wimbleball Lake. Ignore 1st entry (fishing) & take 2nd entry for watersports & camping. (NB care needed - narrow roads)*

Open: Apr-1 Nov, Booking advisable high season, Last departure 14.00hrs

A grassy site overlooking Wimbleball Lake, high up on Exmoor National Park. The lake is renowned for its trout fishing, and boats can be hired with advance notice. A 1.25-acre site with 30 touring pitches and 4 hardstandings.

Facilities: Watersports centre, lakeside walks 🎠 🚿 🔌 💇 📞 🍖 🪑 ♿ **Services:** ☕ ⛽ **Facilities found within 3 miles:** 🐴 ⛵ 🎣 🏄 🛍 **Notes:** Dogs must be kept on leads

LANGPORT ST42

Bowdens Crest Caravan & Camping Park ▶▶▶ 77%

Bowdens TA10 0DD

☎ 01458 250553 🖹 01458 253360

email: bowcrest@btconnect.com

www.bowdenscrest.co.uk

Dir: *Off A372 (Langport to Bridgwater road), signed*

* 🚐 £10-£20 🚌 £10-£20 ▲ £5-£20

Open: Open All Year Booking advisable bank hols & Aug, Last arrival 22.00hrs Last departure noon

A tranquil park with spectacular panoramic views over the Somerset levels and the distant Blackdown Hills. The tasteful restaurant with adjoining patio appeals to both couples and families. A 16.5-acre site with 30 touring pitches, 2 hardstandings and 13 statics.

Facilities: Special diets catered for ◀ 🗛 ☐ ↖ ☉✖ ⓘ 🗑 🖈 🎀 & **Services:** ☎ 🍴 🍷 ⊤ 🖪 🗑 🖻 🕗 🛒 **Facilities found within 3 miles:** ∪ 🖋

MINEHEAD SS94

Minehead & Exmoor Caravan & Camping Park ▶▶▶ 69%

Porlock Road TA24 8SW

☎ 01643 703074

Dir: *1m W of Minehead centre, close to A39*

* 🚐 £10 🚌 £10 ▲ £10

Open: Open All Year (rs Nov-Feb reduced no. of pitches), Booking advisable bank hols & Jul-Aug, Last arrival 22.00hrs Last departure noon

A small terraced park on the edge of Exmoor, spread over five paddocks and screened by the mature trees that surround it. The level pitches provide a comfortable space for each unit on this family-run park. There is a laundrette in nearby Minehead. A 3-acre site with 50 touring pitches and 4 hardstandings.

Facilities: 🗛 ↖ ☉ 🗑✖ ⓘ & **Services:** ☎ 🖪 🕗 🛒 **Facilities found within 3 miles:** ∪ 🎣 18 ⚲ 🖋 ◎ 🐟 🖻 🖼 **Notes:** 🐾

SOMERSET

SOMERSET

...d ST46

...dge Farm Camping & Caravan Park ▶▶▶ 77%

Cowslip Green BS40 5RB

☎ 01934 862311 🗎 01934 862311

email: brooklodgefarm@aol.com

www.brooklodgefarm.com

Dir: *M5 junct 18/22 follow signs for Bristol Airport. Park 3m on left of A38 at bottom of hill after Darlington Arms*

* ⌂ £12.50-£18.50 ⌂ £10-£16.50 ▲ £10.50-£17

Open: Mar-Oct, Booking advisable 22 May-4 Sep, Last arrival 22.30hrs Last departure noon

A naturally sheltered country touring park nestling in a valley of the Mendip Hills, surrounded by trees. A 3.5-acre site with 29 touring pitches and 3 hardstandings.

Facilities: Bicycle hire & walking maps provided ⌂ 🅐 🅡 ☉ 🄿 ☼ ☉ 🅢 🔧 **Services:** 🄰 🔒 🄿 🎺 **Facilities found within 3 miles:** ∪ ☇ 18 🗝 🅢 **Notes:** Small dogs only & must be on lead

RODNEY STOKE ST45

Bucklegrove Caravan & Camping Park Ltd ▶▶▶▶ 71%

Wells Road BS27 3UZ

☎ 01749 870261 🗎 01749 870101

email: info@bucklegrove.co.uk

www.bucklegrove.co.uk

Dir: *On A371 midway between Cheddar & Wells*

* ⌂ £7.50-£21 ⌂ £7.50-£21 ▲ £5-£18

Open: 5 Mar-2 Jan (rs Nov-Dec & Mar-Etr pool closed), Booking advisable bank hols & peak periods, Last arrival 21.00hrs Last departure noon

A well-sheltered site on the southern slopes of the Mendip Hills. Facilities and amenities include an indoor pool and a bar/restaurant. A 7.5-acre site with 120 touring pitches, 24 hardstandings and 35 statics.

Facilities: Tourist information room ⌂ 🔍 🅐 🅡 ☉ 🄿 ☼ ☉ 🅢 🄶 **Services:** 🍽 🛢 🅣 🄿 🄰 🔒 🄿 🎂 **Facilities found within 3 miles:** ∪ ☇ 18 🗝 ◎ 🄿 🅢 ⊗

500 Family Campsites

TAUNTON ST22

Ashe Farm Camping & Caravan Site ►►► 76%

Thornfalcon TA3 5NW

☎ 01823 442567

email: camping@ashe-farm.fsnet.co.uk

Dir: *From M5 junct 25 take A358 E for 2.5m. Turn right at Nags Head pub. Site 0.25m on right*

* ⊕ £9 ⇔ £9 Å £5

Open: Apr-Oct, Booking advisable Jul-Aug, Last arrival 22.00hrs

A well-screened site surrounded by mature trees and shrubs, with two large touring fields. A facilities block includes smart toilets and a separate laundry room, while the old portaloos remain very clean and well-maintained. A 7-acre site with 30 touring pitches and 8 hardstandings.

Facilities: Baby changing facilities ⚠ ⏚ ☊ ⊙ ☞⚡ ⚓ & **Services:** 🗩 🗑 🖴 🛒

Facilities found within 3 miles: ∪ ⅃ 18 ✎ 🗑 🖄 **Notes:** ☻

WATCHET

Home Farm Holiday Cen

►►► 81%

St Audries Bay TA4 4DP

☎ 01984 632487 🗎 01984 634687

email: dib@homefarmholidaycentre.co.uk

www.homefarmholidaycentre.co.uk

Dir: *Follow A39 towards Minehead, fork right onto B3191 at West Quantoxhead after St Audries garage, then right after 0.25m*

⊕ £10-£20 ⇔ £10-£20 Å £10-£20

Open: Open All Year (rs mid Nov-Etr shop & bar closed), Booking advisable all year, Last arrival dusk Last departure noon

In a hidden valley beneath the Quantock Hills, this park overlooks its own private beach. The atmosphere is friendly and quiet, and there are lovely sea views from the level pitches. A 45-acre site with 40 touring pitches, 35 hardstandings and 230 statics.

Facilities: ⌂ ⚠ ⚓ ⊙ ☞⚡ ⌚ ⏚ ☊ ⚓ &

Services: 🔌 🗍 🗩 🗑 🖴 ⚗ ✎ 🗑 🖄

SOMERSET

WESTON-SUPER-MARE ST36
Country View Caravan Park
▶▶▶ 79%
Sand Road Sand Bay BS22 9UJ
☎ 01934 627595
www.cvhp.co.uk
Dir: *M5 junct 21, A370 towards Weston-Super-Mare. Immediately take left lane, follow Kewstoke/Sand Bay signs. Straight over 3 rdbts onto Lower Norton Ln. At Sand Bay right into Sand Rd, site on right*
* ⊕ £11-£21 ⇌ £11-£21 ▲ £10-£20
Open: Mar-Jan, Booking advisable bank hols, wknds & peak periods, Last arrival 20.00hrs Last departure noon
A pleasant open site in a rural area a few hundred yards from Sandy Bay and beach. The park is well placed for walks along the coast. An 8-acre site with 120 touring pitches, 90 hardstandings and 65 statics.
Facilities: ⬤ ✆ 🅰 🄸 🄿 ✳ 🕒 🄶 🛢 ♿
Services: 🔌 🅃 🄰 🛢 🗑 ⊘ **Facilities found within 3 miles:** ∪ ⌽ 18 ⅄ 🖉 ◎ ⅏ 🄶 🅂 **Notes:** 🐾

WINSFORD SS83
Halse Farm Caravan & Camping Park ▶▶▶ 77%
Minehead TA24 7JL
☎ 01643 851259 🖷 01643 851592
email: enquiries@halsefarm.co.uk
www.halsefarm.co.uk
Dir: *Signed from A396 at Bridgetown. In Winsford turn left and bear left past pub. 1m up hill, entrance on left immediately after cattle grid*
* ⊕ £9-£11 ⇌ £9-£11 ▲ £9-£11
Open: 22 Mar-Oct, Booking advisable bank hols & mid Jul-Aug, Last arrival 22.00hrs Last departure noon
A peaceful little site on Exmoor overlooking a wooded valley with glorious views. This moorland site is quite remote. A 3-acre site with 44 touring pitches and 11 hardstandings.
Facilities: 🅰 🄽 ⊙ 🄿 ✳ 🕒 🛏 ♿ **Services:** 🄰 🛢 🗑 ⊘ 🛒 **Facilities found within 3 miles:** ∪ 🖉 🅂

CHEADLE SK04

Quarry Walk Park ▶▶▶ 79%

Coppice Lane Croxden Common ST10 1RQ

☎ 01538 723412 📄 01538 724093

email: quarry@quarrywalkpark.co.uk

www.quarrywalkpark.co.uk

Dir: *From A522 (Uttoxeter-Cheadle road) turn at Crown Inn at Mabberley signed Freehay. In 1m at rdbt by Queen pub turn to Great Gate. Site signed on right in 1.25m*

* 🚐 £15-£15.50 🚌 £15-£15.50 ▲ £10-£11

Open: Open All Year Booking advisable bank hols, Last arrival 21.00hrs Last departure noon

A pleasant park in an old quarry with well-screened pitches, all with water and electricity. Facilities include a shop and family toilets. For children, there is a well equipped play area; Alton Towers is nearby. A 14-acre site with 40 touring pitches and 40 hardstandings.

Facilities: 𝔸 ⌂ ⊙✕ 🏺 🗙 ⌐ ⌂ **Services:** 🚐 🖫 🛋 ∅ **Facilities found within 3 miles:** ✎ 🖫 🖳

OAKAMOOR SK04

The Star Caravan & Camping Park ▶▶▶ 82%

Star Road Cotton Near Alton Towers ST10 3DW

☎ 01538 702219 📄 01538 703704

www.starcaravanpark.co.uk

Dir: *1.25m N of Oakamoor on B5417*

* 🚐 £12-£16 🚌 £12-£16 ▲ £12-£16

Open: Mar-Nov, Booking advisable especially for EHU, bank hols, Last arrival 22.00hrs Last departure noon

This is a well maintained and efficiently managed grassland park with views over the countryside. It is ideally placed for a variety of outdoor leisure activities and convenient for Alton Towers. A 25-acre site with 120 touring pitches, 20 hardstandings and 63 statics.

Facilities: Parent & baby/child bathroom 𝔸 ⌂ ⊙✕ ⓢ 🗙 ⌐ ⌂ **Services:** 🖂 🚐 🖫 🛋 ∅ **Facilities found within 3 miles:** ⚓ 18 ✎ 🖫 🖳 **Notes:** Quiet after 23.00hrs, no ground fires/disposable BBQs, no large groups ⊜

SUFFOLK

FELIXSTOWE   TM23

Peewit Caravan Park ▶▶▶ 71%

Walton Avenue IP11 2HB

☎ 01394 284511

email: peewitpark@aol.com

www.peewitcaravanpark.co.uk

Dir: *Signed from A14 in Felixstowe, 100mtrs past dock gate, 1st on left*

* ⊕ £12-£18 ⇔ £12-£18 ▲ £9-£15

Open: Apr or Etr-Oct, Booking advisable school & bank hols, Last arrival 21.00hrs Last departure 11.00hrs

A grass touring area fringed by trees, with well-maintained grounds and a colourful floral display. This handy urban site is not overlooked by houses, and the toilet facilities are well cared for. A function room contains a TV and library. The beach is a few minutes away by car. A 13-acre site with 45 touring pitches, 1 hardstanding and 200 statics.

Facilities: Boules area, bowling green, adventure trail 🅰 🄽 ⊙ ☞ ✳ ⓢ ☛ ⅙

Services: ⊕ 🄸 🅰 ⅙ 🄻 18 ⅊ ℮ ◎ ⅏ 🄸 ⅙

Notes: 🄬

IPSWICH   TM14

Priory Park ▶▶▶▶ 87%

IP10 0JT

☎ 01473 727393 🄳 01473 278372

email: jwl@priory-park.com

www.priory-park.com

Dir: *Exit A14 at Ipswich southern by-pass towards town centre. 300mtrs left towards Priory Park. Follow single track road into park*

* ⊕ £16-£24 ⇔ £16-£24 ▲ £16-£24

Open: Apr-Oct (rs Apr-Jun & Sep-Oct limited pitches,club & pool closed), Booking advisable at all times, Last arrival 18.00hrs Last departure 14.00hrs

A well-screened and very peaceful south-facing park set close to the banks of the tidal River Orwell, and with panoramic views over the water. A 100-acre site with 75 touring pitches, 59 hardstandings and 260 statics.

Facilities: 9-hole golf, small boat launching, table tennis ⬤ 🄰 ⅊ 🄽 ⊙ ☞ ✳ ⓢ ☛ 🄷 ⅌ 🄰

Services: 🄹 ⅋ 🄸 🄳 ⊕ 🄻 🄰 ⅆ ⅃ 9 ℮ ⅏ 🄸

🄳 **Notes:** No commercial vehicles, pup tents or group bookings 🄬

IPSWICH   TM24

Low House Touring Caravan Centre ►►► 77%

Bucklesham Road Foxhall IP10 0AU

☎ 01473 659437 📠 01473 659880

email: low.house@btopenworld.com

Dir: *From A14 south ring road take slip road to A1156 signed East Ipswich. Right in 1m, right again in 0.5m. Site on left*

* 🚐 £12 🚓 £12 ▲ £20

Open: Open All Year, Booking advisable, Last arrival anytime Last departure 14.00hrs

A secluded site surrounded by hundreds of mature trees. Buildings have been hand-crafted by the owner in stained timber, and there is a children's play area, and a collection of caged rabbits, bantams and guinea fowl. Tents accepted only if room available. A 3.5-acre site with 30 touring pitches.

Facilities: 🅰 🖍 ⊙ 🅿 ✳ 🕒 🕳 **Services:** 🚐 🔒 ⌀ 🍴 **Facilities found within 3 miles:** ∪ ⚓ 18 ⌀ ◎ 🔯 🔯 **Notes:** Dogs must be kept on leads 🐕

KESSINGLAND   TM58

Heathland Beach Caravan Park ►►►► 82%

London Road NR33 7PJ

☎ 01502 740337 📠 01502 742355

email: heathlandbeach@btinternet.com

www.heathlandbeach.co.uk

Dir: *1m N of Kessingland off A12 onto B1437*

🚐 £17-£21 🚓 £17-£21 ▲ £17-£21

Open: Apr-Oct, Booking advisable peak periods, Last arrival 21.00hrs Last departure 11.00hrs

A well-run park offering superb toilet facilities. The park is set in meadowland, with level grass pitches, and mature trees and bushes. There is direct access to the beach, and good provisions for families on site. A 5-acre site with 63 touring pitches and 200 statics.

Facilities: Freshwater & sea fishing ⚓ 🅰 🕳 🖍 ⊙ 🅿 ✳ 🕒 🕳 🍴 🅰 ♿ **Services:** 🚐 🔒 🕒 🔯 ⌀ **Facilities found within 3 miles:** ∪ ⚓ 18 ⚑ ⌀ ⚓ 🔯 🔯 **Notes:** One dog only per unit

SUFFOLK

KESSINGLAND   TM58

Kessingland Beach
Holiday Park 65%

Beach Road NR33 7RW

☎ 01502 740636 📠 01502 740907

email:
holidaysales.kessinglandbeach@park-resorts.com

www.park-resorts.com

* ⊞ £5-£25 ⊞ £5-£25 ▲ £3-£22

Open: Etr-2 Nov, Booking advisable Jul-Aug,
Last arrival 24.00hrs Last departure 10.00hrs
A large holiday centre with direct access onto
the beach, and a variety of leisure facilities.
The touring area is tucked away from the
statics, and served by a clean and functional
toilet block. A fish and chip shop and Boat
House Restaurant are popular features. A 69-
acre site with 90 touring pitches.

Facilities: Kids clubs, entertainment, mini
ten pin bowling 🎦 ⚓ ⚲ ⚠ ⚖ � ⊙✳ ⊙ 🖐
Services: 🐂 🍽 🛢 ⊞ 🛢 🔒 🗑 🚮 **Facilities**
found within 3 miles: ⚄ 🅿 🚤 🗑 🔋

WOODBRIDGE   TM24

Moon & Sixpence ▶▶▶▶▶ 92%

Newburn Road Waldringfield IP12 4PP

☎ 01473 736650 📠 01473 736270

email: info@moonandsixpence.eu

www.moonandsixpence.eu

Dir: *Follow caravan & Moon & Sixpence*
signs from A12 Ipswich (East bypass). Turn
left at x-roads 1.5m from A12

* ⊞ £18-£26 ⊞ £18-£26 ▲ £18-£26

Open: Apr-Oct (rs low season club, shop,
reception open limited hours), Booking
advisable school & bank hols, Last arrival
20.00hrs Last departure noon
Tourers occupy a sheltered position around a
boating lake here. Plenty of leisure facilities
and an adult-only area. A 5-acre site with 65
touring pitches and 225 statics.

Facilities: Lake, cycle trail, 10-acre sports
area/9-hole golf ⚓ ⚠ ⚲ � ⊙ 🅿✳ 🖐 🚮 ⎔
Services: 🍽 🛢 ⚖ ⊞ 🛢 🔒 🗑 🚮 **Facilities**
found within 3 miles: ⚄ 18 🅿 🚤 🗑 🔋
Notes: No group bookings or commercial
vehicles. Quiet 21.00hrs-08.00hrs

CHERTSEY
TQ06

Chertsey Camping & Caravanning Club Site ▶▶▶▶ 83%

Bridge Road KT16 8JX

☎ 01932 562405

www.campingandcaravanningclub.co.uk

Dir: *M25 junct 11, follow A317 to Chertsey. At rdbt take 1st exit to lights. Straight over at next lights. Turn right 400yds, left into site*

🚐 £18.35-£23.25 🚌 £18.35-£23.25

▲ £18.35-£23.25

Open: Open All Year Booking advisable bank hols & peak period, Last arrival 21.00hrs Last departure noon

A pretty Thames-side site set. Some attractive riverside pitches, and fishing and boating is allowed on the river. A 12-acre site with 150 touring pitches and 65 hardstandings.

Facilities: 🔌 🅰 ⛱ 🏕 ⊙ 🅿 ❄ 🕐 🚽 🍴 🔥 ♿

Services: 🔲 ⚡ 🚱 🗑 🛒 🧺 🚿 **Facilities found within 3 miles:** ∪ ⚓ 🎣 ♿

EAST HORSLEY
TQ05

Horsley Camping & Caravanning Club Site ▶▶▶ 80%

Ockham Road North KT24 6PE

☎ 01483 283273

www.campingandcaravanningclub.co.uk

Dir: *M25 junct 10. S & take 1st major turn signed Ockham/Southend/Ripley. Left & site 2.5m on right. From S take A3 past Guildford & take B2215 towards Ripley*

🚐 £17.05-£20.15 🚌 £17.05-£20.15

▲ £17.05-£20.15

Open: Mar-Oct, Booking advisable bank hols & peak period, Last arrival 21.00hrs Last departure noon

A beautiful lakeside site with plenty of trees and separate camping fields, within easy reach of London. A 9.5-acre site with 130 touring pitches and 41 hardstandings.

Facilities: Fishing 🔌 🅰 🏕 ⊙ 🅿 ❄ 🕐 🚽 🍴 ♿ **Services:** 🔲 ⚡ 🗑 🛒 🧺 🚿 **Facilities found within 3 miles:** ∪ ⚓ 🎣 🛶 🍴 ♿

SURREY

EAST SUSSEX

HORAM
TQ51

Horam Manor Touring Park

▶▶▶ 78%

Nr Heathfield TN21 0YD

☎ 01435 813662

email: camp@horam-manor.co.uk

www.horam-manor.co.uk

Dir: *On A267, 3m S of Heathfield and 10m N of Eastbourne*

* 🚐 £14.50 🚙 £14.50 ▲ £14.50

Open: Mar-Oct, Booking advisable peak periods, Last arrival 22.00hrs Last departure 18.00hrs

A well landscaped park in a peaceful location on former estate land, set in gently-sloping grassland surrounded by woods and fishing lakes. There is free entry to nearby nature trails and a farm museum for site visitors. A 7-acre site with 90 touring pitches.

Facilities: Parent and toddler room 🏪 ♨ ᴿ ⊙☼ ⓈΘ☷ 🖈 ♨ & **Services:** 🚱 🖂 🗑 🛢 🧺 ⛟

Facilities found within 3 miles: ∪ ᵤ 18 🎣 🗑 ⑤ **Notes:** ⊕

NORMAN'S BAY
TQ60

Norman's Bay Camping & Caravanning Club Site ▶▶▶ 77%

Pevensey BN24 6PR

☎ 01323 761190

www.campingandcaravanningclub.co.uk

Dir: *From rdbt junct of A27/A259 follow A259 signed Eastbourne. In Pevensey Bay village take 1st left signed Beachlands only. 1.25m site on left*

🚐 £17.05-£20.15 🚙 £17.05-£20.15 ▲ £17.05-£20.15

Open: Mar-Oct, Booking advisable bank hols & peak period, Last arrival 21.00hrs Last departure noon

A well kept site with immaculate toilet block, right beside the sea. This popular family park enjoys good rural views towards Rye and Pevensey. A 13-acre site with 200 touring pitches and 5 hardstandings.

Facilities: ♣ 🏪 ᴿ ⊙℗☼ Ⓢ 🖈 ♨ & **Services:** Ⓣ ⚡ 🚱 🖂 🗑 🛢 🧺 ⛟ ♨ ⑤

ARUNDEL   TQ00

Ship & Anchor Marina ▶▶ 74%

Station Road Ford BN18 0BJ

☎ 01243 551262 📠 01243 555256

email: ysm36@dial.pipex.com

Dir: *From A27 at Arundel take road S signed Ford. Site 2m on left after level crossing*

* 🚐 £11.50-£16.50 🚏 £11.50-£16.50
▲ £11.50-£16.50

Open: Mar-Oct, Booking advisable during Goodwood Motor Festival, Last arrival 21.00hrs Last departure noon

A neat and tidy site in a pleasant position beside the Ship & Anchor pub and the tidal River Arun. There are good walks from the site both to Arundel and to the coast. A 12-acre site with 160 touring pitches.

Facilities: River fishing from site 🔺 🍴 ☉ 🌳✕ ◐ 🚿 🛒 ⅁ **Services:** 🍴 🔌 🔲 🛅 🏧 🔒 🐾 **📶 Facilities found within 3 miles:** ∪ 🎿 18 ⁂ 🏊 ◉ 🗡️ 🗗 🗗 **Notes:** 🐾

BARNS GREEN   TQ12

Sumners Ponds Fishery & Campsite ▶▶▶ 84%

Chapel Road Horsham RH13 0PR

☎ 01403 732539

email: sumnersponds@dsl.co.uk

www.sumnersponds.co.uk

Dir: *From A272 at Coolham x-rds, N towards Barns Green. In 1.5m take 1st left at small x-rds. 1m, over level crossing. Site on left just after right bend*

* 🚐 £14.50-£18.50 🚏 £14.50-£18.50
▲ £14.50-£18.50

Open: Open All Year Booking advisable all year, Last arrival 20.00hrs Last departure 17.00hrs

A site on a working farm on the edge of the quiet village of Barnes Green. Three fishing lakes and a woodland walk. A 40-acre site with 61 touring pitches and 31 hardstandings.

Facilities: Cycling paths 🔺 🍴 ☉ 🌳 🛒 🗡️ 🗗 ⅁ **Services:** 🍴 ⅂ 🔌 ⚑ **Facilities found within 3 miles:** ∪ 🎿 18 🏊 🗗

WEST SUSSEX

WEST SUSSEX

BILLINGSHURST   TQ02

Limeburners (Camping) Ltd

▶▶ 72%

Lordings Rd Newbridge RH14 9JA

☎ 01403 782311

email: chippy.sawyer@virgin.net

Dir: *From A29 turn W onto A272 for 1m, then left onto B2133. Site 300yds on left*

* 🚐 £10 🚗 £10 ⛺ £10

Open: Apr-Oct, Booking advisable bank hols & Jul-Aug, Last arrival 22.00hrs Last departure 14.00hrs

A secluded site in rural West Sussex, at the rear of the Limeburners Arms public house, and surrounded by fields. It makes a pleasant base for touring the South Downs and the Arun Valley. The toilets are basic but very clean. A 2.75-acre site with 40 touring pitches.

Facilities: 🅰 🏠 ⊙⚒ 🕒 **Services:** 🍴🛒
♿ 🚦 🛒 **Facilities found within 3 miles:**
U ♪18 ⚑

CHICHESTER   SU80

Ellscott Park ▶▶▶ 76%

Sidlesham Lane Birdham PO20 7QL

☎ 01243 512003 📄 01243 512003

email: camping@ellscottpark.co.uk

www.ellscottpark.co.uk

Dir: *Take A286 (Chichester/Wittering road) for approx 4m, left at Butterfly Farm sign, site 500yds right*

Open: Mar-Oct, Booking advisable bank hols & Aug

A well-kept park set in meadowland behind the owners' nursery and van storage area. The park attracts a peace-loving clientele, and is handy for the beach and other local attractions. Home-grown produce and eggs are for sale. A 2.5-acre site with 50 touring pitches.

Facilities: 🅰 🏠 ⊙⚒ 🛏🚦♿ **Services:** 🕘
🚦🛢⊘🛒 **Facilities found within 3 miles:** U ♪36 ⚑ 🎣 ⛵🛢⚑ **Notes:** ⚑

DIAL POST TQ11

Honeybridge Park ▶▶▶▶ 86%

Honeybridge Lane Horsham RH13 8NX

☎ 01403 710923 ▤ 01403 712815

email: enquiries@honeybridgepark.co.uk

www.honeybridgepark.co.uk

Dir: *10m S of Horsham on A24. Turn left 1m past Dial Post sign at Old Barn Nurseries, park 300yds on right*

⊞ £15-£23 ⊟ £15-£23 ▲ £15-£19

Open: Open All Year Booking advisable bank hols & high season, Last arrival 20.00hrs Last departure noon

An attractive park with plenty of hardstandings and electric hook-ups. Upmarket toilet facilities, laundry, shop, takeaway and off-licence, and play area. A 15-acre site with 150 touring pitches and 68 hardstandings.

Facilities: Licensed shop ◆ ⋔ ↑ ⊙ ℗ ✻ ⓈⒺ ↬ ☱ ☕ Services: ⊤ ↻ ◖ ⓢ ▮ ⊘ ╘

⚐ **Facilities found within 3 miles:** ∪ ↓ 18 ℘ ⇘ ⓢ ⓢ **Notes:** No groups of under 18s

SELSEY SZ89

Warner Farm Touring Park 78%

Warner Lane Selsey PO20 9EL

☎ 01243 608440 ▤ 01243 604095

email: touring@bunnleisure.co.uk

www.bunnleisure.co.uk

Dir: *Turn right onto School Lane & follow signs*

* ⊞ £17.50-£40 ⊟ £17.50-£40 ▲ £15.50-£28

Open: Mar-Oct, Booking advisable 4 wks prior to arrival, Last arrival 17.30hrs Last departure 10.00hrs

A well-screened touring site adjoining the three static parks under the same ownership. A courtesy bus runs around the complex to entertainment areas and supermarkets. The leisure facilities are also accessible to tourers. A 10-acre site with 250 touring pitches, 60 hardstandings and 1500 statics.

Facilities: ☋ ◄ ◆ ⋔ ⊡ ⒊ ↑ ⊙ ℗ ✻ ⓈⒺ ↬ ☱ ☴ ☕ **Services:** ☎ ⍢ ▮ ⊤ ↻ ◖ ⓢ ▮ ⊘ ⚐ **Facilities found within 3 miles:** ∪ ↓ 18 ⅃ ℘ ◎ ⇘ ⓢ ⓢ

WEST SUSSEX

WEST SUSSEX/WILTSHIRE

WEST WITTERING

SZ79

Wicks Farm Holiday Park ▶▶▶ 78%

Redlands Lane Chichester PO20 8QE

☎ 01243 513116 📄 01243 511296

email: wicks.farm@virgin.net

www.wicksfarm.co.uk

Dir: *From Chichester take A286/B2179 to West Wittering. Follow for 6m and 2nd right after Lamb Inn*

Open: 14 Mar-Oct, Booking advisable peak periods, Last arrival 21.00hrs Last departure noon

A pleasant rural site, well screened by trees and with good clean toilet facilities. The park has a spacious recreation field, and good local walks, with the beach just 2m away. No caravans, only motorhomes and tents. A 14-acre site with 40 touring pitches.

Facilities: ⋀ ⬧ 🐾 ⊙ ⊕ ✳ ⏰ 🅱 🎣

Services: 🆃 ⬇ 🅔 🅑 🅰 🖉 ⬇ 🦺 ◎ 🌊 🅱 🅸 🅱

Notes: No touring caravans

CALNE

ST97

Blackland Lakes Holiday & Leisure Centre ▶▶▶ 72%

Stockley Lane SN11 0NQ

☎ 01249 813672 📄 01249 811346

email: info@blacklandlakes.co.uk

www.blacklandlakes.co.uk

Dir: *From Calne take A4 E for 1.5m, right at camp sign. Site 1m on left*

Open: Open All Year (rs Nov-mid Mar bookings only (pre paid)), Booking advisable all year, Last arrival 23.00hrs Last departure noon

A rural site surrounded by the North and West Downs. The park is divided into paddocks separated by hedges, trees and fences. There are two carp fisheries. A 15-acre site with 180 touring pitches and 25 hardstandings.

Facilities: Wildfowl sanctuary, fishing facilities, bike trail ⋀ 🐾 ⊙ ⊕ ✳ 🅱 🖐 🚻 ♿

Services: 🆃 ⬇ 🅔 🅱 🅰 🖉 🦺 **Facilities found within 3 miles:** ∪ ↓ 18 🖉 🅱

LACOCK ST96

Piccadilly Caravan Park Ltd

▶▶▶ 84%

Folly Lane West SN15 2LP

☎ 01249 730260 📠 01249 730260

email: piccadillylacock@aol.com

Dir: *4m S of Chippenham. On A350 from towards Lacock for 3m. Right at Gastard sign. Site 200yds on left*

🚐 £11.50-£13.50 🚛 £11.50-£13.50
▲ £11.50-£13.50

Open: Apr-Oct, Booking advisable school & bank hols, Last arrival 21.00hrs Last departure noon

A peaceful, pleasant site, well established and beautifully laid out, close to the village of Lacock. Facilities and grounds are immaculately kept, and there is very good screening. A 2.5-acre site with 41 touring pitches and 12 hardstandings.

Facilities: ♨ ❀ ☉ 🅿 ✼ 🕓 ♂ **Services:** 🕿
🖪 🖴 🖉 🛁 **Facilities found within 3 miles:** ∪ ⅃ 18 ♪ 🖪 🖻 **Notes:** 🕲

WESTBURY ST85

Brokerswood Country Park

▶▶▶ 83%

Brokerswood BA13 4EH

☎ 01373 822238 📠 01373 858474

email: woodland.park@virgin.net

www.brokerswood.co.uk

Dir: *From M4 junct 17 south on A350. Right at Yarnbrook to Rising Sun pub at North Bradley, then left at rdbt. Left on bend approaching Southwick, follow lane for 2.5m, site on right*

* 🚐 £10-£25 🚛 £10-£25 ▲ £10-£25

Open: Open All Year Booking advisable peak season & bank hols, Last arrival 21.30hrs Last departure 11.00hrs

A site on the edge of a woodland park with nature trails and fishing lakes. A 5-acre site with 69 touring pitches and 21 hardstandings.

Facilities: ♨ ❀ ☉ 🅿 ✼ 🖪 ♂ 🖻 🔲 ♿

Services: 🕿 🔲 🖪 🖴 🖉 ➡ ♪ 🖻 **Notes:** Families only, no cycling, no disposable BBQs

WILTSHIRE

WORCESTERSHIRE

HANLEY SWAN SO84

Blackmore Camping & Caravanning Club Site ►►►► 79%

Blackmore Camp Site No 2 WR8 0EE

☎ 01684 310280

www.campingandcaravanningclub.co.uk

Dir: *A38 to Upton on Severn. Turn N over river bridge. 2nd left, then 1st left signed Hanley Swan. Site 1m on right*

➡ £18.25–£20.15 ➡ £18.25–£20.15

▲ £18.25–£20.15

Open: Open All Year Booking advisable bank hols & peak period, Last arrival 21.00hrs Last departure noon

Blackmore is a well-established, level wooded park, ideally located for exploring the Malvern Hills and Worcester. The toilet facilities are spotlessly maintained. A 17-acre site with 200 touring pitches and 66 hardstandings.

Facilities: ✎ ♠ ♫ ⊙ ℗ ✳ ℚ ♯ 🛒 ᵫ

Services: ▥ ⌄ ⊕ 🖻 🛢 ∅ 🎦 **Facilities found within 3 miles:** ∪ ℘ ⅍ 🖻

HONEYBOURNE SP14

Ranch Caravan Park ►►►► 82%

Station Road Evesham WR11 7PR

☎ 01386 830744 🖨 01386 833503

email: enquiries@ranch.co.uk

www.ranch.co.uk

Dir: *Through village x-rds towards Bidford, site 400mtrs on left*

* ➡ £15.50–£19.75 ➡ £15.50–£19.75

Open: Mar-Nov (rs Mar-May & Sep-Nov pool closed, shorter club hours), Booking advisable school hols, Last arrival 20.00hrs Last departure noon

An attractive and well-run park set amidst farmland in the Vale of Evesham. Tourers have their own excellent facilities, and the use of an outdoor heated pool. There is also a licensed club. A 12-acre site with 120 touring pitches, 30 hardstandings and 195 statics.

Facilities: ✎ ♠ ♫ ⊡ ♫ ⊙ ℗ ✳ ℚ 🖻 🛒

Services: 🛉 🍴 ▥ ⌄ ⊕ 🖻 🛢 ∅ 🖲 🍺

Facilities found within 3 miles: ∪ ℘ 🖻

🖻 **Notes:** No unaccompanied minors, no tents

MALVERN SO84

Riverside Caravan Park ▶▶▶ 75%

Little Clevelode WR13 6PE

☎ 01684 310475 🖹 01684 310475

Dir: *From A449 signed onto B4424*

* ⊞ £14 ⇔ £14 ▲ £14

Open: Mar-Dec (rs Mar, Nov-Dec closed for tourers), Booking advisable bank hols & end May-end Aug, Last arrival 20.00hrs Last departure noon

An open grassy field close to the Malvern Hills, with fishing in the River Severn which runs past the lower part of the park. The toilet facilities are good, and there is a bar/restaurant/shop. A 25-acre site with 90 touring pitches and 130 statics.

Facilities: ❤ ⚠ ⛔ 🔧 🦊 ⊙✶ 🛢 **Services:** 🔌 ⊤ 🔌 🛢 🛢 ⊘ **Facilities found within 3 miles:** ∪ ⌀ 18 ⚘ 🔎 🛢 🛢 ⊗ **Notes:** No bicycles & skateboards, barrier gate closes at night ⊛

WOLVERLEY SO87

Wolverley Camping & Caravanning Club Site ▶▶▶ 76%

Brown Westhead Park Kidderminster DY10 3PX

☎ 01562 850909

www.campingandcaravanningclub.co.uk

Dir: *From Kidderminster A449 to Wolverhampton, turn left at lights onto B4189 signed Wolverley. Follow brown camping signs, turn right. Site on left*

⊞ £17.05-£20.15 ⇔ £17.05-£20.15 ▲ £17.05-£20.15

Open: Mar-Oct, Booking advisable bank hols & peak periods, Last arrival 21.00hrs Last departure noon

A grassy site on the edge of the village, close to the canal lock and towpath. A 12-acre site with 120 touring pitches.

Facilities: ❤ ⚠ ⛔ 🔧 🦊 ⊙ 🛒✶ ⊙ ⛽ 🍴 ⛓ **Services:** ⊤ 🔌 🛢 🛢 ⊘ 🍴 **Facilities found within 3 miles:** ∪ ⌀ 🔎 🛢 🛢

WORCESTERSHIRE

EAST RIDING OF YORKSHIRE

BRIDLINGTON   TA17

Fir Tree Caravan Park ▶▶▶ 80%

Jewison Lane Sewerby YO16 6YG

☎ 01262 676442 🖨 01262 676442

email: info@flowerofmay.com

www.flowerofmay.com

Dir: *1.5m from centre of Bridlington. Left off B1255 at Marton Corner .Site 600yds on left*

Open: Mar-Oct (rs Early & late season bar & entertainment restrictions), Last arrival 21.00hrs Last departure noon

Fir Tree Park has a well laid out touring area with its own facilities. It has an excellent swimming pool complex, and the bar-cum-conservatory serves meals. There is a family bar, games room and outdoor children's play area. A 22-acre site with 45 touring pitches, 45 hardstandings and 400 statics.

Facilities: 🏠 🔌 Ⓜ ⬧ 🐶 ⊕ ※ Ⓒ 🗑 🚻 ♿

Services: 🚐 🔧 🗑 🛢 🍴 **Facilities found within 3 miles:** ∪ ⅃ 18 ≑ 𝒫 ⊘ 🔥 🗑 🏧

Notes: Dogs by arrangement only 🐾

RUDSTON   TA16

Thorpe Hall Caravan & Camping Site ▶▶▶ 77%

Thorpe Hall YO25 4JE

☎ 01262 420393 🖨 01262 420588

email: caravansite@thorpehall.co.uk

www.thorpehall.co.uk

Dir: *5m from Bridlington on B1253*

* 🚐 £10-£19.50 🚍 £10-£19.50 ▲ £6.50-£15

Open: Mar-Oct (rs reception & shop limited opening hours), Booking advisable bank hols & peak periods, Last arrival 22.00hrs Last departure noon

A delightful small park within the walled gardens of Thorpe Hall yet within a few miles of the seaside resort of Bridlington. The site offers a games field, its own coarse fishery, pitch & putt, and a games and TV lounge. A 4.5-acre site with 90 touring pitches.

Facilities: Golf practice holes 🔌 Ⓜ ⬜ 🐶 ⊕ 𝒫 ※ Ⓒ 🗑 🚻 ♿ **Services:** Ⓣ 🔧 🗑 🛢 🖊

🍴 **Facilities found within 3 miles:** ∪ 𝒫 🗑 🏧

SKIPSEA TA15

Low Skirlington Leisure Park 84%

Driffield YO25 8SY

☎ 01262 468213 ▤ 01262 468105

email: info@skirlington.com

www.skirlington.com

Dir: *From M62 towards Beverley then Hornsea. Between Skipsea & Hornsea on B1242*

Open: Mar-Oct, Booking advisable Mar-Oct

A large well-run park set close to the beach in partly-sloping meadowland. The site has five toilet blocks, supermarket and amusement arcade, with occasional entertainment in the clubhouse. The amenities include an indoor heated pool complex with sauna, jacuzzi and sunbeds, a 10-pin bowling alley and indoor play area. A 24-acre site with 285 touring pitches, 9 hardstandings and 450 statics.

Facilities: Putting green, pony trekking ⛱ ◆ ⚠ ▢ ⋒ ⊙ ☝ ⚓ ◷ ☖ ⚲ ⊼ ⚒ ᷂ **Services:** ⛽ ⛴ ⊗ ◙ ▤ ⊘ ⛟ ⚓ 🛢 **Facilities found within 3 miles:** ∪ ↓ 18 ≑ ⚲ ◎ ⚑ ◙ 🏧

ALLERSTON SE88

Vale of Pickering Caravan Park

▶▶▶▶ 79%

Carr House Farm YO18 7PQ

☎ 01723 859280 ▤ 01723 850060

email: tony@valeofpickering.co.uk

www.valeofpickering.co.uk

Dir: *On B1415, 1.75m off A170 (Pickering-Scarborough road)*

* ◙ £12.50-£15.50 ▲ £10.50-£13.50

Open: 3 Mar (rs Mar), Booking advisable BHs, Last arrival 21.00hrs Last departure noon

A well-maintained, spacious family park with excellent facilities, including a shop, play area and ball sports area. Set in open countryside, the park is handy for the North Yorkshire Moors and Scarborough. A 13-acre site with 120 touring pitches and 80 hardstandings.

Facilities: Microwave ⚠ ⋒ ⊙ ⚲ ☀ ◷ ☖ ⚓ ⚒ **Services:** ⛽ ⊗ ◙ 🛢 ⊘ ⛴ ⚑ **Facilities found within 3 miles:** ∪ ↓ 18 ⚲ ◎ ◙ 🏧

NORTH YORKSHIRE

BOROUGHBRIDGE · SE36

Boroughbridge Camping & Caravanning Club Site ►►►► 77%

Bar Lane Roecliffe YO51 9LS

☎ 01423 322683

www.campingandcaravanningclub.co.uk

Dir: *From A1(M) junct 48 follow signs for Bar Lane Ind Est & Roecliffe. Site 0.25m from rdbt*

⊞ £18.25-£20.15 ⊞ £18.25-£20.15

▲ £18.25-£20.15

Open: Open All Year Booking advisable bank hols & peak periods, Last arrival 21.00hrs Last departure noon

A quiet riverside site with access onto the River Ure, with fishing and boating available. Ripon, Knaresborough, Harrogate and York are within easy reach, and Boroughbridge is just a short walk away. A 5-acre site with 85 touring pitches and 13 hardstandings.

Facilities: ◄ ⋒ ▭ ↸ ⊙ ☞ ✳ ◔ ↦ ☵ ♿

Services: ⊡ ↯ ◙ ◙ ⓘ ∅ ➹ **Facilities found within 3 miles:** ⌀ ⅊ ⓑ

FILEY · TA18

Blue Dolphin Holiday Park 72%

Gristhorpe Bay YO14 9PU

☎ 01723 515155 ▤ 01723 512059

www.havenholidays.com

Dir: *Park off A165, 2m N of Filey*

Open: mid Mar-Oct (rs mid Mar-May & Sep-Oct some facilities may be reduced), Booking advisable school hols, Last arrival 24.00hrs Last departure 10.00hrs

There are great clifftop views to be enjoyed from this fun-filled holiday centre with an extensive and separate touring area. The emphasis is on non-stop entertainment, with sports and clubs, all-weather leisure facilities, heated swimming pools and plenty of well-planned amusements. An 85-acre site with 370 touring pitches and 10 hardstandings.

Facilities: Multi-sports court ⛱ ◄ ◄ ⋒ ⊙ ☞ ✳ ◔ ↦ ♿ **Services:** ☎ ⑩ ⌾ ⊡ ↯ ◙ ◙ ⓘ ∅ ⅏ **Facilities found within 3 miles:** ⚓ 18 ⅊ ⓑ ⓑ **Notes:** Dogs must be on leads, maximum of 2 dogs per group

FILEY
TA18

Flower of May Holiday Park 88%

Lebberston Cliff YO11 3NU

☎ 01723 584311 🖷 01723 581361

email: info@flowerofmay.com

www.flowerofmay.com

Dir: *Signed off A165 on Scarborough side of Filey*

* 🚐 £13.50-£18.50 🚚 £13.50-£18.50 ▲ £11-£18.50

Open: Etr-Oct (rs early & late season restricted opening in café, shop & bars), Booking advisable spring BH wk, Jul-Aug & BHs, Last arrival 21.00hrs Last departure noon

A well-run family holiday park with top class facilities. A 13-acre site with 270 touring pitches, 100 hardstandings and 193 statics.

Facilities: Squash, bowling, 9-hole golf & basketball court 🏊 🐕 🖅 🗖 🐕 ⊙ ℗🛒☀ ① 🚻 ⊁ 🚻 ♿ **Services:** 🕯🗲 ① 🔌 🗑 🛒 🏧 🖴 🛒 **Facilities found within 3 miles:** ∪♪9 ⚓ ℘ ◎ 🛶 🗑 🖫 **Notes:** Dogs by arrangement

FILEY
TA18

Crows Nest Caravan Park ►►► 74%

Gristhorpe YO14 9PS

☎ 01723 582206 🖷 01723 582206

email: enquires@crowsnestcaravanpark.com

www.crowsnestcaravanpark.com

Dir: *5m S of Scarborough & 2m N of Filey. On seaward side of A165, signed off rdbt, near petrol station*

* 🚐 £14-£20 🚚 £14-£20 ▲ £10-£15

Open: Mar-Oct, Booking advisable school hols, Last departure noon

A beautifully situated park with panoramic views on the coast between Scarborough and Filey. This mainly static park offers lively entertainment and two bars. The touring caravan area is near entertainment complex; tenting pitches are at the top of the site. A 20-acre site with 49 touring pitches, 49 hardstandings and 217 statics.

Facilities: Entertainment in bar-no charge 🏊 🐕 🖅 🐕 ⊙☀ ① 🖫 🚻 **Services:** 🕯 ① 🔌 🗑 🖴 �﹍🛒 **Facilities found within 3 miles:** ∪♪18 ℘ ◎ 🛶 🗑 🖫

NORTH YORKSHIRE

FILEY TA18

Filey Brigg Touring Caravan & Country Park ►►► 74%

North Cliff YO14 9ET

☎ 01723 513852

email: fileybrigg@scarborough.gov.uk

Dir: *0.5m from Filey town centre on coast road from Scarborough, A165*

* 🚐 £9-£17 🚙 £9-£17 ▲ £7-£13.50

Open: Etr-30 Oct, Booking advisable bank hols & Jul-Aug, Last arrival 18.00hrs Last departure noon

A municipal park overlooking Filey Brigg with splendid views along the coast, and set in a country park. The beach is just a short walk away, as is the resort of Filey. The main toilet block is heated, and 50 all-weather pitches are available. A 9-acre site with 158 touring pitches and 82 hardstandings.

Facilities: 🏕 🚿 ⊙✳ 📞 [$] 🐕 🪑 ♿ **Services:** 🚰 [T] 💬 🔋 🧺 **Facilities found within 3 miles:** Ω ⚓ ⛳18 🏄 🪶 ◎ 🔋 [$]

FILEY TA17

Reighton Sands Holiday Park 66%

Reighton Gap YO14 9SH

☎ 01723 890476 📠 01723 891043

www.havenholidays.com

Dir: *On A165 5m S of Filey at Reighton Gap, signed*

Open: mid Mar-Oct (rs mid Mar-May & Sep-Oct some facilities may be reduced), Booking advisable school hols, Last arrival 22.00hrs Last departure noon

A lively holiday centre with a wide range of entertainment and all-weather leisure facilities, located just a 10-minute walk from a long sandy beach. Each of the three touring areas has its own facilities block, and the site is geared towards families with young children. A 229-acre site with 160 touring pitches, 160 hardstandings and 800 statics.

Facilities: Indoor play area 🏊 🎱 🏕 🚿 ⊙✳ 📞 [$] 🐕 ♿ **Services:** 🚰 🍴 🍺 💬 🔋 🌿 🧺 **Facilities found within 3 miles:** 🔋 [$]

FILEY TA17

Primrose Valley Holiday Park 80%

YO14 9RF

☎ 01723 513771 📠 01723 513777

www.havenholidays.com

Dir: *Signed off A165 (Scarborough-Bridlington road), 3m S of Filey*

Open: mid Mar-Oct, Booking advisable at all times, Last arrival anytime Last departure 10.00hrs

A large all-action holiday centre with a wide range of sports and leisure activities to suit everyone. The touring area is completely separate from the main park with its own high quality amenity block. All touring pitches are fully-serviced hardstandings with grassed awning strips. A 160-acre site with 49 touring pitches and 1800 statics.

Facilities: ⬥ ⬥ ♠ ⚠ � ⬥ ⊙ ⓢ 🐕 ⬥
Services: 🍴 🔌 🚐 🛢 🛢 ⌀ ⬥ **Facilities found within 3 miles:** ⌂ 19 ⬥ ⌀ ◎ ⬥ 🛢
ⓢ **Notes:** Maximum of 2 dogs per group

HARROGATE SE35

High Moor Farm Park ►►►► 77%

Skipton Road HG3 2LT

☎ 01423 563637 📠 01423 529449

Dir: *On A59 (Harrogate - Skipton road)*

* ⬥ £14-£16 ⬥ £14-£16

Open: Etr or Apr-Oct, Booking advisable public hols, Last arrival 23.30hrs Last departure 15.00hrs

An excellent site with very good facilities, set beside a small wood and surrounded by thorn hedges. The numerous touring pitches are located in meadowland fields, each area with its own toilet block. A large heated indoor swimming pool, games room, golf course, full-sized crown bowling green, and a bar serving meals and snacks are all popular. A 15-acre site with 320 touring pitches, 51 hardstandings and 158 statics.

Facilities: Coarse fishing, 9-hole golf course, bowling green ⬥ ♠ ⚠ ⌂ ⊙ ⓟ ☀ ⓢ
ⓢ 🐕 ⌐ ⬥ **Services:** 🍴 🔌 🅃 🚐 🛢 🛢 ⌀ 🛢
⬥ **Facilities found within 3 miles:** ↻ ⌂
18 ⌀ 🛢 ⓢ

NORTH YORKSHIRE

HARROGATE SE35
Rudding Holiday Park ▶▶▶▶▶ 80%
Follifoot HG3 1JH
☎ 01423 870439 🖹 01423 870859
email: holiday-park@ruddingpark.com
www.ruddingpark.com
*Dir: From A1 take A59 to A658, then S
signed Bradford. 4.5m then right, follow signs*
* ⊕ £15-£29 ⊕ £15-£29 ▲ £15-£29
Open: Mar-Jan (rs Nov-Jan shop & Deer
House - limited opening), Booking advisable
bank hols & wknds, Last arrival 22.30hrs Last
departure 14.00hrs
A spacious park set in stunning Rudding
Park. There are terraced pitches and super
pitches. A 55-acre site with 141 touring
pitches, 60 hardstandings and 95 statics.
Facilities: 18-hole golf course, driving
range ⌂ ♦ ⋔ ↾ ⊙ ⋒ ✳ ⓒ 🖺 🛒 ♿ ⅋
Services: ⓧ 🖘 ⊓ ⊕ 🖺 📦 ⌀ 🛒 ⌘
Facilities found within 3 miles: ∪ ⅃ 18
⅄ ⌀ 🖺 🖺 **Notes:** Under 18s must be
accompanied by adult

HARROGATE SE26
Ripley Caravan Park ▶▶▶▶▶ 72%
Knaresborough Road Ripley HG3 3AU
☎ 01423 770050 🖹 01423 770050
www.ripleycaravanpark.com
*Dir: 3m N of Harrogate on A61. Right at rdbt
onto B6165 signed Knaresborough. Park
300yds left*
* ⊕ £12-£14 ⊕ £12-£14 ▲ £12-£14
Open: Etr-Oct, Booking advisable bank hols,
Last arrival 21.00hrs Last departure noon
A well-run rural site in attractive meadowland.
Well-maintained facilities and a heated
swimming pool and sauna, a games room,
and a covered play room for small children.
An 18-acre site with 100 touring pitches, 35
hardstandings and 50 statics.
Facilities: Nursery playroom, football, TV in
games room ⌂ ♦ ⋔ ↾ ⊙ ⋒ ✳ ⓒ 🖺 ♿ ⅋
Services: ⊓ ⊕ 🖺 📦 ⌀ 🛒 **Facilities found
within 3 miles:** ∪ ⅃ 18 ⅄ ⌀ ◎ 🖺 🖺
Notes: Family camping only, dogs on leads,
BBQs must be off the ground

NORTH YORKSHIRE

HELMSLEY SE68

Golden Square Touring Caravan Park ►►►► 80%

Oswaldkirk YO62 5YQ

☎ 01439 788269 🖺 01439 788236

email: barbara@goldensquarecaravanpark.freeserve.co.uk

www.goldensquarecaravanpark.com

Dir: *1m from Ampleforth towards Helmsley on caravan route. Turn off B1257 to Ampleforth, 0.5m on right*

* ♥ £12.50-£15 ⇌ £12.50-£15 ▲ £10.50-£13

Open: Mar-Oct, Booking advisable bank hols, Last arrival 21.00hrs Last departure noon

A family site with moorland views. Walks and mountain bike trails. Caravans are prohibited from the A170 at Sutton Bank between Thirsk and Helmsley. A 12-acre site with 129 touring pitches, 10 hardstandings and 1 static.

Facilities: Microwave ♠ ⋒ ⋔ ⊙ ℗ ✳ ⊘ 🛍 ⊀ 🏗 ⅋ **Services:** 🖵 ⊍ ⊕ 🖺 🖺 ⊘ 🛒 ⊷ **Facilities found within 3 miles:** ∪ ⌘ 18 ℘ ◎ 🛍 **Notes:** ⊛

HIGH BENTHAM SD66

Riverside Caravan Park ►►►► 81%

Lancaster LA2 7LW

☎ 015242 61272 🖺 015242 62835

email: info@riversidecaravanpark.co.uk

www.riversidecaravanpark.co.uk

Dir: *Off B6480, signed from town centre*

* ♥ £13.50-£26.60 ⇌ £13.50-£26.60 ▲ £13.50-£26.60

Open: Mar-Nov, Booking advisable bank & school hols, Last arrival 20.00hrs Last departure noon

A well-managed riverside park developed to a high standard, with level grass pitches, a well-equipped amenities block, a games room and an adventure playground. The market town of High Bentham is close by. A 12-acre site with 61 touring pitches, 12 hardstandings and 206 statics.

Facilities: Free permits for private fishing ♠ ⋒ ⋔ ⊙ ℗ ✳ ⊘ 🛍 ⊀ ⅋ **Services:** 🖵 ⊍ ⊕ 🛍 🖺 ⊘ ⊷ **Facilities found within 3 miles:** ⌘ 18 ℘ 🛍

NORTH YORKSHIRE

HUNMANBY   TA17
Orchard Farm Holiday Village
▶▶▶ 79%
Stonegate YO14 0PU
☎ 01723 891582 🖷 01723 891582
email: sharon.dugdale@virgin.net
www.orchardfarmholidayvillage.co.uk
Dir: *A165 from Scarborough towards Bridlington. Turn right signed Hunmanby, park on right just after rail bridge*
* 🚐 £12-£16 🚎 £12-£16 ⛺ £12-£16
Open: Mar-Oct (rs Nov-Mar some facilities closed), Booking advisable bank hols & peak season, Last arrival 23.00hrs Last departure 11.00hrs
Pitches are arranged around a coarse fishing lake at this park. There is an indoor heated pool and a bar. A 14-acre site with 91 touring pitches, 34 hardstandings and 46 statics.
Facilities: 🏖 🔌 🛝 🖵 📶 ☉ 🅿✖ 🕔 📧 🚻
🚐 ♿ **Services:** 🍴 📶 🚐 🗑 🛒 🚿 **Facilities found within 3 miles:** ⚓ 18 🎣 ◎ 🍴 🐕
Notes: 🐾

LONG PRESTON   SD85
Gallaber Park ▶▶▶▶ 77%
Skipton BD23 4QF
☎ 01729 851397 🖷 01729 851398
email: info@gallaberpark.co.uk
www.gallaberpark.com
Dir: *On A682 between Long Preston & Gisburn*
* 🚐 £16-£23 🚎 £16-£23 ⛺ £16-£20
Open: mid Mar-Oct, Booking advisable Bank hols, Last arrival 20.00hrs Last departure 13.00hrs
Set in the picturesque Ribble Valley, this park enjoys lovely views across the Dales. A stone barn houses excellent toilets and a family bathroom, and there are various types of pitches including some fully serviced ones. The emphasis is on quiet relaxation, and the spacious grounds and plentiful young shrubs and trees support this impression.
Facilities: Family bathroom 🛝 🔌 ☉ 🅿✖ 🐕
♿ **Services:** ⚡ 🚐 🗑 🛒 📧

MARKINGTON   SE26

Yorkshire Hussar Inn Holiday Caravan Park ▶▶▶ 76%

High Street Harrogate HG3 3NR

☎ 01765 677327

email: yorkshirehussar@yahoo.co.uk

www.yorkshire-hussar-inn.co.uk

Dir: *Between Harrogate & Ripon (A61) turn W at Wormald Green, 1m into Markington, turn left past Post Office into the High Street*

* ♠ £12-£16 ⇌ £12-£16 ▲ £8-£20

Open: Etr-Oct, Booking advisable bank hols & school hols, Last arrival 22.00hrs Last departure noon

A terraced site behind the village inn with well-kept grass. This pleasant site offers spacious pitches with some hardstandings and electricity. A 5-acre site with 20 touring pitches, 2 hardstandings and 73 statics.

Facilities: Paddling pool ⚕ ⚑ ☉ ☊ ⚒ ☀ 🏠 ⚒

Services: 🍴 ♠ 🗑 🛢 🚰 **Facilities found within 3 miles:** ∪ ⚓ 18 🗑 🏠 **Notes:** Dogs must be kept on leads 🐾

NORTHALLERTON   SE38

Otterington Park ▶▶▶▶ 77%

Station Park South Otterington DL7 9JB

☎ 01609 780656

Dir: *Turn W off A168 midway between Northallerton &Thirsk, signed South Otterington. Site on right just before South Otterington*

* ♠ £14-£18 **Open:** Mar-Oct

A high quality park on a working farm with open outlooks across the Vale of York. A peaceful location with a lovely nature walk and on-site fishing which is popular. Young children will enjoy the play area. Toilet facilities are very good. The attractions of Northallerton and Thirsk are a few minutes drive away. A 5-acre site with 40 touring pitches and 40 hardstandings.

Facilities: ⚕ ⚑ ☉ 🏠 ⚒ **Services:** ♠ 🛢 ⚓ 18 ⚓ ⊗

NORTH YORKSHIRE

NORTH YORKSHIRE

OSMOTHERLEY   SE49

Cote Ghyll Caravan & Camping Park ▶▶▶▶ 74%

Northallerton DL6 3AH

☎ 01609 883425

email: hills@coteghyll.com

www.coteghyll.com

Dir: *Exit A19 dual carriageway at A684 (Northallerton junct). Follow signs to Osmotherley. Left in village centre. Site entrance 0.5m on right*

* ⊞ £12-£14 ⊟ £12-£14 ▲ £12-£14

Open: Mar-Oct, Booking advisable bank & school hols, Last arrival 23.00hrs Last departure noon

Quiet site in on the edge of moors, divided into terraces. A 7-acre site with 77 touring pitches, 5 hardstandings and 18 statics.

Facilities: Tourist information, packed lunch service ⋔ ℟ ⊙ ℗ ☼ Ⓢ ⓖ ⌗ ⌷ ╘

Services: 🆃 ⊕ ⓢ ⋔ ∅ ⌷ ╩ **Facilities found within 3 miles:** ∪ ℘ ◙ ⑤ **Notes:** Family park, dogs must be kept on leads at all times ☺

RICHMOND   NZ10

Brompton Caravan & Camping Park ▶▶▶▶ 72%

Brompton-on-Swale DL10 7EZ

☎ 01748 824629 🖹 01748 826383

email: brompton.caravanpark@btinternet.com

www.bromptoncaravanpark.co.uk

Dir: *Take B6271 off A1 signed Richmond, site 1m on left*

* ⊞ £18-£23 ⊟ £18-£23 ▲ £15-£20

Open: Open All Year **Open:** Etr or Mar-Oct (rs Oct-Jan closed to tourers), Booking advisable summer & wknds, Last arrival 20.00hrs Last departure noon

A family riverside park. Fishing is available on the River Swale which flows through the park, and there is a good children's playground. A 14.5-acre site with 177 touring pitches, 6 hardstandings and 22 statics.

Facilities: ⋔ ℟ ⊙ ℗ ☼ Ⓢⓖ ⌗ ⌷ ╘

Services: 🆃 ⊕ ⓢ ⋔ ∅ ╩ ⛟ **Facilities found within 3 miles:** ∪ ⌦ 18 ℘ ╘ ◙ ⑤

Notes: Family park

RICHMOND NZ10

Swale View Caravan Park

▶▶▶ 76%

Reeth Road DL10 4SF

☎ 01748 823106 📠 01748 823106

email: swaleview@teesdaleonline.co.uk

www.swaleviewcaravanpark.co.uk

Dir: *3m W of Richmond on A6108 (Reeth to Leyburn road)*

* ⊞ £18-£20 ⇔ £18 ▲ £18

Open: Mar-Oct, Booking advisable bank & summer hols, Last arrival 21.00hrs Last departure noon

Shaded by trees and overlooking the River Swale, this mainly grassy site has upgraded facilities. It's a short distance from Richmond, and well situated for exploring Swaledale and Wensleydale. A 13-acre site with 50 touring pitches, 50 hardstandings and 130 statics.

Facilities: ♠ ⋒ ⊡ ⋀ ⊙ ℗ ☀ ◐ ☜ 🎜 ⛓ ⛫

Services: ⊡ ⓥ ♨ ⑧ ⋒ ∅ 🚠 ➡ **Facilities found within 3 miles:** ∪ ⅃ 18 ℘ 🗐 🗊

Notes: 1 dog per pitch

RIPON SE37

Riverside Meadows Country Caravan Park ▶▶▶ 80%

Ure Bank Top HG4 1JD

☎ 01765 602964 📠 01765 604045

email: info@flowerofmay.com

www.flowerofmay.com

Dir: *On A61 at N end of bridge out of Ripon, W along river (do not cross river). Site 400yds, signed*

* ⊞ £13.50-£18.50 ⇔ £13.50-£18.50 ▲ £11-£18.50

Open: Etr-Oct (rs Mar-Apr bar open wknds only), Booking advisable bank hols & high season, Last arrival 21.00hrs Last departure noon

This pleasant site stands on high ground overlooking the River Ure. A 28-acre site with 131 touring pitches and 269 statics.

Facilities: ♠ ⋒ ⊡ ⋀ ⊙ ☀ ◐ 🗐 🎜 ⛓ ⛫

Services: ⋒🔦 ⊡ ♨ 🗐 ⋒ ∅ 🚠 **Facilities found within 3 miles:** ∪ ⅃ 18 ⅄ ℘ 🎣 🗐

🗊 **Notes:** Dogs by arrangement only

NORTH YORKSHIRE

ROBIN HOOD'S BAY NZ90
Middlewood Farm Holiday Park

▶▶▶▶ 74%

Middlewood Lane Fylingthorpe Whitby
YO22 4UF

☎ 01947 880414 📄 01947 880871

email: info@middlewoodfarm.com

www.middlewoodfarm.com

Dir: *From A171 towards Robin Hood's Bay &
into Fylingthorpe. Park signed from A171*

🚐 £12.50-£18 ⇌ £12.50-£18 ▲ £8-£17

Open: Mar-4 Jan, Booking advisable bank &
school hols for electric hook ups, Last arrival
22.00hrs Last departure noon

A friendly park with views of Robin Hood's
Bay. A 7-acre site with 100 touring pitches,
16 hardstandings and 30 statics.

Facilities: Pot wash sinks �ΛⲒ☉🌂☀🅒
🛏🅰 **Services:** 🅚🅰🛢🖉🖮🚽🛗
Facilities found within 3 miles: ∪🎣18
🐾🖉🅾🅑 **Notes:** Dogs on leads at all times,
dangerous breeds not accepted, no
radios/noise after 22.00hrs

ROSEDALE ABBEY SE79
**Rosedale Caravan & Camping
Park** ▶▶▶▶ 73%

Pickering YO18 8SA

☎ 01751 417272

email: info@flowerofmay.com

www.flowerofmay.com

Dir: *From Pickering take A170 towards
Sinnington for 2.25m. At Wrelton turn right
onto unclass road signed Cropton &
Rosedale, 7m. Park on left in village*

* 🚐 £13.50-£18.50 ⇌ £13.50-£18.50
▲ £11-£18.50

Open: Mar-Oct, Booking advisable BHs &
high season, Last arrival 21.00hrs Last
departure noon

This park is set in a valley in the North
Yorkshire Moors National Park. A 10-acre site
with 100 touring pitches and 35 statics.

Facilities: ΛⲒ☉🌂☉🅒🛏🚽🅰🛗
Services: 🆃🅚🛢🖉🖮 **Facilities found
within 3 miles:** ∪🎣9🖉🅾🅑 **Notes:**
Dogs by arrangement only

SCARBOROUGH   TA08

Scarborough Camping & Caravanning Club Site ▶▶▶▶ 77%

Field Lane Burniston Road YO13 0DA

☎ 01723 366212

www.campingandcaravanningclub.co.uk

Dir: *On W side of A165, 1m N of Scarborough*

🚐 £18.35-£23.25 🚌 £18.35-£23.25 ▲ £18.35-£23.25

Open: Apr-Oct, Booking advisable bank hols & peak period, Last arrival 21.00hrs Last departure noon

This spacious site has been completely upgraded to a high standard. The majority of pitches are hardstandings of plastic webbing which allow the grass to grow through naturally. A 20-acre site with 300 touring pitches and 100 hardstandings.

Facilities: 🔍 ⚠ 🌂 🔘 🅿 ✳ 🕐 🚗 🚿 ♿

Services: ⊤ 🛁 🚐 🗑 🛢 ⌀ 🚰 **Facilities found within 3 miles:** ∪ ↓ 🦈 ≋ 🗑

SCARBOROUGH   TA08

Jacobs Mount Caravan Park

▶▶▶▶ 83%

Jacobs Mount Stepney Road YO12 5NL

☎ 01723 361178 🖷 01723 361178

email: jacobsmount@yahoo.co.uk

www.jacobsmount.co.uk

Dir: *Direct access from A170*

* 🚐 £10.50-£16.50 🚌 £10.50-£16.50 ▲ £10.50-£16.50

Open: Mar-Nov (rs Mar-May & Oct limited hours at shop/bar), Booking advisable bank hols & late Jun-early Sep, Last arrival 21.00hrs Last departure noon

An elevated family-run park surrounded by woodland and open countryside, 2 miles from the beach. An 18-acre site with 156 touring pitches, 131 hardstandings and 60 statics.

Facilities: Food preparation area 🔍 ⚠ 🔲 🌂 ⊙ 🅿 ✳ 🕐 🗑 🚗 🚿 ♿ **Services:** 🍷 🍴 🚐 🗑 ⊤ 🛁 🚐 🗑 🛢 ⌀ 🚰 🍺 **Facilities found within 3 miles:** ∪ ↓ 18 ≒ 🦈 ◎ ≋ 🗑 🗑 **Notes:** Pets must be kept on leads

NORTH YORKSHIRE

SCARBOROUGH TA08
Arosa Caravan & Camping Park

►►► 74%

Ratten Row Seamer YO12 4QB

☎ 01723 862166 📄 01723 862166

email: info@arosacamping.co.uk

www.arosacamping.co.uk

Dir: *4m from Scarborough. From junct with unclass road & A64 S of Seamer, N into village. Site 250yds along Ratten Row*

* 🚐 £11.50-£17 🚐 £11.50-£16 ▲ £11.50-£17

Open: Mar-4 Jan, Booking advisable bank hols, Jul-Aug, Xmas & New Year, Last arrival 21.00hrs Last departure 11.00hrs

A family-owned park with pitches in small groups screened by trees. There is a clubhouse with café and barbecue patio, and a breakfast takeaway. A 3.5-acre site with 105 touring pitches and 4 hardstandings.

Facilities: 🔌 🛆 🅿 ⊙ 🅿 ✻ 🕒 🖵 🛏 🎗 🚿 🛆 ♿

Services: 🖀 🍴 🍺 🖃 🔲 🗜 🗑 🛢 🥡 🛒 🚮

Facilities found within 3 miles: ∪ 🎣 9 ⅃

🖉 🎿 🖥 🖫

SELBY SE63
The Ranch Caravan Park ►►► 79%

Cliffe Common YO8 6EF

☎ 01757 638984 📄 01757 630089

email: contact@theranchcaravanpark.co.uk

www.theranchcaravanpark.co.uk

Dir: *Exit A63 at Cliffe signed Skipwith. Site 1m N on left*

* 🚐 £12 🚐 £12 ▲ £10

Open: Open All Year Booking advisable bank hols, Last arrival 22.00hrs Last departure noon

A compact, sheltered park in open countryside offering excellent amenities. The enthusiastic and welcoming family owners have created a country club feel, with a tasteful bar, plus a sauna and jacuzzi in a wooden chalet. A 7-acre site with 50 touring pitches and 50 hardstandings.

Facilities: 🛆 🅿 ⊙ 🅿 ✻ 🕒 🛏 🎗 🚿 ♿

Services: 🖀 🍴 🔲 🗜 🗑 🛢 🥡 🚮

Facilities found within 3 miles: 🖉 🖥 🖫

STAINFORTH   SD86

Knight Stainforth Hall Caravan & Campsite ▶▶▶▶ 75%

Settle BD24 0DP

☎ 01729 822200 🖹 01729 823387

email: info@knightstainforth.co.uk

www.knightstainforth.co.uk

Dir: *From W, on A65 take B6480 for Settle, left before swimming pool signed Little Stainforth. From E, through Settle on B6480, over bridge to swimming pool, then turn right*

* ⊞ £12-£14 ⇄ £12-£14 ▲ £12-£14

Open: May-Oct, Booking advisable bank hols & Jul-Aug, Last arrival 22.00hrs Last departure noon

Located near Settle and the River Ribble in the Yorkshire Dales National Park, this is a well-maintained family site. A 6-acre site with 100 touring pitches and 60 statics.

Facilities: Fishing on site 🎣 ♒ ▢ 🖍 ⊙ 🅿✳ ⓒ 🛖 🚻 ♿ **Services:** 🔋 🚽 🛢 🛒 🍴

🛴 🚜 **Facilities found within 3 miles:** ∪ ⚴ 9 🎣 🛢 🅂 **Notes:** No groups of young people

STAXTON   TA07

Spring Willows ▶▶▶▶ 72%

Main Road Staxton Roundabout Scarborough YO12 4SB

☎ 01723 891505 🖹 01723 892123

email: fun4all@springwillows.fsnet.co.uk

www.springwillows.co.uk

Dir: *A64 to Scarborough, then take A1039 to Filey. Entrance on right*

Open: Mar-Jan (rs Mar & Oct bar, pool, take-away, restaurant restricted), Booking advisable bank hols, Etr, Jul & Aug, Last arrival 18.00hrs Last departure 11.00hrs

A lively, popular family park, with a spacious club providing free evening entertainment, the Sharky's Kids Club, swimming pool and games room with video games. Scarborough and Filey are a short drive away. A 26-acre site with 181 touring pitches.

Facilities: 🌐 🎣 ♒ 🖍 ⊙ 🅿✳ ⓒ 🛖 🚻 ♿ **Services:** 🍽 🔋 🚽 🛢 🛒 🍴 🛴 🚽

Facilities found within 3 miles: ∪ ⚴ 18 ◎ 🛢 🅂 **Notes:** No gazebos

NORTH YORKSHIRE

NORTH YORKSHIRE

SUTTON-ON-THE-FOREST SE65

Goosewood Caravan Park

▶▶▶▶ 83%

YO61 1ET

☎ 01347 810829 🖺 01347 811498

email: edward@goosewood.co.uk

www.goosewood.co.uk

Dir: *From A1237 take B1363. After 5m turn right. Take right turn after 0.5m & site on right*

* 🚐 £12.50-£20 🚏 £12.50-£20

Open: Feb-14 Jan, Booking advisable BHs, Jul & Aug, Last arrival 20.00hrs Last departure noon An immaculately maintained park with its own lake and seasonal fishing, set in attractive woodland just six miles north of York. The generous patio pitches are randomly spaced throughout the site, and there's a good play area for younger children, with a recreation barn for teenagers, plus a health spa. A 20-acre site with 75 touring pitches, 75 hardstandings and 35 statics.

Facilities: 🍴🔍🛝🔲🏧⊙🖉✳🕙📵🚕🎢🕭 **Services:** 🚽⚡📻🔲🛒🗑🛒⚙18🖊🗑 🗑

THIRSK SE48

Sowerby Caravan Park ▶▶▶ 64%

Sowerby YO7 3AG

☎ 01845 522753 🖺 01845 574520

Dir: *From A19 approx 3m S of Thirsk, turn W for Sowerby. Turn right at junct. Site 1m on left*

* 🚐 £9-£10.30 🚏 £9-£10.30 **Open:** Mar-Oct, Booking advisable bank hols, Last arrival 22.00hrs

A grassy site beside a tree-lined river bank, with basic but functional toilet facilities. Tourers enjoy a separate grassed area with an open outlook, away from the statics. A 1-acre site with 25 touring pitches, 5 hardstandings and 85 statics.

Facilities: 🔍🛝🏧⊙✳🕙📵♿ **Services:** 🔲⚡🗑🛒⚙🛒 **Facilities found within 3 miles:** ∪🖊🗑 **Notes:** 🚫

TOWTHORPE SE65

York Touring Caravan Site

▶▶▶▶ 76%

Greystones Farm Towthorpe Moor Lane York
YO32 9ST

☎ 01904 499275 📠 01904 499271

email: info@yorkcaravansite.co.uk

www.yorkcaravansite.co.uk

Dir: *Leave A64 at exit for Strensall/Haxby,
site 1.5m on left*

* ⊞ £11.50-£18.50 ⊟ £11.50-£18.50
▲ £10-£16.50

Open: Open All Year Booking advisable bank
hols, Last arrival 20.00hrs Last departure
noon

A purpose-built, high quality site with a select
'country club' feel. Part of a leisure complex
with a golf driving range, a 9-hole putting
course, a bar and bistro. A 6-acre site with
44 touring pitches and 12 hardstandings.
Facilities: 🅰🔲🅽🏵☉🅿☀️🕔🔚🎢🍴🏃‍♂️🅰️🛁 **Services:** 🍴🍽🅰️🔋🗑🛒 **Facilities found
within 3 miles:** ∪♨27🏌️ ◎🗑🕹

WHITBY NZ81

Rigg Farm Caravan Park ▶▶▶ 75%

Stainsacre YO22 4LP

☎ 01947 880430 📠 01947 880430

Dir: *From A171 Scarborough road left onto
B1416 signed Ruswarp. Right in 3.25m onto
unclass road signed Hawsker. Left in 1.25m.
Site in 0.5m*

* ⊞ £14-£15 ⊟ £14-£18 ▲ £11-£12

Open: Mar-Oct, Booking advisable bank hols
& Jul-Aug, Last arrival 22.00hrs Last
departure noon

A neat rural site with distant views of the coast
and Whitby Abbey, set in peaceful
surroundings. The former farm buildings are
used to house reception and a small games
room. A 3-acre site with 14 touring pitches,
14 hardstandings and 15 statics.
Facilities: 🚿🅰️🅽☉❄☉🔚🎢 **Services:**
🔋🅰️🗑🔋📶🛒 **Facilities found within 3
miles:** ∪♨9🏌️🏌️ ◎🗑🕹 **Notes:** No ball
games, cycling, skateboards, roller skating or
kite flying

NORTH YORKSHIRE

WYKEHAM   SE98
St Helens Caravan Park ▶▶▶▶ 83%
St Helens in the Park Scarborough YO13 9QD
☎ 01723 862771 🖷 01723 866613
email: caravans@wykeham.co.uk
www.wykeham.co.uk
Dir: *On A170 in village, 150yds on left
beyond Downe Arms Hotel towards
Scarborough*

* 🚐 £8.50-£10.60 🚏 £8.50-£10.60 ▲ £6-£10.60
Open: Feb-Jan (rs Nov-Jan shop/laundry
closed), Booking advisable bank hols & Jul-
Aug, Last arrival 22.00hrs Last departure
17.00hrs

On the edge of the North York Moors National
Park, this delightfully landscaped park is well-
maintained with top quality facilities. The site
is divided into terraces. A 25-acre site with
250 touring pitches and 2 hardstandings.
Facilities: Caravan storage 🔍 Å ➟ ⊙ 🅿 ✳
🕒 🖫 🛏 🚻 🛒 ♿ **Services:** 🕎 🌐 🔟 🔯 🛢 🛎 🍴
🛳 🛒 🧹 **Facilities found within 3 miles:**
∪ ♪ 18 ✚ 🖉 ◎ 🛂 🛢 🖇

YORK   SE54
**Riverside Caravan & Camping
Park** ▶▶▶ 61%
Ferry Lane Bishopthorpe YO23 2SB
☎ 01904 705812 🖷 01904 705824
email: info@yorkmarine.co.uk
www.yorkmarine.co.uk
Dir: *From A64 take A1036. Right at lights
signed Bishopthorpe, left into main street at
T-junct. At end of road right into Ancaster
Lane, left in 150yds*

Open: Apr-Oct, Booking advisable Jul-Sep,
bank hols, Last arrival 22.00hrs Last
departure noon

A small level grassy park in a hedged field on
the banks of the River Ouse, on the outskirts
of York. This is a popular site with those who
enjoy messing about on the river. A 1-acre
site with 25 touring pitches.
Facilities: Boat hire, slipway, fishing Å ℟
⊙ 🅿 ✳ 🛏 🚻 🛒 **Services:** 🕎 🍴 🔟 🔯 🛎 🍴
🛳 **Facilities found within 3 miles:** ∪ ♪
✚ 🖉 🛂 🛢 🖇 **Notes:** Dogs must be kept
on leads

HATFIELD SE60

Hatfield Waterpark ►►► 70%

Old Thorne Road Doncaster DN7 6EQ

☎ 01302 841572 ▤ 01302 846368

Dir: *Signed from Hatfield off A18*

* **Open:** Apr-Oct (rs Nov-Mar reduced visitor centre opening times), Booking advisable bank hols, Last arrival 17.30hrs Last departure noon

A parkland setting offering instruction in a variety of sports from kayaking to power boating. There is something for everyone here, whether taking part or just watching the action. A seasonal warden keeps the centre running well, and there is also bunkhouse accommodation for 36, handy for tenters in very wet weather. A 10-acre site with 48 touring pitches.

Facilities: Canoeing, rowing, sailing, windsurfing, fishing ⚠ ⋔ ⊙ ☼ ⏰ ☴ ☵ ⊼ ☞ ♿

Services: ⊡ ⇥ **Facilities found within 3 miles:** ∪ ⚲ 18 ⚓ ⚬ ≽ ⊡ ⑂

KIRK MICHAEL SC39

Glen Wyllin Campsite ►►► 76%

IM6 1AL

☎ 01624 878231 ▤ 01624 878836

email: michaelcommissioners@manx.net

www.michaelcommissioners.com

Dir: *From Douglas take A1 to Ballacraine, right at lights onto A3 to Kirk Michael. Left onto A4 signed Peel. Site 100yds on right*

Open: Apr-mid Sep, Booking advisable end May-mid Jun & Aug, Last departure noon

Set in a beautiful wooded glen with bridges over a pretty stream dividing the camping areas. A gently-sloping tarmac road gives direct access to a good beach. Hire tents available. A 9-acre site with 90 touring pitches.

Facilities: ⚠ ▢ ⋔ ⊙ ℗ ☼ ⊙ ⑂ ⊼ ☴ ☵ ⊼ ♿

Services: ⊡ ⑂ ▯ ⊘ ☴ ⊞ **Facilities found within 3 miles:** ∪ ⚲ ⊡ ⑂ **Notes:** No excess noise after midnight, dogs must be kept under control ⊛

GUERNSEY

CASTEL
Fauxquets Valley Farm ▶▶▶ 79%
GY5 7QA
☎ 01481 255460 ▤ 01481 251797
email: info@fauxquets.co.uk
www.fauxquets.co.uk
Dir: *Off pier. 2nd exit off rdbt. Top of hill left onto Queens Rd. Continue for 2m. Turn right onto Candie Rd. Opposite sign for German Occupation Museum*
Open: mid Jun-Aug (rs May-mid Jun & 1-15 Sep Haybarn restaurant & bar closed), Booking advisable last 2 wks Jul-1st 3 wks Aug
A beautiful, quiet farm site in a hidden valley close to the sea. Friendly, helpful owners offer good quality facilities and amenities, including an outdoor swimming pool, bar/restaurant, nature trail and sports areas. A 3-acre site with 100 touring pitches.
Facilities: Bird watching ⚓ ⚲ ⚠ ▢ ▩ ☉ ☇ ✳ ◔ ▣ ▤ ⌁ ☰ **Services:** ☎ ⊗ ☷ ▣ ⊠ ▢ ⊘ ▩ ⚒ **Facilities found within 3 miles:** ∪ ⚐ 9 ⚟ ◎ ▣ ☷

ST SAMPSON
Le Vaugrat Camp Site ▶▶▶ 80%
Route de Vaugrat GY2 4TA
☎ 01481 257468 ▤ 01481 251841
email: enquiries@vaugratcampsite.com
www.users.globalnet.co.uk/~adgould
Dir: *From main coast road on NW of island, site is signed at Port Grat Bay into Route de Vaugrat, near Peninsula Hotel*
Open: May-mid Sep, Booking advisable all year
Overlooking the sea and set within the grounds of a lovely 17th-century house, this level grassy park is backed by woodland, and close to lovely sandy beaches of Port Grat and Grand Havre. It is run by a warm and welcoming family who pride themselves on their magnificent floral displays. A 6-acre site with 150 touring pitches.
Facilities: ⚓ ⚠ ▢ ▩ ☉ ☇ ✳ ◔ ▣ ⚒ ☰ ⌁ **Services:** ▢ ⊘ ⚒ **Facilities found within 3 miles:** ∪ ⚐ 18 ⚟ ▣ ☷ ⊗ **Notes:** No animals

VALE

La Bailloterie Camping & Leisure

▶▶▶ 77%

GY3 5HA

☎ 01481 243636 📠 01481 243225

email: info@campinginguernsey.com

www.campinginguernsey.com

Dir: *3m N of St Peter Port, take Vale road to Crossways, turn right into Rue du Braye. Site 1st left at sign*

Å £11-£12

Open: 15 May-15 Sep, Booking advisable all times, Last arrival 23.00hrs

A pretty rural site with one large touring field and a few small, well-screened paddocks. This delightful site has been in the same family ownership for over 30 years, and offers super facilities in converted outbuildings. A 12-acre site with 100 touring pitches.

Facilities: Volleyball net, boules pitch 🔍 /A ⬜ ⛧ ☉ ℗ ※ 🗑 🚰 🚻 🚮 **Services:** 🛒 ⊞ 🗑 🛢 🧺 🚽 🛁 ♿ **Facilities found within 3 miles:** ∪ ♨ 18 ✦ 🎣 ◎ 🛥 🗑 🗑 **Notes:** Dogs allowed in restricted areas

ST MARTIN

Rozel Camping Park ▶▶▶▶ 77%

Summerville Farm JE3 6AX

☎ 01534 855200 📠 01534 856127

email: rozelcampingpark@jerseymail.co.uk

www.rozelcamping.co.uk

Dir: *Take A6 from St Helier through Five Oaks to St Martins Church, turn right onto A38 towards Rozel, site on right*

🚐 £15.20-£18 🚎 £15.20-£18 **Å** £15.20-£18

Open: May-mid Sep, Booking advisable Jul-Aug, Last departure noon

An attractive and secluded holiday site offering excellent amenities in a lovely farm location. The site is divided into paddocks, with hedges, and there are ready-erected tents for hire. Close to Rozel Bay. A 4-acre site with 100 touring pitches and 20 statics.

Facilities: Mini golf 🔍 🔍 /A ⬜ ⛧ ☉ ℗ ※ ☉ 🗑 🚰 ♿ **Services:** ⊞ ⊔ ♨ 🗑 🛢 🧺 🚽 ♿ **Facilities found within 3 miles:** ∪ ♨ 18 ✦ 🎣 🛥 🗑 🗑 ⊗ **Notes:** Dogs only during low season

JERSEY

ST MARTIN
Beuvelande Camp Site
▶▶▶▶▶ 80%

Beuvelande JE3 6EZ

☎ 01534 853575 📠 01534 857788

email: info@campingjersey.com

www.campingjersey.com

Dir: *Take A6 from St Helier to St Martin & follow signs to campsite before St Martins church*

🚐 £6-£9 🚍 £6-£9 ▲ £6-£9

Open: Apr-Sep (rs Apr-May & Sep restaurant closed, shop hours limited)

A well-established site with excellent toilet facilities, an attractive bar/restaurant, a small swimming pool and playground. Motorhomes and towed caravans will be met at the ferry and escorted to the site if requested when booking. A 6-acre site with 150 touring pitches and 75 statics.

Facilities: 🌣 🔍 🄰 🖵 🅛 ⊙✕ ⓢ 🗓 🏴 ঙ
Services: 🕯 🍴 🍷 🔟 ↯ 🍵 🗓 📦 ⌀ 🍴
Facilities found within 3 miles: ∪ ⅃ 18 ⅄ 🐾 ⅂ ⓢ

ST OUEN
Bleu Soleil Campsite ▶▶▶▶ 72%
La Route de Vinchelez Leoville JE3 2DB

☎ 01534 481007 📠 01534 481525

email: info@bleusoleilcamping.com

www.bleusoleilcamping.com

Dir: *From St Helier ferry port take A2 towards St Aubin then turn right onto A12 passing airport to Leoville. Site on right of La Route de Vinchelez*

▲ £12-£50

Open: 28 Apr-Sep, Booking advisable Jul-Aug, Last arrival 23.00hrs Last departure 10.00hrs

A compact tent park set in the NW corner of the island. Greve-de-Lacq beach is close by, and the golden beaches at St Ouen's Bay and St Brelade's Bay are a short drive away. There are 45 ready-erected tents for hire. A 1.5-acre site with 55 touring pitches, 8 hardstandings and 45 statics.

Facilities: 🌣 🔍 🄰 🖵 🅛 ⊙ 🅟✕ ⓢ 🗓 🍴
Services: 🕯 🍴 🍷 🔌 📦 ⌀ 🍺 **Facilities found within 3 miles:** ∪ ⅃ 18 ⅄ ◎ ⅂ ⓢ

ABOYNE   NO59

Aboyne Loch Caravan Park

▶▶▶ 68%

AB34 5BR

☎ 013398 86244 📠 01330 811669

Dir: *On A93, 1m E of Aboyne*

* 🚐 £14 🚎 £14 ⏏ £10

Open: 31 Mar-Oct, Booking advisable Jul-Aug, Last arrival 20.00hrs Last departure 11.00hrs

Attractively-sited caravan park set amidst woodland on the shores of the lovely Aboyne Loch in scenic Deeside. The facilities are modern and immaculately maintained, and amenities include boat-launching, boating and fishing. An ideally-situated park for touring Royal Deeside and the Aberdeenshire uplands. A 6-acre site with 35 touring pitches, 25 hardstandings and 80 statics.

Facilities: Coarse & pike fishing, boats for hire 🔌 🛝 🐾 ☺ 🅿 ☀ 🕒 🛒 🎄 🚻 ♿ **Services:** 🛢 🚻 🚐 🔘 🍴 🚮 **Facilities found within 3 miles:** ∪ ♨ 18 ⚓ 🎣 ⛵ 🅿 ☺ 💲 **Notes:** 🐕

HUNTLY   NJ54

Huntly Castle Caravan Park

▶▶▶▶ 84%

The Meadow AB54 4UJ

☎ 01466 794999

email: enquiries@huntlycastle.co.uk

www.huntlycastle.co.uk

Dir: *From Aberdeen on A96 to Huntly. 0.75m after rdbt on outskirts of Huntly turn right towards town centre, left into Riverside Drive*

* 🚐 £13.50-£17.50 🚎 £13.50-£17.50 ⏏ £8.50-£15

Open: Apr-Oct, Last arrival 20.00hrs Last departure noon

A parkland site close to the Speyside Malt Whisky Trail, the Moray coast, and Cairngorm Mountains. The park has exceptional toilet facilities, some serviced pitches and an Indoor Activity Centre. A 15-acre site with 90 touring pitches, 46 hardstandings and 40 statics.

Facilities: Indoor activity centre, badminton, table tennis 🔌 🛝 🐾 ☺ 🅿 ☀ 🕒 🛒 🚻 ♿ **Services:** 🛢 🚻 🚐 🔘 🍴 🛎 🚮 🚮 18 🅿 💲 🔘

ABERDEENSHIRE

ABERDEENSHIRE

MACDUFF NJ76
Wester Bonnyton Farm Site
▶▶ 68%
Gamrie AB45 3EP
☎ 01261 832470 📄 01261 831853
email: taylor@westerbonnyton.freeserve.co.uk
Dir: *From A98 (1m S of Macduff) take B9031 signed Rosehearty. Site 1.25m on right*
* 🚐 £10 🚏 £10 ▲ £7
Open: Mar-Oct, Booking advisable Jul-Aug
A spacious farm site in a screened meadow, with level touring pitches enjoying views across Moray Firth. The site is continually improving, and offers some electric hook-ups and a laundry. A 4-acre site with 10 touring pitches, 5 hardstandings and 45 statics.
Facilities: Children's playbarn ❤ ⚲ 📡 ☉ 📶 🖾 🚻 🍽 A **Services:** 🔌 🛢 🛍 🖹 ⚡ 18 ⚡ 🖋 ⚵ 🗑 🗊 **Notes:** 🐕

NORTH WATER BRIDGE NO66
Dovecot Caravan Park ▶▶▶ 74%
Laurencekirk AB30 1QL
☎ 01674 840630 📄 01674 840630
email: dovecotcaravanpark@tinyworld.co.uk
www.dovecotcaravanpark.com
Dir: *Take A90, 5m S of Laurencekirk. At Edzell Woods sign turn left. Site 500yds on left*
* 🚐 £10-£11 🚏 £10-£11 ▲ £7.50-£8.50
Open: Apr-Oct, Booking advisable Jul & Aug for hook ups, Last arrival 20.00hrs Last departure noon
A level grassy site in a country area close to the A90, with mature trees screening one side and the River North Esk on the other. The immaculate toilet facilities make this a handy overnight stop in a good touring area. A 6-acre site with 25 touring pitches, 8 hardstandings and 44 statics.
Facilities: ❤ ⚲ 📡 ☉ 📶 🖾 🗙 🕐 🖹 🖋 ♿ **Services:** 🆃 🔌 🛢 🗑 **Notes:** 🐕

TARLAND   NJ40

Tarland Camping & Caravanning Club Site ►►► 77%

Aboyne AB34 4UP

☎ 013398 81388

www.campingandcaravanningclub.co.uk

Dir: *A93 from Aberdeen turn right in Aboyne at Struan Hotel onto B9094. After 6m take next right, then fork left before bridge, 600yds site on left*

🚐 £14.05-£18.85 🚙 £14.05-£18.85
▲ £14.05-£18.85

Open: Apr-Oct, Booking advisable bank hols & peak periods, Last arrival 21.00hrs Last departure noon

A pretty park, laid out on two levels. The upper area has hardstandings and electric hook-ups, and views over hills and moorland, while the lower level is well screened with mature trees and grassy. An 8-acre site with 90 touring pitches and 32 hardstandings.

Facilities: ♦ ⚲ □ ⚑ ⊙ ℗ ✳ ⊙ ⊣ 🚽
Services: 🔲 🚐 🗑 🔒 🖋 🛒 Facilities found within 3 miles: ∪ 🎣 ⚓ 🛒 🛒

EDZELL   NO67

Glenesk Caravan Park ►►► 69%

Brechin Angus DD9 7YP

☎ 01356 648565

email: warden@gleneskcaravanpark.fsnet.co.uk

www.caravancampingsites.co.uk

Dir: *Turn off B966, 1.25m NE of Edzell signed Glenest. Park 0.75m on right*

* 🚐 £12.25-£14.25 🚙 £12.25-£14.25
▲ £6-£9

Open: Apr-Oct, Booking advisable public hols & mid Jun-Aug, Last arrival 22.00hrs Last departure 16.00hrs

A carefully-maintained woodland site with caravans spread amongst the trees around a fishing lake, and tents located in a separate area. An 8-acre site with 45 touring pitches, 45 hardstandings and 10 statics.

Facilities: ♦ ⚲ □ ⚑ ⊙ ℗ ✳ ⊙ ⊣ 🚽 🛒 ♿
Services: 🔲 🚐 🗑 🔒 🖋 🛒 **Facilities found within 3 miles:** ∪ 🎣 18 ⚓ 🛒 🛒
Notes: Dogs must be kept on leads, no ground fires 🐕

ABERDEENSHIRE/ANGUS

ANGUS/ARGYLL & BUTE

MONIFIETH   NO43
Riverview Caravan Park ▶▶▶▶ 78%
Marine Road DD5 4NN
☎ 01382 535471 🖷 01382 535375
email: riverviewcaravan@btinternet.com
www.ukparks.co.uk/riverview
Dir: *Signed in both directions from A930 in centre of Monifieth*
Open: Apr-Oct (rs Nov-Mar holiday homes open), Booking advisable Jul-Aug, Last arrival 22.00hrs Last departure 12.30hrs
A well-landscaped seaside site with individual hedged pitches, and direct access to the beach. The modernised toilet block has excellent facilities which are immaculately maintained. Amenities include a multi-gym, sauna and steam rooms. A 5.5-acre site with 60 touring pitches, 40 hardstandings and 25 statics.
Facilities: 🔌 🏕 🏞 ⊙ ⌨ 𝄃 ※ ⊗ 🚿 🗑 ♨ 🚻 ♿
Services: 🚰 🔌 🗑 🛢 🏪 🍽 **Facilities found within 3 miles:** ∪ ↕ 18 🔗 ◉ 🏊 🗑 🏦

CRAIGNURE   NM73
Shieling Holidays ▶▶▶ 81%
Isle of Mull PA65 6AY
☎ 01680 812496
www.shielingholidays.co.uk
Dir: *From ferry left onto A849 to Iona. 400mtrs left at church, follow site signs towards sea*
🚐 £14-£15 ⇌ £14-£15 ▲ £14-£15
Open: Apr-Oct, Booking advisable Spring bank hol & Jul-Aug, Last arrival 22.00hrs Last departure noon
A lovely water's edge site. Hardstandings and service points are provided for motorhomes, and there are astro-turf pitches for tents. The park offers bunkhouse accommodation for families. A 6-acre site with 90 touring pitches, 27 hardstandings and 15 statics.
Facilities: Adventure playground, bikes 🔌 🏞 🗖 🏞 ⊙ ⌨ ※ ⊗ 🗑 🚿 🚻 ♿ **Services:** 🏧 🚰 🔌 🗑 🛢 🌀 **Facilities found within 3 miles:** ↕ 9 🔗 🗑 🏦

GLENDARUEL NR98

Glendaruel Caravan Park ►►► 76%

PA22 3AB

☎ 01369 820267 📠 01369 820367

email: mail@glendaruelcaravanpark.co.uk

www.glendaruelcaravanpark.co.uk

Dir: *From A83 take A815 to Strathur, then 13m to park on A886. By ferry from Gourock to Dunoon then B836, then A886 for approx 4m N. (NB this route not recommended for towing vehicles - 1:5 uphill gradient on B836)*

* 🚐 £13-£16 🚌 £11-£16 ⛺ £11-£13

Open: Apr-Oct, Booking advisable spring bank hol & mid Jul-Aug, Last arrival 22.00hrs Last departure noon

A very pleasant site in the Victorian gardens of Glendaruel House. Grass and hardstanding pitches are set in 23 acres of wooded parkland. A 3-acre site with 35 touring pitches, 24 hardstandings and 30 statics.

Facilities: Sea trout & salmon fishing 🔍 🛝 🚿 ⊙ 🔌 ✲ ✆ [$] 🐕 ♨ ⛩ **Services:** [T] 🚐 🗄 🔒 🍃 ☕ 🏌 🗄 [$] **Notes:** Dogs must be kept on lead at all times

INVERUGLAS NN30

Loch Lomond Holiday Park

►►► 79%

Tarbet G83 7DW

☎ 01301 704224 📠 01301 704206

email: enquiries@lochlomond-caravans.co.uk

www.lochlomond-lodges.co.uk

Dir: *On A82 3.5m N of Tarbet*

* 🚐 £15-£17 🚌 £15-£17 **Open:** Mar-Oct (rs Dec-Jan main amenity building restricted hours), Booking advisable May-Aug, Last arrival 20.00hrs Last departure 11.45hrs

A lovely setting on the shores of Loch Lomond with views of forests and mountains, and boat hire available. The small touring area is beautifully situated overlooking the loch, and handily placed for the toilets and clubhouse. A 6-acre site with 18 touring pitches and 72 statics.

Facilities: Satellite TV, pool tables 🔍 🛝 📺 🚿 ⊙ 🔌 ✲ ✆ [$] 🐕 ♨ ⛩ ♿ **Services:** [T] 🚐 🗄 🔒 🍃 🛒 **Facilities found within 3 miles:** U 🏌 🏌 🌊 🗄 [$]

ARGYLL & BUTE/DUMFRIES & GALLOWAY

OBAN   NM82

Oban Caravan & Camping Park

▶▶▶ 78%

Gallanachmore Farm Gallanach Road
PA34 4QH

☎ 01631 562425 📠 01631 566624

email: info@obancaravanpark.com

www.obancaravanpark.co.uk

Dir: *From Oban centre follow signs for Mull
Ferry. Take turn past terminal signed
Gallanach. 2m to site*

* 🚐 £10-£12.50 🚍 £10-£12.50 ▲ £10-
£12.50

Open: Etr/Apr-Oct, Last arrival 23.00hrs Last
departure noon

A tourist park in an attractive location close to
sea and ferries. This family park is an ideal
boating centre, and offers two large rally
areas. A 15-acre site with 150 touring pitches,
35 hardstandings and 12 statics.

Facilities: Indoor kitchen for tent campers
🔌 🗚 🕭 ⊙ 🅿 ✳ 🕓 🖻 ⛵ 🗒 **Services:** 🔟 ⚡
🚰 🖻 🛢 🖉 🛒 **Facilities found within 3
miles:** ∪ ⚓ 18 🛶 🖉 👟 🖻 🖻

BALMINNOCH   NX26

Three Lochs Holiday Park

▶▶▶▶ 80%

Kirkcowan Newton Stewart DG8 0EP

☎ 01671 830304 📠 01671 830335

email: info@3lochs.co.uk

www.3lochs.co.uk

Dir: *Follow A75 W towards Stranraer. Approx
10km from Newton Stewart rdbt turn right at
small x-roads, follow signs, park 4m on right*

* 🚐 £11-£12 🚍 £11-£12 ▲ £6.50-£11

Open: Mar-Oct, Booking advisable bank hols
& Jul-Aug, Last arrival 22.00hrs Last
departure 11.00hrs

A remote park set in beautiful moorland on
the banks of Loch Heron. This spacious grass
park offers some fully-serviced pitches. Also
provides a heated indoor pool and games
room. A 22.5-acre site with 45 touring
pitches, 20 hardstandings and 90 statics.

Facilities: Snooker 🕭 🔌 🗚 🕭 ⊙ 🅿 ✳ 🕓 🖻
🗒 🏪 ♿ **Services:** 🔟 🚐 🖻 🛢 🖉 🛒 🍴
Facilities found within 3 miles: 🖉 🖻 🖻

Notes: 🐾

BEATTOCK
NY00

Craigielands Country Park

►►► 77%

Moffat DG10 9RE

☎ 01683 300591 ▤ 01683 300105

email: admin@craigielandsleisure.com

www.craigielandsleisure.com

Dir: *A74(M) junct 15 follow Beattock. Site in 350yds*

* ➡ £14-£20 ⇌ £14-£20 ▲ £10-£16

Open: Mar-6 Jan (rs pub open wknds only), Last arrival 23.00hrs Last departure 14.00hrs
A relaxed park in part of a former country estate on the edge of the village of Beattock. There is a coarse fishing lake. A bar and restaurant serve home cooking, and there is some entertainment at weekends during the high season. A 56-acre site with 125 touring pitches, 6 hardstandings and 104 statics.

Facilities: ⚓ ⋔ ℝ ⊙ ℗ ☺ ⊁ ⊞ ⅃

Services: ⑩ 🛒 ⊍ 🅿 🗑 🛢 ⌀ 🚽 **Facilities found within 3 miles:** ∪ ⅃ 30 ⊁ ℓ ◎ 🖥

🖥 **Notes:** Dogs must be kept on leads

BRIGHOUSE BAY
NX64

Brighouse Bay Holiday Park

►►►►► 93%

Borgue Kirkcudbright DG6 4TS

☎ 01557 870267 ▤ 01557 870319

email: aa@brighouse-bay.co.uk

www.gillespie-leisure.co.uk

Dir: *Off B727 (Kirkcudbright to Borgue) or take A755 (Kirkcudbright) off A75 2m W of Twynholm. Site signed*

➡ £12.50-£17.60 ⇌ £12.50-£17.60
▲ £12.50-£17.60

Open: Open All Year (rs Nov-Mar leisure club closed 2 days each week), Booking advisable Etr, Spring bank hol & Jul-Aug, Last arrival 21.30hrs Last departure 11.30hrs
A 30-acre grassy site in a coastal setting, with 190 touring pitches and 120 statics.

Facilities: Mini golf, 18-hole golf, riding, fishing, quad bikes ⌂ ⚓ ⋔ ℝ ⊙ ℗ ⊁ ⊙ 🖥
⊁ ⊞ ⅃ **Services:** 🐟 ⑩ 🛒 ⊞ 🅿 🗑 🛢 ⌀ 🛒
🚽 **Facilities found within 3 miles:** ∪ ⅃ 9
⊁ ℓ ◎ ⊱ 🖥 🖥

DUMFRIES & GALLOWAY

CASTLE DOUGLAS NX76
Lochside Caravan & Camping Site

▶▶▶ 78%

Lochside Park DG7 1EZ

☎ 01556 502949 📄 01556 503806

email: scottg2@dumgal.gov.uk

www.dumgal.gov.uk/lochsidecs

Dir: *Off A75 towards Castle Douglas by Carlingwark Loch*

* 🚐 £10.20-£14.60 🚃 £10.20-£14.60
▲ £10.20-£14.60

Open: Etr-Oct, Last arrival 19.30hrs Last departure noon

Well-managed municipal touring site in a pleasant location adjacent to Carlingwark Loch and parkland but close to the town. A 5.5-acre site with 161 touring pitches and 74 hardstandings.

Facilities: Putting & pedalo boats (wknds & high season) 🄟 🎖 🏷 ⊙ ☀ ⓒ 🖇 🗐 ❤ ♿

Services: 🔌 🗐 🛒 **Facilities found within 3 miles:** ↓ 9 ∻ 🖉 ⓒ 🗐 **Notes:** Height restriction barrier 🐾

CREETOWN NX45
Castle Cary Holiday Park

▶▶▶▶▶ 84%

Newton Stewart DG8 7DQ

☎ 01671 820264 📄 01671 820670

email: enquiries@castlecarypark.f9.co.uk

www.castlecary-caravans.com

Dir: *Signed with direct access off A75, 0.5m S of village*

* 🚐 £10.80-£13.50 🚃 £10.80-£13.50
▲ £10.80-£13.50

Open: Open All Year (rs Oct-Mar reception/shop, no heated outdoor pool), Booking advisable BHs & Jul-Aug, Last arrival anytime Last departure noon

This site is set in the grounds of Cassencarie House. A 12-acre site with 50 touring pitches, 50 hardstandings and 26 statics.

Facilities: Bike hire, crazy golf, fishing, football pitch 🄟 🎖 🏊 🄟 ⊙ 🖇 🗐 🄟 ⊙ ⓟ ☀ ⓒ 🗐 🏌 🎖 ❤ ♿ **Services:** 🍴 🍽 🔌 🗐 🛒 🖉 🗑 📶 🛒 🛗 **Facilities found within 3 miles:** ↓ 18 🖉 ⓒ 🗐 🗐 **Notes:** Dogs must be kept on leads at all times

CREETOWN   NX45

Creetown Caravan Park ▶▶▶ 78%

Silver Street DG8 7HU

☎ 01671 820377 🖷 01671 820377

email: creetowncaravan@btconnect.com

www.creetown-caravans.co.uk

Dir: *Off A75 into Creetown, turn between clock tower & hotel, then left along Silver Street*

* 🚐 £10–£12.50 🚌 £10–£12.50 ▲ £7–£12.50

Open: Mar-Oct, Booking advisable Jul-Aug, Last arrival 22.30hrs Last departure 14.00hrs

A neat and well-maintained park set in the village centre with views across the estuary on the coast of Wigtown Bay. Its attractive setting is beside the Moneypool Burn on the River Cree. Plenty of good amenities, including a heated outdoor swimming pool. A 3-acre site with 20 touring pitches and 54 statics.

Facilities: Games room, indoor hot tub 🛁 🔍 🛆 📡 ⊙ 🖤 ✳ ⓛ & **Services:** 🆃 🚐 🛢 🛢 🥜 🚢 **Facilities found within 3 miles:** 𝒫 🖢

CROCKETFORD   NX87

Park of Brandedleys ▶▶▶▶ 84%

DG2 8RG

☎ 0845 4561760 🖷 01556 690681

email: brandedleys@holgates.com

www.holgates.com

Dir: *In village on A75, from Dumfries towards Stranraer site on left up minor road, entrance 200yds on right*

* 🚐 £12.50–£21 🚌 £12.50–£21 ▲ £12.50–£21

Open: Open All Year (rs Nov-Mar bar/restaurant open Fri-Sun afternoon), Booking advisable public hols & Jul-Aug, Last arrival 22.00hrs Last departure noon

A well-maintained site with fine views of Auchenreoch Loch, and offering a range of amenities. A 24-acre site with 80 touring pitches, 40 hardstandings and 63 statics.

Facilities: Badminton court 🛋 🛆 🔍 🛆 🌡 🛐 ⊙ 🖤 ✳ ⓛ 🛆 🗟 🚽 🎾 🛏 & **Services:** 🐧 🍴 🍷 🆃 🚐 🛢 🛢 🥜 🚢 🛒 🏧 **Facilities found within 3 miles:** ∪ 🎣 𝒫 🛥 🖢 **Notes:** Guidelines issued on arrival

DUMFRIES & GALLOWAY

DUMFRIES & GALLOWAY

DALBEATTIE   NX86

Glenearly Caravan Park ►►►► 75%

DG5 4NE

☎ 01556 611393 ▤ 01556 612058

Dir: *From Dumfries take A711 towards Dalbeattie. Park entrance is past Edingham Farm on right, 200yds before boundary sign*

* ⚏ £11-£13 ⚏ £11-£13 ▲ £11-£13

Open: Open All Year Booking advisable Jun-Aug, Last arrival 19.00hrs Last departure noon

An excellent park set in open countryside with panoramic views of Long Fell, Maidenpap and Dalbeattie Forest. The park is located in 84 acres of farmland which visitors can enjoy. Luxury extras are provided in the laundry and toilets. A 10-acre site with 39 touring pitches, 33 hardstandings and 57 statics.

Facilities: ♠ ⚑ ♠ ⊙✕ ⓒ ⊣ & **Services:** ⚏ ☒ ♠ ⚏ **Facilities found within 3 miles:** ∪ ♨ 18 ✦ ∅ ☒ ☺ **Notes:** No commercial vehicles, dogs must be kept on leads ⊛

ECCLEFECHAN   NY17

Hoddom Castle Caravan Park ►►►►► 77%

Hoddom DG11 1AS

☎ 01576 300251 ▤ 01576 300757

email: hoddomcastle@aol.com

www.hoddomcastle.co.uk

Dir: *M74 junct 19, follow signs to site. From A75 W of Annan take B723 for 5m, follow signs to site*

* ⚏ £7.50-£17 ⚏ £7.50-£17 ▲ £6.50-£17

Open: Etr or Apr-Oct (rs early season cafeteria closed), Booking advisable bank hols & Jul-Aug, Last arrival 21.00hrs Last departure 14.00hrs

A well-equipped park on the banks of the River Annan. A 28-acre site with 200 touring pitches, 150 hardstandings and 44 statics.

Facilities: Visitor centre ♠ ⚑ ▤ ♠ ⊙ ℘✕ ⓒ ☒ ⊣ ☶ ☒ & **Services:** ☎ ⍟ ⚏ ☒ ⊤ ⇞ ⚏ ☒ ♠ ∅ ⚏ ⇘ 曲 **Facilities found within 3 miles:** ♨ 18 ∅ ◎ ☒ ☺

GATEHOUSE OF FLEET NX55

Auchenlarie Holiday Park 77%

DG7 2EX

☎ 01557 840251 📠 01557 840333

email: enquiries@auchenlarie.co.uk

www.auchenlarie.co.uk

Dir: *Direct access off A75, 5m W of Gatehouse of Fleet*

* 🚐 £20-£25 🚛 £20-£25 Å £20-£25

Open: Mar-Oct, Booking advisable all year, Last arrival 20.00hrs Last departure noon

A family park on cliffs overlooking Wigtown Bay, with its own sandy beach. The tenting area, in sloping grass, has its own sanitary facilities; the caravan pitches are in paddocks with open views, and have high quality toilets. Leisure centre. A 32-acre site with 49 touring pitches, 49 hardstandings and 350 statics.

Facilities: Baby changing facilities 🐕 🔍 ∧ 🐾 ↻ 🕭 ⊙ ☞ ✻ Ⓒ 🖫 ⊀ 🛒 🚽 ᕇ **Services:** 🍴 ⦿ 🐠 📋 🚐 🔋 🛢 🖉 🚽 ⛢ **Facilities found within 3 miles:** ∪ 🚴 18 🎣 ⊚ 🖭 🖼

GLENTROOL VILLAGE NX47

Glentrool Holiday Park ►►► 77%

Bargrennan Newton Stewart DG8 6RN

☎ 01671 840280 📠 01671 840342

email: enquiries@glentroolholidaypark.co.uk

www.glentroolholidaypark.co.uk

Dir: *Leave Newton Stewart on A714 towards Girvan, right at Bargrennan towards Glentrool. Park on left before village*

* 🚐 £8.50-£9.50 🚛 £8.50-£9.50 Å £8.50-£9.50

Open: Mar-Oct, Booking advisable Jul-Aug & BHs, Last arrival 21.00hrs Last departure noon

A small park close to the village of Glentrool, and bordered by the Galloway National Park. The keen owners keep their site neat, clean and freshly painted. The on-site shop is well stocked. A 6.75-acre site with 14 touring pitches, 12 hardstandings and 26 statics.

Facilities: ∧ 🐾 ↻ 🕭 ⊙ ☞ ✻ Ⓒ 🖫 🛒 ᕇ **Services:** 🖫 🚐 🛢 🖉 🚽 **Facilities found within 3 miles:** 🎣 **Notes:** ⦿

DUMFRIES & GALLOWAY

GRETNA   NY36

Braids Caravan Park ▶▶▶▶ 73%

Annan Road DG16 5DQ

☎ 01461 337409 🖹 01461 337409

email: enquiries@thebraidscaravanpark.co.uk

www.thebraidscaravanpark.co.uk

Dir: *On B721, 0.5m from village on right, towards Annan*

* 🚐 £12.50-£15 🚐 £12.50-£15 ▲ £10-£20

Open: Open All Year Booking advisable Jul-Sep, Last arrival 21.00hrs Last departure noon

A well-maintained grassy site in the centre of the village just inside Scotland. A good toilet block provides a high standard of facilities, and several hard pitches further enhance this busy and popular park. A 6-acre site with 74 touring pitches and 29 hardstandings.

Facilities: � ₦ ⊙ ₱✳ ⓚ ♿ 🛒 **Services:** ⊤ ⇩ ⊕ 🖃 🔋 ⊘ ✐ 🖻

GRETNA   NY36

Bruce's Cave Caravan & Camping Park ▶▶▶ 81%

Cove Estate Kirkpatrick Fleming DG11 3AT

☎ 01461 800285 🖹 01461 800269

email: enquiries@brucescave.co.uk

www.brucescave.co.uk

Dir: *Exit A74(M) junct 21 for Kirkpatrick Fleming follow N through village, pass Station Inn, at Bruce's Court turn left. Over rail crossing to site entrance.*

* 🚐 £10 🚐 £10 ▲ £8.50-£16

Open: Open All Year (rs Nov-Mar Shop closed, water restriction), Last arrival 23.00hrs Last departure 19.00hrs

An 80-acre site set in the wooded grounds of an old castle and mansion, with 75 touring pitches, 60 hardstandings and 35 statics.

Facilities: BMX bike hire, coarse fishing, buggy & travel cot � ₦ ⊙ ₱✳ ⓚ 🛢 ✝ 🏕 ♿ **Services:** 🐶 ⊤ ⇩ ⊕ 🖃 🔋 ⊘ 🏕 🚽

Facilities found within 3 miles: ∪ ⚓ 18 ✐ ⚓ 🛆 🖻 **Notes:** Dogs must be on lead 🐾

KIRKCUDBRIGHT NX64

Seaward Caravan Park ►►►► 82%

Dhoon Bay DG6 4TJ

☎ 01557 870267 📠 01557 870319

email: aa@seaward-park.co.uk

www.gillespie-leisure.co.uk

Dir: *2m SW off B727 (Borgue road)*

* 🚐 £10.25-£14.60 🚍 £10.25-£14.60

▲ £10.25-£14.60

Open: Mar-Oct (rs Mar-mid May & mid Sep-Oct swimming pool closed), Booking advisable Spring bank hols & Jul-Aug, Last arrival 21.30hrs Last departure 11.30hrs
An attractive elevated park with outstanding views over Kirkcudbright Bay. Access to a sandy cove with rock pools is just across the road. Leisure facilities of the other Gillespie parks are available to guests. An 8-acre site with 26 touring pitches and 30 statics.

Facilities: Pitch & putt 🛶 🔦 🗚 🐾 ☉ 🅿 �️ 🕔 🖭 🚻 🎝 👤 **Services:** 🚻 🗑 🔋 🗑 🛒

Facilities found within 3 miles: ∪ 🎣 18 🖋 ◎ 🗑 🗐

LOCHMABEN NY08

Kirkloch Caravan & Camping Site

►► 80%

DG11 1PZ

☎ 01556 503806 📠 01556 503806

email: scottg2@dumgal.gov.uk

www.dumgal.gov.uk/kirklochcs

Dir: *In Lochmaben enter via Kirkloch Brae*

* 🚐 £8.20-£12 🚍 £8.20-£12 ▲ £8.20-£12

Open: Etr-Oct, Last departure noon
A grassy lochside site with superb views and well-maintained facilities. Some hard pitches are available at this municipal park, which is adjacent to a golf club, and close to three lochs. A 1.5-acre site with 30 touring pitches and 14 hardstandings.

Facilities: 🗚 🐾 ☉ 🅿 🗐 🚻 **Services:** 🚻

Facilities found within 3 miles: 🎣 18 🕊 🖋 🏌 🗐 **Notes:** Dogs must be kept on leads 🐕

DUMFRIES & GALLOWAY

DUMFRIES & GALLOWAY

NEWTON STEWART   NX46
Creebridge Caravan Park ▶▶▶ 67%

Minnigaff DG8 6AJ

☎ 01671 402324 🖹 01671 402324

email: johnsharples1@btopenworld.co.uk

www.creebridgecaravanpark.com

Dir: *0.25m E of Newton Stewart at Minnigaff on bypass, signed off A75*

* 🚐 £12-£14 🚌 £12-£14 ▲ £8-£12

Open: Open All Year (rs Mar only one toilet block open), Booking advisable Jul-Aug, Last arrival 20.00hrs Last departure 10.00hrs

A small family-owned site a short walk from the town's amenities. The site is surrounded by mature trees, and offers good facilities including an indoor games room and outdoor draughts. A 5.5-acre site with 36 touring pitches, 12 hardstandings and 50 statics.

Facilities: Security street lighting 🔍 Ⓜ ⚘ ☉ 🅿 ✳ 🕐 🗑 📬 🍴 **Services:** 🚰 🗑 🛢 🧴 🚿

Facilities found within 3 miles: ∪ ♨ 18 ✐ 🗑 🛒 **Notes:** 🐾

PALNACKIE   NX85
Barlochan Caravan Park ▶▶▶ 77%

Castle Douglas DG7 1PF

☎ 01556 600256 🖹 01557 870319

email: aa@barlochan.co.uk

www.gillespie-leisure.co.uk

Dir: *On A711, N of Palnackie, signed*

🚐 £10.25-£14.70 🚌 £10.25-£14.70

▲ £10.25-£14.70

Open: Apr-Oct, Booking advisable Spring bank hol & Jul-Aug, Last arrival 21.30hrs Last departure 11.30hrs

A small terraced park with quiet landscaped pitches in a level area backed by rhododendron bushes. There are spectacular views over the River Urr estuary, and the park has its own coarse fishing loch nearby. A 9-acre site with 20 touring pitches and 40 statics.

Facilities: Fishing, pitch & putt ⚘ 🔍 Ⓜ 🔲 ⚘ ☉ 🅿 ✳ 🕐 🗑 📬 ⛲ 🛒 **Services:** 🔲 🚰 🗑 🛢 🧴 🚿 **Facilities found within 3 miles:** ♨ 9 ✐ ◎ 🗑 🛒

SANDHEAD   NX15

Sands of Luce Holiday Park

▶▶▶▶ 74%

Sands of Luce Stranraer DG9 9JN

☎ 01776 830456 📠 01776 830477

email: info@sandsofluceholidaypark.co.uk

www.sandsofluceholidaypark.co.uk

Dir: *From S & E - left off A75 onto B7084*
signed Drummore. Site signed at junct with
A716. From N - A77 through Stranraer
towards Portpatrick, 2m & follow A716
signed Drummore, site signed in 5m

* 🚐 £17 🚎 £17 ▲ £10-£15

Open: Mar-Oct, Booking advisable Jul-Aug,
Last arrival 20.00hrs Last departure noon
A friendly site on the grassy banks at the edge
of a sandy beach, with views across Luce Bay.
Surrounding area is protected by the Nature
Conservancy Council. A 30-acre site with 100
touring pitches and 190 statics.

Facilities: Boat launching 🏊 🄰 🄽 ⊙ 🄿 ✳
🕓 🖪 🚻 🕭 **Services:** 🗄 🔌 🖳 🗑 🔋 ⊘ 🚮 🛒
Facilities found within 3 miles: 🏌 🖥 💲

SANDYHILLS   NX85

Sandyhills Bay Leisure Park

▶▶▶ 78%

Dalbeattie DG5 4NY

☎ 01557 870267 📠 01557 870319

email: info@sandyhills-bay.co.uk

www.gillespie-leisure.co.uk

Dir: *On A710, 7m from Dalbeattie, 6.5m from*
Kirkbean

🚐 £10.25-£14.70 🚎 £10.25-£14.70
▲ £10.25-£14.70

Open: Apr-Oct, Booking advisable Spring
bank hol & Jun-Aug, Last arrival 21.30hrs
Last departure 11.30hrs
A well-maintained park in a superb location
beside a 'blue-flag' beach, and close to many
attractive villages. The level, grassy site is
sheltered by woodland, and the south-facing
Sandyhills Bay and beach are ideal for all the
family, with caves and rock pools. A 6-acre
site with 26 touring pitches and 34 statics.

Facilities: 🄰 🄽 ⊙ 🄿 ✳ 🕓 🖪 🚻 🕭
Services: 🗄 🔌 🖳 🗑 🔋 ⊘ 🚮 🛒 **Facilities**
found within 3 miles: ⛳ 🏊 9 🖥 💲

DUMFRIES & GALLOWAY

DUMFRIES & GALLOWAY

SOUTHERNESS NX95

Southerness Holiday Village 79%

DG2 8AZ

☎ 01387 880256 📠 01387 880429

email: enquiries@parkdeanholidays.co.uk

www.parkdeanholidays.co.uk

Dir: *From S take A75 from Gretna to Dumfries. From N take A74, exit at A701 to Dumfries. Take A710 coast road. Approx 16m, site easily seen*

* 🚐 £10-£24.50 ⛺ £10-£24.50 ▲ £8-£21

Open: Mar-Oct, Booking advisable Jul-Aug & bank hols, Last arrival 21.00hrs Last departure 10.00hrs

A holiday centre with stunning views of the Solway Firth. A 50-acre site with 90 touring pitches, 45 hardstandings and 72 statics.

Facilities: Amusement centre, live entertainment, kids' clubs 🎣 🔍 🛝 🛖 ⊙ 🅿 ✳ 🌙 🖥 🚻 🛁 ⅙ 👶 **Services:** 🛢 🍴 🛒 ⚡ 🅣 🚽 💩 🗑 🛢 🔥 🚛 **Facilities found within 3 miles:** 🏖 18 🎣 🐾 ◎ 🛢 🗑

WIGTOWN NX45

Drumroamin Farm Camping & Touring Site ►►► 85%

1 South Balfern Newton Stewart DG8 9DB

☎ 01988 840613

email: enquiry@drumroamin.co.uk

www.drumroamin.co.uk

Dir: *A75 towards Newton Stewart, turn onto A714 for Wigtown. Left on B7005 through Bladnock, A746 through Kirkinner. Take B7004 Garlieston, 2nd left opposite Kilsture Forest, site 0.75m at end of lane*

* 🚐 £12.50 ⛺ £12.50 ▲ £11

Open: Open All Year Booking advisable Last arrival 21.00hrs Last departure noon

An open, spacious park in a quiet spot a mile from the main road, and close to Wigton Bay. There's a superb toilet block, a lounge/games room and room for children to play. A 5-acre site with 48 touring pitches and 2 statics.

Facilities: Ball games area 🔍 🛝 ⊙ 🅿 ✳ 🚻 🛁 🛒 🚻 & **Services:** 💩 🗑 🛒 🚿 9 🎣 🛢 **Notes:** No fires 🐕

DUNBAR   NT77

Thurston Manor Holiday Home Park ▶▶▶▶▶ 84%

Innerwick EH42 1SA

☎ 01368 840643 📠 01368 840261

email: mail@thurstonmanor.co.uk

www.thurstonmanor.co.uk

Dir: *4m S of Dunbar, signed off A1*

* ⊕ £15-£25 ⊕ £15-£25 ▲ £15-£20

Open: Mar-8 Jan (rs 1-23 Dec weekends only), Booking advisable Etr, bank hols & high season, Last arrival 23.00hrs Last departure noon

A pleasant park set in 250 acres of unspoilt countryside. The park boasts a fishing loch, indoor pool, steam room, sauna, jacuzzi, mini-gym and fitness room and entertainment. A 250-acre site with 100 touring pitches, 45 hardstandings and 420 statics.

Facilities: ⌂ ♠ ⋒ ☐ ⋔ ⊙ ℘ ☀ ☉ 🛈 ⊁ ⤸

�& **Services:** ⌾ ⏻ ⤖ ⏟ 🛈 ⊕ ⟐ ⌷ ⊘ 🛒 ⤸

⚕ **Facilities found within 3 miles:** ✎ 🛈

🛈

LONGNIDDRY   NT47

Seton Sands Holiday Village **V** 66%

EH32 0QF

☎ 01875 813333 📠 01875 813531

www.havenholidays.com

Dir: *Take A1 to A198 exit, then B6371 to Cockenzie. Right onto B1348. Park 1m on right*

Open: mid Mar-Oct (rs mid Mar-May & Sep-Oct some facilities may be reduced), Booking advisable school hols, Last arrival 23.00hrs Last departure 10.00hrs

A well-equipped holiday centre with plenty of organised entertainment, clubs and bars, restaurants, and sports and leisure facilities. The good touring facilities are separate from the large static areas. A 1.75-acre site with 38 touring pitches and 648 statics.

Facilities: ⌂ ⋒ ⚲ ⋔ ⊙ ℘ 🛈 & **Services:** ⌾ ⏻ ⤖ ⊕ 🛈 ⊕ ⟐ ⌷ ⚕ **Facilities found within 3 miles:** ↻ ⌿ 18 ↯ ≋ 🛈 ⊗ **Notes:** Dogs not allowed at peak periods, max 2 dogs per pitch

EAST LOTHIAN

ST ANDREWS NO41
Craigtoun Meadows Holiday Park
▶▶▶▶▶ 90%
Mount Melville KY16 8PQ
☎ 01334 475959 ▤ 01334 476424
email: craigtoun@aol.com
www.craigtounmeadows.co.uk
Dir: *From M90 junct 8 onto A91 to St Andrews. Just after Guardbridge turn right for Strathkinness. At 2nd x-rds after Strathkinness turn left for Craigtoun*
⊞ £18-£25 ⊞ £17-£23 Å £17-£18
Open: 13 Mar-15 Nov (rs Mar-Etr & Sep-Oct shops & restaurant open shorter hours), Booking advisable bank hols & Jun-Aug, Last arrival 21.00hrs Last departure noon
An attractive site set in woodlands near sandy beaches. A 32-acre site with 58 touring pitches, 58 hardstandings and 157 statics.
Facilities: ⬥ ⬜ ♨ ⬤ ⊙ ℘ ⤬ ⊙ ▤ ☰ ⤒ ⬥
Services: ⬥ ⨉ Ⓣ ⬥ ⊙ ⬥ ∅ ⤒ **Facilities found within 3 miles:** ∪ ↓ 18 ℘ ◎ ⬥ ⬥
⊗ **Notes:** No groups under 18yrs

BOAT OF GARTEN NH91
Campgrounds of Scotland
▶▶▶ 76%
PH24 3BN
☎ 01479 831652 ▤ 01479 831450
email: briangillies@totalise.co.uk
www.campgroundsofscotland.com
Dir: *From A9 take A95 to Grantown-on-Spey, then follow signs for Boat of Garten. Park in village centre.*
* ⊞ £12.50-£17.50 ⊞ £12.50-£17.50
Å £5.50-£17.50
Open: Open All Year Booking advisable 26 Dec-2 Jan & 25 Jul-7 Aug, Last arrival 22.00hrs Last departure 11.00hrs
A very attractive site set in mountainous woodland near the River Spey and Loch Garten, with outstanding views. Young trees and bushes enhance the park. A 3.5-acre site with 37 touring pitches, 20 hardstandings and 60 statics.
Facilities: ⬜ ⬤ ⊙ ℘ ⤬ ⊙ ⬥ ⬥ **Services:** ⬥ Ⓣ ⬥ ⊙ ⬥ ∅ ⤒ **Facilities found within 3 miles:** ↓ 18 ℘ ⬥ ⬥ **Notes:** ⊜

CANNICH NH33

Cannich Caravan and Camping Park ▶▶▶ 72%

Strathglass IV4 7LN

☎ 01456 415364 📠 01456 415364

email: enquiries@highlandcamping.co.uk

www.highlandcamping.co.uk

Dir: *On A831, 200yds SE of Cannich Bridge*

* 🚐 £9 🚌 £9 ⛺ £9

Open: Mar-Oct (rs Dec-Feb winter opening by arrangement), Booking advisable Jul & Aug, Last arrival 23.00hrs Last departure noon

Quietly situated in Strath Glass, close to the River Glass and Cannich village. This family-run park has attractive mountain views, and is set in ideal walking and naturalist country. A 6-acre site with 43 touring pitches, 15 hardstandings and 15 statics.

Facilities: Mountain bike hire 🔍 ⛬ ▭ 🚿 ⊙ 🚿 ✲ ✆ 🛒 ⛩ ♿ **Services:** [T] ⛰ 🚐 🗄 🔒 🌿 🍴 ⚲ 🔌 [$] **Notes:** Dogs must be kept on lead

CORPACH NN07

Linnhe Lochside Holidays ▶▶▶▶▶ 83%

Fort William PH33 7NL

☎ 01397 772376 📠 01397 772007

email: relax@linnhe-lochside-holidays.co.uk

www.linnhe-lochside-holidays.co.uk

Dir: *On A830, 1m W of Corpach, 5m from Fort William*

* 🚐 £15-£17 🚌 £15-£17 ⛺ £11-£13

Open: Etr-Oct (rs 15 Dec-Etr shop/main wc block closed), Booking advisable school hols & peak periods, Last arrival 21.00hrs Last departure 11.00hrs

An excellently maintained site in a beautiful setting on the shores of Loch Eil, with Ben Nevis to the east and the mountains and Sunart to the west. Highest standards of maintenance. A 5.5-acre site with 85 touring pitches, 63 hardstandings and 20 statics.

Facilities: Launching slipway, free fishing ⛬ 🚿 ⊙ 🚿 ✲ ✆ [$] 🐕 🛒 ⛩ ♿ **Services:** [T] ⛰ 🚐 🗄 🔒 🌿 🍴 ⛳ 18 🔌 ◎ [$]

HIGHLAND

DAVIOT NH73

Auchnahillin Caravan and Camping Park ▶▶▶ 76%

IV2 5XQ

☎ 01463 772286

email: info@auchnahillin.co.uk

www.auchnahillin.co.uk

Dir: *7m S of Inverness, just off A9 on B9154 (Daviot-East & Moy road)*

⊞ £10-£15 ⛺ £8-£15 ▲ £8-£10

Open: 15 Mar-Oct, Booking advisable Jun-Aug, Last arrival 21.00hrs Last departure 17.00hrs

Surrounded by hills and forests, this level, grassy site offers clean and spacious facilities. The owner lives in a bungalow on the site. A 10-acre site with 75 touring pitches, 4 hardstandings and 35 statics.

Facilities: ⚒ ₨ ⊙ ☺ ☞ ⚡ ✲ ① ☺ ☞ ☷ ☷ ♿

Services: ① ⊞ ⓢ ▣ 🖆 ∅ ☕ Facilities found within 3 miles: ℘ **Notes:** No noise after midnight, limited facilities for disabled visitors

DORNOCH NH78

Grannie's Heilan' Hame Holiday Park 73%

Embo IV25 3QD

☎ 01862 810383 🖨 01862 810368

email: enquiries@parkdeanholidays.co.uk

www.parkdeanholidays.co.uk

Dir: *A949 to Dornoch, left in square. Follow Embo signs*

* ⊞ £12-£26.50 ⛺ £10-£24.50 ▲ £8-£21

Open: Mar-Oct, Booking advisable Jul-Aug & bank hols, Last arrival 21.00hrs Last departure 10.00hrs

A holiday centre on the Highland coast, with a range of leisure facilities, including indoor pool with sauna and solarium, separate play areas for under and over fives, putting green, tennis courts and very much more. A 60-acre site with 220 touring pitches and 186 statics.

Facilities: Spa bath, sauna, solarium, family entertainment ☎ ♦ ⚒ ₷ ₨ ⊙ ☺ ✲ ① ☺ ☞

Services: ⑩ ▦ ① ⊞ ⓢ ▣ 🖆 ∅ ☕ 🍺

Facilities found within 3 miles: ♨ 18 ℘ ⊙ ▣ ⓢ

GAIRLOCH NG77

Sands Holiday Centre ►►► 75%

IV21 2DL

☎ 01445 712152 🖷 01445 712518

email: litsands@aol.co.uk

www.highlandcaravancamping.co.uk

Dir: *3m W of Gairloch on B8021*

* ⛟ £9-£17 ⛺ £8.50-£15 Å £9-£17

Open: 20 May-10 Sep (rs Apr-19 May & 11
Sep-mid Oct shop & some toilets closed),
Booking advisable Jul-Aug, Last arrival
22.00hrs Last departure noon

Close to a sandy beach with a panoramic
outlook towards Skye, a well-maintained park
with very good facilities. A large laundry and
refitted toilets make this an ideal family site.
A 51-acre site with 360 touring pitches and
20 statics.

Facilities: Boat slipway 🔍 ⚠ 🅿 ☉ 🅿 ⚒ 🕒
🅗 🚻 🛒 🚽 🕭 **Services:** 🆃 🚰 🛢 🍴 🗑 🏕
Facilities found within 3 miles: ∪ ↓ 9 🅿
◎ 🗑 🅕

GRANTOWN-ON-SPEY NJ02

Grantown on Spey Caravan Park

►►►► 84%

Seafield Avenue PH26 3JQ

☎ 01479 872474 🖷 01479 873696

email: warden@caravanscotland.com

www.caravanscotland.com

Dir: *From town turn N at Bank of Scotland,
park in 0.25m*

* ⛟ £16-£20 ⛺ £16-£20 Å £12-£16

Open: 15 Dec-Oct, Booking advisable Etr,
May Day, spring BH & Jul-Aug, Last arrival
22.00hrs Last departure noon

A scenic park in a mature setting near the
river, surrounded by hills, mountains, moors
and woodland. In a good location for outdoor
activities. A 29-acre site with 120 touring
pitches, 60 hardstandings and 45 statics.

Facilities: Freezer facility 🔍 ⚠ 🅿 ☉ 🅿 ⚒
🕒 🅗 🚻 🛒 🚽 🕭 **Services:** 🆃 🚰 🚰 🛢 🍴 🗑
🏕 🚗 **Facilities found within 3 miles:** ∪
↓ 18 🅿 ◎ ⚓ 🗑 🅕

HIGHLAND

HIGHLAND

LAIRG NC51
Woodend Caravan & Camping Site

►►► 63%

Achnairn IV27 4DN

☎ 01549 402248 📄 01549 402248

Dir: *4m N of Lairg off A836 onto A838, signed at Achnairn*

* 🚐 £9 🚌 £8-£9 ⛺ £6-£7

Open: Apr-Sep, Last arrival 23.00hrs

A clean, fresh site set in hilly moors and woodland with access to Loch Shin. The area is popular with fishing and boating enthusiasts, and there is a choice of golf courses within 30 miles. A spacious camper's kitchen is a useful amenity. A 4-acre site with 55 touring pitches.

Facilities: ⚠ ⬆ ⊙ ⏚ ☀ **Services:** 🔌 🗑 🚾 🍴 🚰 ≒ **Facilities found within 3 miles:** 🎣 🗑 **Notes:** ⌽

NAIRN NH85
Nairn Camping & Caravanning Club Site ►►► 75%

Delnies Wood Inverness IV12 5NX

☎ 01667 455281

www.campingandcaravanningclub.co.uk

Dir: *Off A96 (Inverness to Aberdeen road). 2m W of Nairn*

🚐 £12.75-£16.75 🚌 £12.75-£16.75 ⛺ £12.75-£16.75

Open: Apr-Oct, Booking advisable BHs & peak periods, Last arrival 21.00hrs Last departure noon

An attractive site set amongst pine trees, with facilities maintained to a good standard. The park is close to Nairn with its beaches, shopping, golf and leisure activities. A 14-acre site with 75 touring pitches.

Facilities: Fishing 🍴 ⚠ ⬆ ⊙ ⏚ ☀ 🕐 🚾 🏪 **Services:** 🚽 🔌 🗑 🚾 🍴 ≒ **Facilities found within 3 miles:** ∪ ⬇ 🎣 ≒ 🗑

THURSO ND16

Thurso Caravan & Camping Site

►►► 69%

Smith Terrace Scrabster Road KW14 7JY

☎ 01847 895782 📠 01847 893156

Dir: *Signed on A836 W of town*

Open: May-Sep

A large grassy site set high above the coast
on the west side of town, with panoramic
views out to sea and the Orkney island of Hoy.
Convenient for ferries to the islands, and all
the town's facilities. A 4.5-acre site with 95
touring pitches and 10 statics.

Facilities: 🅰 🦮 ☺ ⊙ 🖬 🛧 ⅋ **Services:**
🔌 🗑 ⅃ 18 🕎 ⅊ 🛒 🗑 🗑 **Notes:** ☺

ULLAPOOL NH19

Broomfield Holiday Park ►►► 69%

West Shore Street IV26 2UT

☎ 01854 612020 📠 01854 613151

email: sross@broomfieldhp.com

www.broomfieldhp.com

Dir: *Take 2nd right past harbour*

🚐 £13 �", £12 ▲ £11-£13

Open: Etr/Apr-Sep, Booking advisable for
group bookings only, Last departure noon
Set right on the water's edge of Loch Broom
and the open sea, with lovely views of the
Summer Isles. The park is close to the
harbour and town centre with their
restaurants, bars and shops. A 12-acre site
with 140 touring pitches.

Facilities: 🅰 🦮 ⊙ ⋇ 🖬 🍴 ⅋ **Services:** 🔌
🔌 🗑 🎖 ⅃ 9 🕎 ⅊ 🛒 🗑 🗑 **Notes:** Pets must
be kept on leads, no noise at night

HIGHLAND

MORAY

ALVES
NJ16

North Alves Caravan Park ►►► 67%

Elgin IV30 8XD

☎ 01343 850223

Dir: *1m W of A96, halfway between Elgin & Forres. Site signed on right*

* ⊕ £7.50-£10.50 ⊕ £7-£10 ▲ £6-£10

Open: Apr-Oct, Booking advisable peak periods, Last arrival 23.00hrs Last departure noon

A quiet rural site in attractive rolling countryside within three miles of a good beach. The site is on a former farm, and the stone buildings are quite unspoilt. A 10-acre site with 45 touring pitches and 45 statics.

Facilities: ◀ ⋀ ☐ ⋔ ☉ ℗ ✕ ⓒ 📵 ⋈

Services: ⊤ ⊕ 🖅 🆘 ⊘ 🖿 **Facilities found within 3 miles:** ∪ ⌟ 18 ⫛ ℘ ⓞ **Notes:** 🐾

FOCHABERS
NJ35

Burnside Caravan Park ►►► 72%

IV32 7ET

☎ 01343 820511 📄 01343 820511

Dir: *0.5m E of town off A96*

* ⊕ £12-£14 ⊕ £12-£14 ▲ £12-£14

Open: Apr-Oct, Booking advisable Jul-Aug, Last departure noon

Attractive site in a tree-lined, sheltered valley with a footpath to the village. Owned by the garden centre on the opposite side of the A96. A 5-acre site with 51 touring pitches, 30 hardstandings and 101 statics.

Facilities: Jacuzzi & sauna ⌂ ◀ ⋀ ☐ ⋔ ☉ ℗ ⓒ 📵 ⋈ ⭐ **Services:** ⊤ ⊍ ⊕ 🆘 ⊘

Facilities found within 3 miles: ∪ ⌟ 18 ℘ ⓞ ⓢ

LOSSIEMOUTH NJ08
Silver Sands Leisure Park

▶▶▶▶ 73%

Covesea West Beach IV31 6SP

☎ 01343 813262 📠 01343 815205

email: holidays@silversands.freeserve.co.uk

www.travel.to/silversands

Dir: *From Lossiemouth, B9040, 2m W to site*

* 🚐 £7.50-£16.25 ⛺ £7.50-£16.25
▲ £6.20-£12.50

Open: Apr-Oct (rs Apr, May & Oct shops & entertainment restricted), Booking advisable Jul-Aug, Last arrival 22.00hrs Last departure noon

A holiday park with entertainment during peak season, on the links beside the shore of the Moray Firth. Touring campers and caravans are catered for in three areas. A 7-acre site with 140 touring pitches and 200 statics.

Facilities: Children's entertainment 🔦 🗚 🗖 🌢 📻 ⊙ 🅿 ❄ ⓧ 🗟 🚗 ☵ 🚃 **Services:** 🐟 📞 🎵 🎔 🗟 🛢 🌢 ⇌ 🌰 **Facilities found within 3 miles:** ∪ 🎣 18 ⛷ ℘ ◎ 🛥 🗟 🗟 **Notes:** Over 14yrs only in bar

ABERFELDY NN84
Aberfeldy Caravan Park ▶▶▶ 73%

Dunkeld Road PH15 2AQ

☎ 01887 820662 📠 01738 475210

Dir: *Off A827, on E edge of town*

* 🚐 £13 ⛺ £13 ▲ £9.35

Open: late Mar-late Oct, Booking advisable Jun-Aug, Last arrival 20.00hrs Last departure noon

A very well-run and well-maintained site, with good facilities and some landscaping, at the eastern end of the town and lying between main road and banks of the River Tay. Good views from site of surrounding hills. A 5-acre site with 92 touring pitches.

Facilities: 🗚 🌢 ⊙ 🅿 ⓧ 🗟 🚗 ☵ 🚃 ↺ 🛒 **Services:** 🐟 📞 🗟 🗟 🎔 🎵 🎣 18 ℘ ◎ 🛥 🗟 🗟

MORAY/PERTH & KINROSS

PERTH & KINROSS

BLAIR ATHOLL   NN86

Blair Castle Caravan Park

▶▶▶▶▶ 80%

Pitlochry PH18 5SR

☎ 01796 481263 📠 01796 481587

email: mail@blaircastlecaravanpark.co.uk

www.blaircastlecaravanpark.co.uk

Dir: *From A9 junct with B8079 at Aldclune,*
then NE to Blair Atholl. Park on right after
crossing bridge in village

🚐 £12-£15 🚎 £12-£15 ▲ £12-£15

Open: Mar-Nov, Booking advisable bank hols
& Jul-Aug, Last arrival 21.30hrs Last
departure noon

Attractive site in impressive seclusion within
the Atholl estate. Groups of pitches; choice of
grass pitches, hardstandings, fully-serviced.
Good for larger type of motorhome. A 32-acre
site with 280 touring pitches and 101 statics.

Facilities: Internet gallery with broadband
access 🔌 🛁 🛉 🕙 🅿 🎇 🕓 🕯 🚻 🛒 🛒 ᴫ ♿

Services: 🎛 🛠 🚐 🛢 🛢 🧺 📶 🚰 **Facilities**
found within 3 miles: ∪ ↓ 9 🖉 ◎ 🛢 🖾

PITLOCHRY   NN95

Faskally Caravan Park ▶▶▶▶ 73%

PH16 5LA

☎ 01796 472007 📠 01796 473896

email: info@faskally.co.uk

www.faskally.co.uk

Dir: *1.5m N of Pitlochry on B8019*

* 🚐 £14.40-£16 🚎 £14.40-£16 ▲ £14.40-£16

Open: 15 Mar-Oct, Booking advisable Jul-
Aug, Last arrival 23.00hrs

A large park attractively divided into sections
by mature trees, set in gently-sloping
meadowland beside the tree-lined River Garry.
The excellent amenities include a leisure
complex with heated indoor swimming pool,
spa, sauna and steam room, bar, restaurant
and indoor amusements. The park is close to,
but unaffected by, the A9. A 27-acre site with
300 touring pitches and 130 statics.

Facilities: 🛖 🔌 🛁 🛉 🕙 🅿 🎇 🕓 🖾 ♿

Services: 🚰 🍽 🍺 🎛 🚐 🛢 🛢 🧺 **Facilities**
found within 3 miles: ∪ ↓ 18 ⅄ 🖉 🛢 🖾

Notes: Dogs must be kept on leads

SCONE NO12

Scone Camping & Caravanning
Club Site ▶▶▶ 69%

Scone Palace Perth PH2 6BB

☎ 01738 552323

www.campingandcaravanningclub.co.uk

Dir: *Follow signs for Scone Palace, once*
through Perth continue for 2m. Turn left,
follow site signs. 1m left onto Racecourse
Road. Site entrance from car park

🚐 £14.05-£18.85 🚎 £14.05-£18.85
▲ £14.05-£18.85

Open: Mar-Oct, Booking advisable bank hols
& peak periods, Last arrival 21.00hrs Last
departure noon

A delightful woodland site, sheltered and well
screened from the adjacent Scone racecourse.
Super pitches add to the park's appeal. A
16-acre site with 150 touring pitches and 40
hardstandings.

Facilities: 🔌 ♨ 🛱 ⊙ ℗ ✳ 🕙 🛒 🛁 ♿
Services: ▯ 🚽 🚭 🖵 🖴 🗑 🚿 **Facilities**
found within 3 miles: ∪ 🖉 🛥 🏌 🏙

TUMMEL BRIDGE NN75

Tummel Valley
Holiday Park 71%

Pitlochry PH16 5SA

☎ 01882 634221 📄 01882 634302

email: enquiries@parkdeanholidays.co.uk

www.parkdeanholidays.co.uk

Dir: *From Perth take A9 N to bypass*
Pitlochry. 3m after Pitlochry turn onto B8019
signed Tummel Bridge. Park 11m on left

* 🚐 £10-£24.50 🚎 £10-£24.50
▲ £10-£24.50

Open: Mar-Oct, Booking advisable at all
times, Last arrival 21.00hrs Last departure
10.00hrs

Set amongst mature forest in a valley beside
the famous bridge on the banks of the River
Tummel. Play areas, bar, indoor pool,
children's clubs, entertainment. A 55-acre
site with 33 touring pitches and 159 statics.

Facilities: Cycle hire, fishing rod hire 🏞 🔌
♨ 🛱 ⊙ ℗ ✳ 🕙 🗑 🛒 🚻 ♿ **Services:** 🐟 🍴
🍽 🚭 🗑 🛁 🚾 **Facilities found within 3**
miles: 🖉 🖴 🏙

PERTH & KINROSS

COLDINGHAM NT96

Scoutscroft Holiday Centre

►►►► 79%

St Abbs Road TD14 5NB

☎ 018907 71338 📠 018907 71746

email: holidays@scoutscroft.co.uk

www.scoutscroft.co.uk

Dir: *From A1 take B6438 signed Coldingham & Scoutscroft on right; on Coldingham outskirts*

* 🚐 £16-£23 🚗 £16-£23

Open: Mar-Nov (rs Mar-May, Sep, Oct Crofters Bar only, arcade wknds only), Booking advisable Bank hols, Jul-Aug, wknds, Last arrival midnight Last departure noon

A large family-run site with good facilities and amenities. A 16-acre site with 60 touring pitches, 32 hardstandings and 120 statics.

Facilities: Sub Aqua Centre, cash machine 🔍 ⛺ 📺 🚿 ⊙ 🔌 ✲ 📞 [$] 🚰 ⛩ ♿ **Services:** 🍴 🍷 [T] 🎮 🧺 🔒 🍃 🛏 🧁 **Facilities found within 3 miles:** ∪ ⛳ 18 🎣 ≋ 🧺 [$]

JEDBURGH NT61

Jedwater Caravan Park ►►► 72%

TD8 6PJ

☎ 01835 869595 & 📠 01835 869595

email: jedwater@clara.co.uk

www.jedwater.co.uk

Dir: *3.5m S of Jedburgh on A68*

Open: Etr-Oct, Booking advisable high season, Last arrival midnight Last departure noon

A quiet riverside site in a beautiful valley, run by resident owners as a peaceful retreat. The touring area is separate from statics, and this site is an ideal touring base. A 10-acre site with 30 touring pitches and 75 statics.

Facilities: Bike hire, trampoline, football field 🔍 ⛺ 📺 🚿 ⊙ 🔌 ✲ 📞 [$] 🐕 🚰 ⛩ **Services:** [T] 🎮 🧺 🔒 🍃 🛏 **Facilities found within 3 miles:** ∪ ⛳ 9 🎣 🧺 [$] **Notes:** 🚫

KELSO NT73

Springwood Caravan Park

►►►► 78%

TD5 8LS

☎ 01573 224596 📠 01573 224033

email: tourers@springwood.biz

www.springwood.biz

Dir: *On A699, signed Newton St Boswells*

* 🚐 £17 🚌 £17 **Open:** 30 Mar-9 Oct, Booking advisable bank hols & Jul-Aug, Last arrival 23.00hrs

Set in a secluded position on the banks of the tree-lined River Teviot, this well-maintained site enjoys a pleasant and spacious spot in which to relax. It offers a high standard of modern toilet facilities which are mainly contained in cubicled units. Floors Castle and the historic town of Kelso are close by. A 2-acre site with 20 touring pitches, 20 hardstandings and 212 statics.

Facilities: 🛁 🧒 🚿 ⊙ 💨 ❄ ✆ 🐕 ♿

Services: 🚐 🧺 🔥 **Facilities found within 3 miles:** 🐎 🏌 18 🎣 🧺 🛍 **Notes:** Dogs must be kept on leads

PEEBLES NT24

Rosetta Caravan & Camping Park

►►► 75%

Rosetta Rd EH45 8PG

☎ 01721 720770 📠 01721 720623

www.rosettacaravanpark.co.uk

Dir: *Signed from all main roads from Peebles*

* 🚐 £15 🚌 £15 ⛺ £15

Open: Apr-Oct, Booking advisable BHs, Jul-Aug, Last arrival 23.00hrs Last departure 15.00hrs

A pleasant site set in 40 acres of parkland around a late Georgian mansion and stable block. Some of the stable buildings house the toilet facilities and bar. A 25-acre site with 160 touring pitches and 60 statics.

Facilities: 🛁 🧒 📺 🚿 ⊙ 💨 ❄ ✆ 🛍 🐕 🍖

Services: 🍷 [T] 🚐 🧺 🔥 🍃 **Facilities found within 3 miles:** 🐎 🏌 18 ⛵ 🎣 🧺 🛍

Notes: ⊘

SCOTTISH BORDERS

PEEBLES NT24

Crossburn Caravan Park ▶▶▶▶ 77%

Edinburgh Road EH45 8ED

☎ 01721 720501 📠 01721 720501

email: enquiries@crossburncaravans.co.uk

www.crossburncaravans.com

Dir: *0.5m N of Peebles on A703*

* 🚐 £15-£17 �caravan £15-£17 ▲ £15

Open: Apr-Oct, Booking advisable Jul-Aug, Last arrival 21.00hrs Last departure 14.00hrs A peaceful site in a relatively quiet location, despite the proximity of the main road which partly borders the site, as does the Eddleston Water. The park is well stocked with trees, flowers and shrubs. Facilities are maintained to a high standard, and fully-serviced pitches are available. A large caravan dealership is on the same site. A 6-acre site with 45 touring pitches, 15 hardstandings and 85 statics.

Facilities: 🔧 🄰 🌂 ⊙ 🅿 🖻 🗙 🎄 🕭

Services: 🕕 ↯ 🚐 🖻 🛢 🖉 🛒 🚮 Facilities found within 3 miles: ∪ ⅃ 18 🖋 🖻

Notes: Dogs must be kept on leads

SELKIRK NT42

Victoria Park Caravan & Camping Park ▶▶▶ 70%

Victoria Park Buccleuch Road TD7 5DN

☎ 01750 20897 📠 01750 20897

www.bstt.org.uk

Dir: *From A707/A708 N of town, cross river bridge & take 1st left, then left again*

* 🚐 £9.10 �caravan £9.10 ▲ £8.05

Open: Open All Year (rs mid-late Jun), Booking advisable Jul-Aug, Last arrival 20.00hrs Last departure 14.00hrs A consistently well-maintained site with good basic facilities forming part of public park and swimming pool complex close to River Ettrick. A 3-acre site with 60 touring pitches and 9 hardstandings.

Facilities: Fitness room, sauna, small soft play area 🄰 🄰 🌂 ⊙ 🅿 🗙 🖻 🗙 🎄 🕭

Services: 🐟 🚐 🖻 Facilities found within 3 miles: ∪ ⅃ 9 🖋 🖻 🖻

AYR NS31

Craig Tara Holiday Park 75%

KA7 4LB

☎ 01292 265141 📠 01292 445206

www.havenholidays.com

Dir: *From Ayr take A77 towards Stranraer, then 2nd right after Bankfield Rdbt. Left at Doonholm Rd, then right into Greenfield Ave, left at next junct, then follow signs*

Open: mid Mar-Oct (rs mid Mar-May & Sep-Oct some services may be limited), Booking advisable school hols, Last departure 10.00hrs

A large, well-maintained holiday centre with on-site entertainment and sporting facilities. The touring area is set apart from the main complex. A 213-acre site with 29 touring pitches, 29 hardstandings and 608 statics.

Facilities: Access to beach from park 🏖 /\\ 🐾 ⊙ 🕒 🔥 ♿ **Services:** 🚰 🍴 🛢 📞 🛢 🛒 ⛴ **Facilities found within 3 miles:** ∪ ↓ 9 ⛵ 🅿 ◎ 🔲 📷 **Notes:** Max 2 dogs per pitch

BARRHILL NX28

Windsor Holiday Park ►►►► 77%

Girvan KA26 0PZ

☎ 01465 821355 📠 01465 821355

email: windsorholidaypark@barrhillgirvan.freeserve.co.uk

www.windsorholidaypark.com

Dir: *On A714 (Newton Stewart to Girvan road). 1m N of Barrhill*

* 🚐 £10 �caravan £10 ▲ £5-£10

Open: Mar-Nov (rs Nov-Feb closed Tue to Thu)

A small, friendly park in a tranquil rural location, screened from the A714 by trees. The park is terraced and well landscaped, and a high quality amenity block includes disabled facilities. A 6-acre site with 30 touring pitches, 9 hardstandings and 29 statics.

Facilities: /\\ 🐾 ⊙ ⊙ 🅿 ✕ 🕒 🔲 ♨ 🚻 ♿ **Services:** 🔌 🛢 🛢 🛒 **Facilities found within 3 miles:** 🅿 🔲 **Notes:** ◎

SOUTH AYRSHIRE

SOUTH AYRSHIRE/SOUTH LANARKSHIRE

COYLTON
NS42

**Sundrum Castle
Holiday Park** 74%

By Ayr KA6 5JH

☎ 01292 570057 📄 01292 570065

email: enquiries@parkdeanholidays.co.uk

www.parkdeanholidays.co.uk

Dir: *Just off A70, 4m E of Ayr near Coylton*

* ⊕ £12-£26 ⇔ £12-£26 ▲ £10-£22.50

Open: Mar-Oct, Booking advisable all times,
Last arrival 21.00hrs Last departure 10.00hrs

A large family holiday centre in rolling
countryside, with plenty of on-site
entertainment, and just a 10-minute drive
from the centre of Ayr. Leisure facilities
include an indoor swimming pool complex
with flume, crazy golf, clubs for young
children and teenagers, and the touring area
is adequate and clean. A 30-acre site with 32
touring pitches and 245 statics.

Facilities: Amusement arcade, live family
entertainment 🥤 🔌 🛒 🗗 🏠 ⊙ 🅿 🕓 🖎

Services: 🕯 🍴 🛒 🕹 🖲 🛢 🗗 �∅ 🚐 🏧

Facilities found within 3 miles: ∪ ⅃ 18
🖋 🗗 🖎

ABINGTON
NS92

Mount View Caravan Park

▶▶▶ 78%

ML12 6RW

☎ 01864 502808 📄 01864 502808

email: info@mountviewcaravanpark.co.uk

www.mountviewcaravanpark.co.uk

Dir: *M74 junct 13 onto A702 S into
Abington. Left into Station Road, over river &
railway. Park on right*

* ⊕ £13.50 ⇔ £13.50 ▲ £5

Open: Mar-Oct

A developing park, surrounded by the
Southern Uplands and handily located
between Carlisle and Glasgow. It is an
excellent stopover site for those travelling
between Scotland and the South. The West
Coast railway passes beside the park. A 5.5-
acre site with 51 touring pitches, 51
hardstandings and 20 statics.

Facilities: Emergency phone 🔌 🏠 ⊙ 🅿 🖎

&. Services: 🕯 🛢 🛢 🖋 🛢 🖎 **Notes:** Dogs
must be kept on leads

ABERFOYLE NS59

Trossachs Holiday Park ►►►► 78%

FK8 3SA

☎ 01877 382614 📠 01877 382732

email: info@trossachsholidays.co.uk

www.trossachsholidays.co.uk

Dir: *Access on E side of A81, 1m S of junct A821 & 3m S of Aberfoyle*

* 🚐 £12-£18 🚎 £12-£18 ▲ £10-£16

Open: Mar-Oct, Booking advisable anytime, Last arrival 21.00hrs Last departure noon An imaginatively designed terraced site offering a high degree of quality, with fine views across Flanders Moss. All touring pitches are fully serviced with water, waste, electricity and TV aerial. Set in 20 acres of ground within the Queen Elizabeth Forest Park, with opportunities for cycling off-road on mountain bikes, which can be hired or bought on site. A 40-acre site with 66 touring pitches, 46 hardstandings and 84 statics.

Facilities: ♠ ⚠ ⛛ ♠ ♦ 🅿️✲ ⊙ 🛢 ♣ ☰

Services: 🔲 🚐 🛢 🔋 ⊘ 🍴 Facilities found within 3 miles: ∪ ⚓ 18 ≜ ✐ 🅑

BLAIRLOGIE NS89

Witches Craig Caravan & Camping Park ►►►► 84%

FK9 5PX

☎ 01786 474947 📠 01786 447286

email: info@witchescraig.co.uk

www.witchescraig.co.uk

Dir: *3m NE of Stirling on A91 (Hillfoots-St Andrews road)*

* 🚐 £12-£16 🚎 £12-£16 ▲ £12-£16

Open: Apr-Oct, Booking advisable Jul-Aug, Last arrival 21.00hrs Last departure 13.00hrs In an attractive setting with direct access to the lower slopes of the dramatic Ochil Hills, this is a well-maintained family-run park. It is in the centre of Braveheart country, with easy access to historical sites and many popular attractions. A 5-acre site with 60 touring pitches and 26 hardstandings.

Facilities: Food preparation, baby bath & changing area ⚠ ♠ ⊙ 🅿️✲ ⊙ 🛒 🍴 ☰ ♣ ♿

Services: 🔲 ⬆ 🚐 🛢 🔋 ⊘ 🍴 Facilities found within 3 miles: ∪ ⚓ 18 ✐ ◎ 🛢 🅑

STIRLING

STIRLING/WEST DUNBARTONSHIRE

CALLANDER NN60

Gart Caravan Park ▶▶▶ 86%

The Gart FK17 8LE

☎ 01877 330002 📠 01877 330002

email: enquiries@theholidaypark.co.uk

www.theholidaypark.co.uk

Dir: *1m E of Callander on A84*

* ➡ £17 ⊞ £17

Open: Etr or Apr-15 Oct, Booking advisable
Bank hols & Jul-Aug, Last arrival 22.00hrs
Last departure 11.30hrs

A well-screened caravan park bordered by
trees and shrubs, near to the Queen Elizabeth
Park amidst ideal walking and climbing
country. A feature of the park is the careful
attention to detail in the maintenance of
facilities, and the owners are very helpful and
friendly. A 26-acre site with 128 touring
pitches and 66 statics.

Facilities: Fishing on site 🅰 🅡 ⊕※ 🕔 🗟
🚲 ♿ **Services:** 🛢 ⊕ 🗟 🚰 **Facilities found
within 3 miles:** ∪ ⌀ 18 ⌀ ⚱ 🗟 🗟 **Notes:**
No commercial vehicles

BALLOCH NS38

Lomond Woods Holiday Park
▶▶▶▶ 80%

Old Luss Road Loch Lomond G83 8QP

☎ 01389 755000 📠 01389 755563

email: lomondwoods@holiday-parks.co.uk

www.holiday-parks.co.uk

Dir: *From A82, 17m N of Glasgow, take A811
(Stirling to Balloch road). Left at 1st rdbt,
follow holiday park signs, 150yds on left*

➡ £15-£20 ⊞ £15-£20

Open: Open All Year Booking advisable all
dates, Last arrival 21.00hrs Last departure
noon A mature park with well-laid out pitches
screened by trees and shrubs. The park is
within walking distance of 'Loch Lomond
Shores', a complex of leisure and retailing
experiences. A 13-acre site with 110 touring
pitches and 35 statics.

Facilities: 🔌 🅰 🖵 🅡 ⊕ ⌀※ 🕔 🗟 🚲 🚻 ♿
Services: 🎞 🛢 ⊕ 🗟 🚰 ⌀ ⚱ 🚲 **Facilities
found within 3 miles:** ∪ ⌀ 18 ⚱ ⌀
⚱ 🗟 🗟

EAST CALDER   NT16

Linwater Caravan Park ▶▶▶ 83%

West Clifton EH53 0HT

☎ 0131 333 3326 📠 0131 333 1952

email: linwater@supanet.com

www.linwater.co.uk

Dir: *M9 junct 1, signed from B7030 or from Wilkieston on A71*

🚐 £11-£14 🚐 £11-£14 ▲ £9-£12

Open: late Mar-late Oct, Booking advisable BHs & Aug, Last arrival 21.00hrs Last departure noon

A farmland park in a peaceful rural area within easy reach of Edinburgh. The very good facilities are housed in a Scandinavian-style building, and are well maintained by resident owners. Nearby are plenty of pleasant woodland walks. A 5-acre site with 60 touring pitches and 11 hardstandings.

Facilities: 🚿 📻 ⊙ 🅿 ✕ ◑ 🚻 ♿ **Services:** 🔌 🔋 🛢 ⊘ 🍴 Facilities found within 3 miles: ∪ ⅃ 27 ✦ 🎣 🛒 🔵 📵

LINLITHGOW   NT07

Beecraigs Caravan & Camping Site ▶▶▶▶ 79%

Beecraigs Country Park The Park Centre EH49 6PL

☎ 01506 844516 📠 01506 846256

email: mail@beecraigs.com

www.beecraigs.com

Dir: *From Linlithgow on A803 or from Bathgate on B792, follow signs to country park. Reception either at restaurant or park centre*

* 🚐 £11.50-£14.50 🚐 £11.50-£14.50 ▲ £7-£16

Open: Open All Year (rs 25 -26 Dec, 1-2 Jan no new arrivals), Booking advisable all year, Last arrival 22.00hrs Last departure noon

A wildlife enthusiast's paradise. A 6-acre site with 36 touring pitches and 36 hardstandings.

Facilities: Children's bath, country park facilities 🚿 📻 ⊙ 🅿 ✕ ◑ 🚻 🍴 🎯 ♿

Services: 🔌 Ⓣ 🔋 🛢 🍴 🚐 **Facilities found within 3 miles:** ∪ ⅃ 18 🎣 🏊 🛒 🔵 📵

Notes: No ball games near caravans, no noise after 22.00hrs

CARMARTHENSHIRE

CROSS HANDS SN51

Black Lion Caravan & Camping Park ▶▶▶ 89%

78 Black Lion Road Gorslas Llanelli SA14 6RU

☎ 01269 845365

email: blacklionsite@aol.com

www.caravansite.com

Dir: *M4 junct 49 onto A48 to Cross Hands rdbt, right onto A476 (Llandeilo). 0.5m at Gorslas sharp right into Black Lion Rd. Site 0.5m on right, (follow brown tourist signs from Cross Hands rdbt)*

* ➡ £12 ⇌ £12 ▲ £8

Open: Apr-Oct (rs Oct-Mar main toilet block closed), Booking advisable all times, Last arrival 22.00hrs Last departure 11.00hrs
Well maintained park with very good toilet and shower facilities. A 12-acre site with 45 touring pitches and 10 hardstandings.
Facilities: Caravan storage, spa hot tub /A
♠ ⊙ �ℱ ✕ ⓢ ⌁ ⊞ ⊓ ♿ **Services:** ⬛ ⬜ ⬛
⬤ ≟ Facilities found within 3 miles: ⅃
ℰ ⬜ ⬜

LLANGADOG SN62

Abermarlais Caravan Park

▶▶▶ 76%

SA19 9NG

☎ 01550 777868

www.ukparks.co.uk/abermarlais

Dir: *On A40 midway between Llandovery & Llandeilo, 1.5m NW of Llangadog*

* ➡ £8.50 ⇌ £8.50 ▲ £8.50

Open: 15 Mar-15 Nov (rs Nov, Dec & Mar 1 toilet block, water point no hot water), Booking advisable bank hols & 15 Jul-Aug, Last arrival 23.00hrs Last departure noon
An attractive, well-run site with a welcoming atmosphere. This part-level, part-sloping park is in a wooded valley on the edge of the Brecon Beacons National Park. A 17-acre site with 88 touring pitches and 2 hardstandings.
Facilities: Volleyball, badminton court, softball tennis net /A ♠ ⊙ ✕ ⓢ ⬛ ⊓
Services: ⊤ ⬛ ⬛ ⬜ ≟ Facilities found within 3 miles: ∪ ℰ ⬜ **Notes:** Dogs must be kept on leads, no open fires, silence from 23.00hrs-08.00hrs

NEWCASTLE EMLYN   SN34

Afon Teifi Caravan & Camping Park ▶▶▶ 74%

Pentrecagal SA38 9HT

☎ 01559 370532

email: afonteifi@btinternet.com

www.afonteifi.co.uk

Dir: *Signed off A484, 2m E of Newcastle Emlyn*

* ⊕ £13-£14 ⇌ £13-£14 ▲ £8-£13

Open: Apr-Oct (rs Nov-Mar when facilities limited, no toilet block), Booking advisable peak periods, Last arrival 23.00hrs

This secluded park is set on the banks of the River Teifi, a famous salmon and sea trout river. Family owned and run, and only 2 miles from the market town of Newcastle Emlyn. A 6-acre site with 110 touring pitches, 22 hardstandings and 10 statics.

Facilities: 15 acres of woodland, fields & walks, ball area ♣ /Λ ⋒ ⊙ ☞ ⋇ ⊙ 🖻 ⊣ 🛒 ⊓

& **Services:** ⊺ ⊘ 🖻 🛅 ⊘ 🖆 **Facilities found within 3 miles:** ∪ ⅃ 9 ⌀ 🖢 🖻 🖻

Notes: 🐾

NEWCASTLE EMLYN   SN34

Dolbryn Camping & Caravanning ▶▶▶ 78%

Capel Iwan Road SA38 9LP

☎ 01239 710683

email: dolbryn@btinternet.com

www.dolbryn.co.uk

Dir: *A484 (Carmarthan to Cardigan road). At Newcastle Emlyn (signed) turn to Capel Iwan. Follow signs*

* ⊕ £8.50-£10 ⇌ £8.50-£10 ▲ £8.50-£10

Open: Mar-Nov, Last arrival 23.30hrs Last departure 19.00hrs

A secluded park set in a peaceful valley with a stream, ponds, mature trees and an abundance of wildlife in 13 acres, that include a vineyard and plenty of nature walks. Cosy bar. A 6-acre site with 60 touring pitches.

Facilities: Fishing, children's activities ♣ /Λ ⋒ ⋇ ⊙ ⊣ 🛒 ♁ & **Services:** ⊺ 🛒 🖻 🛅 🖆

Facilities found within 3 miles: ∪ ⌀ 🖻

🖻 **Notes:** Dogs must be kept on leads, quiet after 23.30hrs 🐾

CARMARTHENSHIRE

NEWCASTLE EMLYN   SN34
Moelfryn Caravan & Camping Site
▶▶▶ 74%

Ty-Cefn Pant-y-Bwlch SA38 9JE

☎ 01559 371231 📄 01559 371231

email: moelfryn@tinyonline.co.uk

Dir: *A484 from Carmarthen towards Cynwyl Elfed. Pass Blue Bell Inn on right, 200yds take left fork onto B4333 towards Hermon. In 7m brown sign on left. Turn left, site on right*

* 🚐 £7-£11 🚙 £7-£11 ▲ £6-£10

Open: Mar-10 Jan, Booking advisable Jul-Aug, Last arrival 22.00hrs Last departure noon

A small family-run park in an elevated location overlooking the valley of the River Teifi. Pitches are level and spacious, and well screened by hedging and trees. Facilities are well maintained, and the playing field is well away from the touring area. A 3-acre site with 25 touring pitches and 13 hardstandings.

Facilities: Caravan storage 🅰 🏕 ⊙ 🏳✳ 🖾 🍖 **Services:** 🚾 Facilities found within 3 miles: ∪ ↓ ⚓ ⌁ 🍴 🖾 🖲 **Notes:** 🐾

NEWCASTLE EMLYN   SN34
Cenarth Falls Holiday Park
▶▶▶▶▶ 79%

Cenarth SA38 9JS

☎ 01239 710345 📄 01239 710344

email: enquiries@cenarth-holipark.co.uk

www.cenarth-holipark.co.uk

Dir: *Off A484 on outskirts of Cenarth towards Cardigan*

🚐 £13-£23 🚙 £13-£23 ▲ £13-£23

Open: Mar-16 Dec, Booking advisable bank hols & Jul-Aug, Last arrival 20.00hrs Last departure 11.00hrs

Close to the village of Cenarth where the famous salmon and sea trout River Teifi cascades through the Cenarth Falls Gorge. Excellent facilities, indoor pool, restaurant and bar. A 2-acre site with 30 touring pitches, 30 hardstandings and 89 statics.

Facilities: Pool table, health & leisure complex 🏊 🍴 ⚓ 🅰 🏕 ⊙ 🏳✳ ⊙ ♿ **Services:** 🍴 🍷 ⬆ 🚽 🖾 🛢 🖊 🍴 ⌁ 🖾 🖲 **Notes:** No dogs 15 Jul-2 Sep

ABERAERON SN46

Aeron Coast Caravan Park

▶▶▶ 77%

North Road SA46 0JF

☎ 01545 570349 ▤ 01545 571289

email: enquiries@aeroncoast.com

www.aeroncoast.com

Dir: *On A487 (coast road) on N edge of Aberaeron, signed. Filling station at entrance*

⊞ £12-£17 ⊟ £12-£17 ▲ £12-£17

Open: Mar-Oct, Booking advisable bank & school hols, Last arrival 23.00hrs Last departure 11.00hrs

A holiday park on the edge of the resort of Aberaeron, with access to the beach. Facilities include an outdoor pool complex and multi-activity sports. A 22-acre site with 100 touring pitches, 23 hardstandings and 200 statics.

Facilities: Indoor leisure rooms ⊛ ◕ ⋀ ▱ ⊰ ⋔ ⊙❄ ◔ ⓖ ⓹ **Services:** ⊞ ⊤ ⋃ ⊡ ⓖ ⓸ ⌀ ⥤ ⌂ **Facilities found within 3 miles:** ⌀ ◎ ⋛ ⓖ **Notes:** Families only, no motorcycles, no letting static caravans

BETTWS EVAN SN34

Pilbach Holiday Park ▶▶▶ 72%

Rhydlewis Llandysul SA44 5RT

☎ 01239 851434 ▤ 01239 851969

email: info@pilbach.com

www.pilbach.com

Dir: *S on A487, turn left onto B4333*

* ⊞ £12-£20 ⊟ £12-£20 ▲ £12-£20

Open: Mar-Oct (rs Mar-Spring BH & Oct swimming pool closed), Booking advisable Spring BH & Jul-Aug, Last arrival 22.00hrs Last departure noon

Set in secluded countryside, with two separate paddocks and pitches clearly marked in the grass, close to nearby seaside resorts. It has a heated outdoor swimming pool, and entertainment in the club two or three times a week in high season. A 15-acre site with 65 touring pitches, 10 hardstandings and 70 statics.

Facilities: Bike/skateboard parks ⊛ ◕ ⋀ ◔ ⊙ ⓟ ◔ ⊬ ⋒ **Services:** ⓸ ⊞ ⊡ ⓖ ⌂ ⥤ **Facilities found within 3 miles:** ∪ ⋛ 18 ⌀ ⋛ ⓖ ⓹

CEREDIGION

CEREDIGION/CONWY

BORTH SN68

Brynowen Holiday Park 68%

Aberystwyth SY24 5LS

☎ 01970 871366

email: gmbrynowen@park-resorts.com

www.park-resorts.com

Dir: *Signed off B4353, S of Borth*

* ⊞ £5-£26 ⇆ £5-£26 **Open:** Etr-1 Nov, Booking advisable Jul-Aug, Last arrival 19.00hrs Last departure 10.00hrs

Enjoying spectacular views across Cardigan Bay and the Cambrian Mountains, a small touring park in a large and well-equipped holiday centre. The well-run park offers a wide range of organised activities and entertainment for all the family from morning until late in the evening. A long sandy beach is a few minutes drive away. A 52-acre site with 13 touring pitches and 480 statics.

Facilities: Kids' clubs, mini ten-pin bowling

🛋 🖄 🎧 🕒 🗑 🕂 🕹 **Services:** 🍸 🍽 🗐 🖾 📵 🛏 👜 **Facilities found within 3 miles:** ∪ ↓ 18 🖾 🕏

CERRIGYDRUDION SH94

Glan Ceirw ▶▶▶ 77%

Ty Nant LL21 0RF

☎ 01490 420346 📠 01490 420346

email: glanceirwcaravanpark@yahoo.co.uk

www.ukparks.co.uk/glanceirw

Dir: *From A5 Betws-y-Coed onto unclass road 1m after Cerrig-y-Drudion. Park 0.25m on left. From Corwen for 8m, then 2nd left onto unclass road after Country Cooks*

* ⊞ £18 ⇆ £18 ▲ £12-£20

Open: Mar-Oct, Booking advisable bank hols & Jul-Sep, Last arrival 22.00hrs Last departure noon

A small riverside site in a rural location, with pleasant owners. Guests can enjoy the use of two games rooms, a bar lounge and a jacuzzi, and an amenity block. An ideal touring point for Snowdonia and North Wales. A 4.5-acre site with 15 touring pitches, 9 hardstandings and 29 statics.

Facilities: 🔦 🖄 🗆 🎧 ⊗ ✴ 🕒 🕂 🚻 🛒 **Services:** 🗐 🖾 🛏 🚼 ℓ 🕏 **Notes:** 🐾

TAL-Y-BONT SH76

Tynterfyn Touring Caravan Park

► 88%

LL32 8YX

☎ 01492 660525

Dir: *5m S of Conwy on B5106, road sign Tal-y-Bont, 1st on left*

* 🚐 £7.50 🚐 £8 ▲ £2

Open: Mar-Oct (rs (tent pitches only for 28 days in year)), Booking advisable bank hols & Jul-Aug, Last arrival 22.00hrs Last departure noon

A quiet, secluded little park set in the beautiful Conwy Valley, and run by family owners. The grounds are tended with care, and the older-style toilet facilities sparkle. There is lots of room for children and dogs to run around. A 2-acre site with 15 touring pitches and 4 hardstandings.

Facilities: ⋒ 🐾 ☉ 🅟 ☼ 🚼 **Services:** 🚫 🔒 ⌀ 🎯 🏕 🐾 🅟 🗑 **Notes:** ☺

TOWYN SH97

Ty Mawr Holiday Park 63%

Towyn Road LL22 9HG

☎ 01745 832079 📄 01745 827454

email: admin.tymawr@parkresorts.com

www.park-resorts.com

Dir: *On A548, 0.25m W of Towyn*

Open: Etr-Oct (rs Apr excluding Etr), Booking advisable at all times, Last arrival 24.00hrs Last departure 10.00hrs

A very large coastal holiday park with extensive leisure facilities including sports and recreational amenities, and club and eating outlets. The touring facilities are rather dated but clean. An 18-acre site with 400 touring pitches and 464 statics.

Facilities: Free evening entertainment 🎬 🎣 ⋒ 🐾 ☉ 🅟 ☼ ⌚ 🗑 🚼 ♿ **Services:** 🐓 🍴 🎯 🚫 🗑 🔒 ⌀ 🏛 **Facilities found within 3 miles:** ∪ 🎿 18 ◎ 🗑 🗑

CONWY

DENBIGHSHIRE

CORWEN SJ04
Llawr-Betws Farm Caravan Park
►► 70%
Near Corwen LL21 0HD
☎ 01490 460224
www.ukparks.co.uk/llawrbetws
Dir: *3m W of Corwen off A494 (Bala road)*
* 🚐 £8 🚐 £8 ▲ £6-£8
Open: Mar-Oct, Booking advisable bank hols & Jul-Aug, Last arrival 23.00hrs Last departure noon

A quiet grassy park with mature trees and gently sloping pitches. The friendly owners keep the facilities in good condition. A 12.5-acre site with 35 touring pitches and 68 statics.

Facilities: Fishing 🔦 ♨ 🐾 ⊙✳ 🕐 🚻 🎏
Services: 🖵 🚽 🗑 🔋 ⊘ 🚰 **Facilities found within 3 miles:** 🚵 18 🎣 🗑 🗑 **Notes:** ⊗

PRESTATYN SJ08
Presthaven Sands 78%
Gronant LL19 9TT
☎ 01745 856471 🖷 01745 886646
www.havenholidays.com
Dir: *A548 from Prestatyn towards Gronant. Park signed*
Open: mid Mar-Oct (rs mid Mar-May & Sep-Oct facilities may be reduced), Booking advisable school hols, Last arrival 22.00hrs Last departure noon

Set beside two miles of superb sandy beaches and dunes, this large holiday centre offers extensive leisure and sports facilities and lively entertainment for all the family. The leisure complex houses clubs, swimming pools, restaurants, shops, launderette and pub, and the touring area is separate from the much larger static section. A 130-acre site with 34 touring pitches and 672 statics.

Facilities: 📶 📶 🔦 ♨ 🗖 🏊 🐾 🌳✳ 🕐 🗑 🗑
🎏 **Services:** 🍺 🍴 🗑 🖵 🚽 🗑 🚰 🚮
Facilities found within 3 miles: 🚵 🗑 🗑

ABERSOCH   SH32

Deucoch Touring & Camping Park

▶▶▶ 72%

Sarn Bach LL53 7LD

☎ 01758 713293

Dir: *From Abersoch take Sarn Bach road, at*
x-rds turn right, site on right in 800yds

* ⊕ £18 ⌮ £18 ▲ £14-£15

Open: Mar-Oct, Booking advisable school
hols, Last arrival 22.00hrs Last departure
11.00hrs

A sheltered site with sweeping views of
Cardigan Bay and the mountains, just a mile
from Abersoch and a long sandy beach. The
facilities block is well maintained, and this
site is of special interest to watersports
enthusiasts and those touring the Llyn
Peninsula. A 5-acre site with 68 touring
pitches and 10 hardstandings.

Facilities: ✎ ⋒ ⋒ ⊙ ℱ ✳ ◔ ☷ ⎲
Services: ⊞ ⊠ **Facilities found within 3**
miles: ∪ ⅃ 18 ⚹ ⌀ ⇃ ⊠ ⍟ **Notes:** Families
only ⊜

ABERSOCH   SH32

Bryn Bach Caravan & Camping
Site ▶▶▶ 78%

Tyddyn Talgoch Uchaf Bwlchtocyn LL53 7BT

☎ 01758 712285

email: brynbach@abersochcamping.co.uk

www.abersochcamping.co.uk

Dir: *From Abersoch take Sarn Bach road for*
approx 1m, left at sign for Bwlchtocyn. Site
approx 1m on left

* ⊕ £14-£17 ⌮ £13-£17 ▲ £12-£17

Open: Mar-Oct, Booking advisable at all
times, Last arrival 22.00hrs Last departure
11.00hrs

This park overlooks Abersoch Bay, with sea
views towards the Snowdonia mountain
range. Pitches in sheltered paddocks. A 4-
acre site with 30 touring pitches and 2 statics.

Facilities: Private shortcut to beach, boat
storage ⋒ ⋒ ⊙ ✳ ☷ ⋒ ⎲ **Services:** ⎗ ⊞
⊠ **Facilities found within 3 miles:** ∪ ⅃
18 ⚹ ⌀ ⇃ ⊠ ⍟ **Notes:** Families & couples
only ⊜

GWYNEDD

GWYNEDD

BALA · SH93

Tytandderwen Caravan Park

▶▶▶ 73%

LL23 7EP

☎ 01678 520273 📄 01678 521393

Dir: *From B4401 take B4391 then unclass road signed Tytandderwen*

* 🚐 £8 🚏 £8 ▲ £8

Open: Mar-Oct, Booking advisable peak periods

A secluded family park with superb views, and fishing on site in the River Dee. A large modern facilities block includes laundry, dishwashing and disabled unit, and this is an ideal base for watersports, walking and climbing. An 8-acre site with 55 touring pitches and 60 statics.

Facilities: ◣ ⚠ ℝ ☉ 𝒫 ✖ ◯ 🛲 ♿

Services: 🔌 🗑 🏠 🥤 🎣 🚽 **Facilities found within 3 miles:** 🚣 9 🏇 🗑 🗑

Notes: 🐾

BALA · SH83

Glanllyn Lakeside Caravan & Camping Park ▶▶▶ 91%

Llanuwchllyn LL23 7ST

☎ 01678 540227

email: info@glanllyn.com

www.glanllyn.com

Dir: *2.5m SW of Bala on A494*

* 🚐 £12-£18 🚏 £12-£18 ▲ £12-£16

Open: mid Mar-mid Oct, Booking advisable bank hols, Last arrival 22.00hrs Last departure 14.00hrs

A spacious park set in parkland on the south shore of Bala Lake. An ideal base for walking, or watersports on the lake; equipment can be hired nearby. The modern toilet facilities are excellent. A 16-acre site with 100 touring pitches and 19 hardstandings.

Facilities: Baby changing area ⚠ ℝ ☉ 𝒫 ✖ ◯ 🗑 🛒 ♿ **Services:** 🎬 ↻ 🔌 🗑 🏠 🥤 🚽

Facilities found within 3 miles: 🚣 18 🏇 🗑 🗑

Notes: No fires or disposable BBQs

BARMOUTH · SH61

Hendre Mynach Touring Caravan & Camping Park ▶▶▶▶ 79%

Llanaber Road LL42 1YR

☎ 01341 280262 📠 01341 280586

email: mynach@lineone.net

www.hendremynach.co.uk

Dir: *0.75m N of Barmouth on A496*

* 🚐 £10-£24 🚃 £10-£21 ▲ £10-£20

Open: Mar-9 Jan (rs Nov-Etr shop closed), Booking advisable bank hols & Jul-Aug, Last arrival 22.00hrs Last departure noon

A lovely site with immaculate facilities and almost direct access to beach. Caravanners should not be put off by the steep descent as park staff are always on hand if needed. Pitches have TV and satellite hook-up as well as water and electricity. A 10-acre site with 240 touring pitches and 50 hardstandings.

Facilities: 50 TV hook ups 🕭 🖡 ⊙ 🅿 ☀ ⓒ 🖻 🛏 ﴾ **Services:** 🐛 🅣 🕁 🖭 🖳 🛢 🗋 🧀 🚮

Facilities found within 3 miles: ∪ 🖉 🖻 🖻

BARMOUTH · SH51

Trawsdir Touring & Camping Park ▶▶▶ 83%

Caerddaniel Caravan Park LL42 1RR

☎ 01341 280999 📠 01341 280740

email: enquiries@barmouthholidays.co.uk

www.barmouthholidays.co.uk

Dir: *3m N of Barmouth on A496, just past Wayside pub on right*

* 🚐 £20-£25 🚃 £20-£25 ▲ £12-£19

Open: Mar-Oct, Booking advisable Etr, Whitsun & Jul-Aug, Last arrival 21.00hrs Last departure noon

A good quality park on a sheep farm with sea and hill views. Modern facilities are clean. Tents and caravans have their own areas divided by dry-stone walls. A 15-acre site with 70 touring pitches and 40 hardstandings.

Facilities: Milk/bread etc available from reception 🕭 🖡 ⊙ 🅿 ☀ ⓒ 🖻 🛏 ﴾ **Services:** 🕁 🖭 🛢 🗋 🧀 🚆 **Facilities found within 3 miles:** ∪ 🖉 🖻 🖻 **Notes:** Families & couples only

GWYNEDD

GWYNEDD

BETWS GARMON   SH55

Bryn Gloch Caravan & Camping Park ►►►► 78%

Caernarfon LL54 7YY

☎ 01286 650216 🖹 01286 650591

email: eurig@bryngloch.co.uk

www.bryngloch.co.uk

Dir: *On A4085, 7m SE of Caernarfon*

* 🚐 £14-£21 🚗 £14-£21 ▲ £14-£19

Open: Open All Year Booking advisable school & bank hols, Last arrival 23.00hrs Last departure 17.00hrs

An excellent family-run site with modern facilities, and all level pitches. The park offers bustling holiday atmosphere and peaceful natural surroundings. There are walks and a stream. A 12-acre site with 160 touring pitches, 40 hardstandings and 40 statics.

Facilities: Family bathroom, mother & baby room ◀ ⌂ ⌷ ⌸ ⟲ ⊙ 🅿 ✕ ⊙ 🅢 ㎮ ㅐ ⚲ ⅋

Services: ⊤ ⅃ ⊕ 🅢 🅰 ⌀ 🚂 ⛟ Facilities found within 3 miles: ∪ ⌇ 18 ⅄ ⋏ ⌓ ◎ 🖰 🖸

CAERNARFON   SH46

Riverside Camping ►►► 79%

Seiont Nurseries Pont Rug LL55 2BB

☎ 01286 678781 🖹 01286 677223

email: brenda@riversidecamping.co.uk

www.riversidecamping.co.uk

Dir: *2m from Caernarfon on right of A4086 towards Llanberis, also signed Seiont Nurseries*

* 🚐 £12-£18 🚗 £12-£15 ▲ £12-£15

Open: Etr-end Oct, Booking advisable May-Aug & bank hols, Last arrival anytime Last departure noon

Set in the grounds of a large garden centre beside the small River Seiont, this park has very good facilities. A 4.5-acre site with 60 touring pitches and 4 hardstandings.

Facilities: Family shower room & baby changing facilities ⌂ ⌷ ⊙ 🅿 ✕ ㎮ ㅐ ⚲

Services: ⌷ 🍴 ⊕ 🅢 🖮 Facilities found within 3 miles: ∪ ⌇ 18 ⅄ ⌓ ⋧ 🖰 🖸

Notes: No fires, no loud music, dogs must be kept on leads ⊜

CAERNARFON   SH46

**Ty'n yr Onnen Mountain Farm
Caravan & Camping** ►►► 71%

Waunfawr LL55 4AX

☎ 01286 650281 📠 01286 650043

email: tynronnen.farm@btconnect.com

Dir: *At Waunfawr on A4085, onto unclass
road opposite church. Site signed*

* 🚐 £14-£17 🚃 £14-£17 ▲ £14-£17

Open: Etr bank hol-Oct (rs Etr & May Day
bank hol open if weather permitting), Booking
advisable spring bank hol & Jul-Aug, Last
arrival 21.00hrs Last departure 10.00hrs
A gently-sloping site on a 200-acre sheep
farm, set in magnificent surroundings with
mountain views. This secluded park is well
equipped, with quality toilet facilities. Access
is by single track unclassified road. A 4-acre
site with 20 touring pitches and 4 statics.

Facilities: Fishing & nature park 🔌 ▲ ⊡ 📡
☉ 🅿 ⚡ 🕐 🛉 🚻 🚮 🛒 🛆 **Services:** 🚽 🛢 🛒
🔓 🖉 🎣 **Facilities found within 3 miles:**
∪ ⚓ 18 ⅃ 🎣 🎿 🛆 🛆 **Notes:** No music after
22.00hrs

CRICCIETH   SH53

Eisteddfa ►►►► 80%

Eisteddfa Lodge Pentrefelin LL52 0PT

☎ 01766 522696

email: eisteddfa@criccieth.co.uk

www.eisteddfapark.co.uk

Dir: *From Porthmadog take A497 towards
Criccieth. After approx 3.5m, through
Pentrefelin, park signed 1st right after Plas
Gwyn Nursing Home*

* 🚐 £10.60-£14.80 🚃 £10.60-£14.80
▲ £8.80-£12.95

Open: Mar-Oct, Booking advisable bank &
school hols, Last arrival 22.30hrs Last
departure 11.00hrs
A quiet park on elevated ground, with views of
Cardigan Bay. There's a field and play area,
and woodland walks. An 11-acre site with 100
touring pitches and 17 hardstandings.

Facilities: Football pitch, baby bath 🔌 ▲ 📡
☉ 🅿 ⚡ 🕐 🛉 🚻 🚮 🛒 🛆 **Services:** 🚽 🔓 🖉 🎣
Facilities found within 3 miles: ∪ ⅃ 18
🎿 🎣 ◎ 🎿 🛆 🛆 **Notes:** 🐾

GWYNEDD

GWYNEDD

DINAS DINLLE — SH45
Dinlle Caravan Park ►►►► 78%

Caernarfon LL54 5TW

☎ 01286 830324 📠 01286 831526

email: enq@thornleyleisure.co.uk

www.thornleyleisure.co.uk

Dir: *Turn right off A499 at sign for Caernarfon Airport. 2m W of Dinas Dinlle coast*

* ⬠ £6.50-£17 ⬡ £6.50-£17 ▲ £6.50-£17

Open: May-Aug (rs Mar-Apr & Sep-Nov club & swimming pool restricted hours), Booking advisable spring bank hol & Jul-Aug, Last arrival 23.00hrs Last departure noon

A well-kept grassy site, adjacent to sandy beach, with views to Snowdonia. There's a lounge bar, family room and adventure playground. Beach road access to golf club, a nature reserve, and to Air World at Caernarfon Airport. A 20-acre site with 175 touring pitches, 20 hardstandings and 167 statics.

Facilities: ⬠ ◉ ⋒ ⋒ ⊙ ⊕ ✗ ⚲ ⊙ ⬢

Services: ⬠ ⬢ ⬡ ⬠ ⬢ 🍴 ⬡ ⬠ 🗑 **Facilities found within 3 miles:** ∪ ⌒ 🗐

LLANDWROG — SH45
White Tower Caravan Park
►►►► 75%

Caernarfon LL54 5UH

☎ 01286 830649 📠 01286 830649

email: whitetower@supanet.com

www.whitetower.supanet.com

Dir: *1.5m from village along Tai'r Eglwys road. From Caernarfon take A487 Porthmadog road. Cross rdbt, take 1st right. Park 3m on right*

⬠ £16-£24 ⬡ £16-£24 ▲ £16-£24

Open: 1 Mar-10 Jan (rs Mar-mid May & Sep-Oct bar open wknds only), Booking advisable bank hols & Jul-Aug, Last arrival 23.00hrs Last departure noon

This park is 2 miles from the beach. Toilet block has key access; hard pitches have water and electricity. A 6-acre site with 104 touring pitches, 80 hardstandings and 54 statics.

Facilities: ⬠ ◉ ⋒ ⬜ ⋒ ⊙ ⊕ ✗ ⚲ ⊙ ⬢

Services: ⬠ 🍴 ⬡ ⬠ ⬢ 🗑 🛢 ⬡ **Facilities found within 3 miles:** ∪ ⬡ 18 ⚲ ⌒ 🗐 ⬢
🗐

PORTHMADOG SH53

Greenacres 77%

Black Rock Sands

Morfa Bychan LL49 9YF

☎ 01766 512781 ≡ 01766 512084

www.havenholidays.com

Dir: *After high street, turn between Woolworths & post office towards Black Rock Sands. 2m park entrance on left*

Open: mid Mar-Oct (rs mid Mar-May & Sep-Oct some facilities may be reduced), Booking advisable school hols, Last arrival 18.00hrs Last departure 10.00hrs

A quality holiday park on level ground just a short walk from Black Rock Sands. All touring pitches are on hardstandings surrounded by grass. Entertainment, clubs, indoor and outdoor sports, pubs, and shows. A 121-acre site with 48 touring pitches and 370 statics.

Facilities: 🌳 🔍 🕊 🏍 ⊙ 🅿 🕒 🛁 🚻 🚿

Services: 🍴 🔌 🐕 🗑 🛢 🖉 ⚙ Facilities found within 3 miles: ✦ 18 ⌀ ◎ ⚓ 🗑 🛢

Notes: Dogs not allowed during school holidays

PWLLHELI SH43

Abererch Sands Holiday Centre

▶▶▶ 75%

LL53 6PJ

☎ 01758 612327 ≡ 01758 701556

email: enquiries@abererch-sands.co.uk

www.abererch-sands.co.uk

Dir: *On A497 (Porthmadog-Pwllheli road), 1m from Pwllheli*

✱ 🚐 £18-£20 🚃 £16-£18 ⏶ £17.50-£19.50

Open: Mar-Oct, Booking advisable school & bank hols, Last arrival 21.00hrs Last departure 21.00hrs

Glorious views of Snowdonia and Cardigan Bay from this very secure, family-run site, adjacent to a long sandy beach. Indoor pool, snooker room, pool room, fitness centre and play area. An 85-acre site with 70 touring pitches, 70 hardstandings and 90 statics.

Facilities: 🌳 🔍 🕊 🏍 ⊙ 🅿 🕒 🛁 🚻 🛒 🚿

Services: 🖵 ♨ 🐕 🗑 🛢 🖉 🍴 Facilities found within 3 miles: ∪ ✦ 18 ⚓ 🖉 ⚓ 🗑 🛢

GWYNEDD

GWYNEDD/ISLE OF ANGLESEY

TYWYN   SH60

Ynysymaengwyn Caravan Park

►►► 79%

LL36 9RY

☎ 01654 710684 📠 01654 710684

email: rita@ynysy.co.uk

www.ynysmaengwyn.co.uk

Dir: *On A493, 1m N of Tywyn, towards
Dolgellau*

* 🚐 £10–£13 🚎 £10–£13 ▲ £8–£13

Open: Etr or Apr-Oct, Booking advisable Jul-
Aug, Last arrival 23.00hrs Last departure
noon

A lovely park set in the wooded grounds of a
former manor house, with woodland and river
walks, fishing and a sandy beach nearby. The
amenity block is clean and well kept, and this
smart park is ideal for families. A 4-acre site
with 80 touring pitches and 115 statics.

Facilities: ⚘🖲🌣🏕🍴🛝🐾🚻🏃♿

Services: 🔌🛢🚽🤵🛒 Facilities found
within 3 miles: ∪🎣18🎯◉⛳🚲🖲🛒

Notes: Dogs must be kept on leads at all
times 🐕

DULAS   SH48

Tyddyn Isaf Caravan Park

►►►► 77%

Lligwy Bay Anglesey LL70 9PQ

☎ 01248 410203 📠 01248 410667

email: enquiries@tyddynisaf.demon.co.uk

www.tyddynisaf.demon.co.uk

Dir: *Take A5025 through Benllech to Moelfre
rdbt, left towards Amlwch to Brynrefail village.
Turn right opposite craft shop. Park 0.5m
down lane on right*

* 🚐 £18–£23 🚎 £18–£23 ▲ £15–£23

Open: Mar-Oct (rs Mar-Jul & Sep-Oct bar &
shop opening limited), Booking advisable
May bank hol & Jun-Aug, Last arrival
22.00hrs Last departure 11.00hrs

A 16-acre site with 80 touring pitches, 20
hardstandings and 56 statics.

Facilities: Baby changing unit ⚘🖲🌣🏕☺
🖲🍴🕐🚽🐾🚻♿ **Services:** 🔌🍴🛒 🖵
🔌🛢🚽🤵🚰🛒 **Facilities found within 3
miles:** ∪🎣18🎿🎯🛒 **Notes:** Dogs must
be kept on leads, no groups 🐕

LLANBEDRGOCH SH58

Ty Newydd Leisure Park ▶▶▶ 76%

LL76 8TZ

☎ 01248 450677 📠 01248 450711

email: mike@tynewydd.com

www.tynewydd.com

Dir: *A5025 from Brittania Bridge. Through Pentraeth, bear left at layby. Site 0.75m on right*

* 🚐 £10–£27 🚎 £10–£27 ▲ £10–£27

Open: Whit-mid Sep (rs Mar-Whit & mid Sep-Oct club/shop wknds only, outdoor pool closed), Booking advisable Etr, Whit & Jul-Aug, Last arrival 23.30hrs Last departure 10.00hrs

A low-density park. Many facilities, including heated outdoor pool, club with restaurant, and a playground. A 4-acre site with 48 touring pitches, 15 hardstandings and 62 statics.

Facilities: Sauna & jacuzzi 🏖 🍴 🔌 🕭 🛒 ⊙ 🅿 ✕ 🕚 🗴 🚻 🚽 ⏶ **Services:** 🏊 🍴 🍺 📶 🖵 🗑 🗄 🛢 🧺 ⛟ **Facilities found within 3 miles:** ∪ ♨ 9 🎣 ⛵ 🗑 🗄

MARIAN-GLAS SH48

Home Farm Caravan Park

▶▶▶▶ 92%

LL73 8PH

☎ 01248 410614 📠 01248 410900

email: enq@homefarm-anglesey.co.uk

www.homefarm-anglesey.co.uk

Dir: *on A5025, 2m N of Benllech. Park 300mtrs beyond church*

* 🚐 £11.25–£23.75 🚎 £11.25–£23.75 ▲ £11.25–£19.50

Open: Apr-Oct, Booking advisable bank hols, Last arrival 21.00hrs Last departure noon

A first class park in an elevated and secluded position sheltered by trees. The peaceful rural setting affords views of farmland, the sea, and mountains. There is a modern toilet block and excellent play facilities for children, both indoors and out. A 6-acre site with 98 touring pitches, 21 hardstandings and 84 statics.

Facilities: Indoor adventure playground 🔌 ⏶ 🗆 🔌 🕭 ⊙ 🅿 ✕ 🕚 🗴 🚻 🚽 ⏶ **Services:** 🖵 ⏚ 🍺 🗑 🛢 🧺 ⛟ **Facilities found within 3 miles:** ∪ ♨ 18 🎣 ⛵ 🗑 🗄

ISLE OF ANGLESEY

ISLE OF ANGLESEY

PENTRAETH   SH57

Rhos Caravan Park ►►► 77%

Rhos Farm LL75 8DZ

☎ 01248 450214 📄 01248 450214

Dir: *Site on left of A5025, 1m N of Pentraeth*

🚐 £10-£12 🚎 £10-£12 ▲ £10-£12

Open: Etr-Oct (rs Mar shop restricted),
Booking advisable Spring bank hol & Jul-
Aug, Last arrival 22.00hrs Last departure
16.00hrs

A warm welcome awaits families at this
spacious park on level, grassy ground with
easy access to the main road to Amlwch. This
200-acre working farm has a games room,
two play areas and farm animals to keep
children amused, with good beaches, pubs,
restaurants and shops nearby. The two toilet
blocks are kept to a good standard by
enthusiastic owners, who are constantly
improving the facilities. A 15-acre site with
98 touring pitches and 66 statics.

Facilities: 🛆 🅿 ⊙ ⚡ 🖎 🔭 🍔 **Services:** 🔟
🔌 🖬 🛆 🍴 🍴 **Facilities found within 3
miles:** ∪ 🎣 9 ⅞ 🖉 🔲 🔲

RHOSNEIGR   SH37

Ty Hen ►►► 77%

Station Road LL64 5QZ

☎ 01407 810331 📄 01407 810331

email: bernardtyhen@hotmail.com

www.tyhen.com

Dir: *A55 across Anglesey. At exit 5 follow
signs to Rhosneigr, at clock turn right.
Entrance adjacent to Rhosneigr railway station*

🚐 £17-£19 🚎 £17-£19 **Open:** mid Mar-Oct,
Booking advisable all year, Last arrival
21.00hrs Last departure noon

Attractive seaside position near a large fishing
lake and riding stables, in lovely countryside.
A smart toilet block offers a welcome amenity
at this popular family park. A 7.5-acre site
with 38 touring pitches, 5 hardstandings and
42 statics.

Facilities: Fishing, family room 🚿 🔍 🛆 🅿
⊙ 🅿 ⚡ 🕘 🔭 ⅃ & **Services:** 🔌 🖬 🛆 🍴 🖬 & 18
🖉 🖫 **Notes:** 1 motor vehicle per pitch, dogs
on leads, children in tents/tourers/statics by
22.00hrs

EAST WILLIAMSTON SN00

Masterland Farm Touring Caravan Park ►►► 70%

Broadmoor SA68 0RH

☎ 01834 813298 🖹 01834 814408

email: bonsermasterland@aol.com

www.ukparks.co.uk/masterland

Dir: *Exit A4777 at Broadmoor onto B4586. Site 400yds on right*

🚐 £9.50-£18 🚏 £9.50-£18 ▲ £9.50-£18 (rs off season bar & restaurant open at wknds only), Last arrival 21.00hrs Last departure 10.30hrs

A small site on a working farm set on edge of the Pembrokeshire Coast National Park. An ideal centre for touring the area. Only 4 miles from the beaches at Tenby. Restaurant and bar open during high season (evenings only) and most weekends. A 2.5-acre site with 38 touring pitches and 23 hardstandings.

Facilities: Library ♦ ⚠ ➊ ⚫ ☺ ☞ ※ 🖾 ✠ 🖳
🚌 **Services:** ⚏ ☎ 🖳 🖾 🛢 ⊘ 🖾 **Facilities found within 3 miles:** ∪ ✐ ≩ 🖾 🖾

Notes: No bicycles ⊛

FISHGUARD SM93

Fishguard Bay Caravan & Camping Park ►►► 77%

Garn Gelli SA65 9ET

☎ 01348 811415 🖹 01348 811425

email: enquiries@fishguardbay.com

www.fishguardbay.com

Dir: *Take A487 (Fishguard-Cardigan road). Park (signed) 3m from Fishguard, on left*

* 🚐 £12-£14 🚏 £12-£14 ▲ £11-£17

Open: Mar-9 Jan, Booking advisable Jul-Aug, Last arrival after noon Last departure noon

Set high up on cliffs with outstanding views of Fishguard Bay, and the Pembrokeshire Coastal Path running right through the centre. The park is extremely well kept, with three good toilet blocks, a common room with TV, a lounge/library, decent laundry, and well-stocked shop. A 5-acre site with 50 touring pitches, 4 hardstandings and 50 statics.

Facilities: ♦ ⚠ ☐ ➊ ⚫ ☺ ☞ ※ ⊕ 🖾
Services: ⊤ 🖳 🖾 🛢 ⊘ 🖾 **Facilities found within 3 miles:** ∪ ≩ ✐ 🖾 🖾

PEMBROKESHIRE

PEMBROKESHIRE

FISHGUARD SM93
Gwaun Vale Touring Park ▶▶▶ 74%

Llanychaer SA65 9TA

☎ 01348 874698

email: margaret.harries@talk21.com

Dir: *From Fishguard take B4313. Site 1.5m on right*

Open: Apr-Oct, Booking advisable Jul-Aug, Last arrival anytime Last departure noon Located at the opening of the beautiful Gwaun Valley, this well-kept park is set on the hillside with pitches tiered on two levels. There are lovely views of the surrounding countryside, and good facilities. A 1.6-acre site with 29 touring pitches and 5 hardstandings.

Facilities: Guidebooks available ♠ ♠ ☺ ♺ ✻ ☉ 🏧 🍴 🛒 🏕 **Services:** 🕚 🖴 🍷 🗑 ✉ **Facilities found within 3 miles:** ∪ ≯ ☀ ✐ 🗑 🏧 **Notes:** Dogs must be kept on leads ✉

HAVERFORDWEST SM81
Nolton Cross Caravan Park ▶▶ 78%

Nolton SA62 3NP

☎ 01437 710701 ▤ 01437 710329

email: noltoncross@nolton.fsnet.co.uk

www.noltoncross-holidays.co.uk

Dir: *1m off A487 (Haverfordwest to St David's road) at Simpson Cross*

* 🚐 £7-£11 🚛 £7-£11 ▲ £7-£11

Open: Mar-Dec, Booking advisable high season, Last arrival 22.00hrs Last departure noon

High grassy banks surround the touring area of this park next to the owners' working farm. It is located on open ground above the sea and St Bride's Bay which are both 1.5m away, and there is a coarse fishing lake close by. A 4-acre site with 15 touring pitches and 30 statics.

Facilities: ♠ ♠ ☺ ✻ ☉ 🏧 🍴 🛒 **Services:** 🖴 🗑 🍷 ✉ 🛒 ➙ **Facilities found within 3 miles:** ∪ ✐ ≋ 🗑

TAVERNSPITE SN11

Pantglas Farm Caravan Park

▶▶▶ 76%

Whitland SA34 0NS

☎ 01834 831618 📠 01834 831193

email: neil.brook@btinternet.com

www.pantglasfarm.com

Dir: *Leave A477 to Tenby at Red Roses x-roads onto B4314 to Tavernspite. Take middle road at village pumps. Site 0.5m on left*

* 🚐 £10.25-£12.50 🚙 £10.25-£12.50 ▲ £6-£11

Open: Etr-17 Oct, Booking advisable Spring bank hol & Jul-Aug, Last arrival 23.00hrs Last departure 10.30hrs

A rural site with pitches in three enclosures. There is an activity play area, indoor games room, and a licensed bar. A 10-acre site with 86 touring pitches and 3 hardstandings.

Facilities: Year round caravan weekly storage 🔌 🏕 🐕 ⊕✕ 🕒 🍴 🚻 🔥 **Services:** 🔌 🚐 🔋 🛢 ⌀ 🚰 **Facilities found within 3 miles:** ∪ ℘ 🔋 🛢 **Notes:** Children must be supervised/controlled at all times 🐕

TENBY SN10

Kiln Park
Holiday Centre 77%

Marsh Road SA70 7RB

☎ 01834 844121 📠 01834 845387

www.havenholidays.com

Dir: *Follow A477/A478 to Tenby for 6m, then follow signs to Penally, park 0.5m on left*

Open: mid Mar-Oct (rs mid Mar-May & Sep-Oct some facilities may be reduced), Booking advisable school hols, Last arrival 22.00hrs Last departure 10.00hrs

A large holiday complex complete with leisure and sports facilities, and lots of entertainment. There are bars and cafés, and plenty of security. The well-equipped toilet block is very clean. A 103-acre site with 240 touring pitches and 620 statics.

Facilities: Entertainment complex, bowling & putting green 🏊 🏊 🔌 🏕 🏠 🕒 🐕 ⊕ ℘✕ 🕒 🛢 🔥 🚻 🚰 🍴 **Services:** 🔌 🍴 🚐 🛢 **⛪ Facilities found within 3 miles:** ∪ 🎿 18 🐟 ℘ ◎ 🛥 🔋 🛢

Notes: No dogs Jul & Aug

PEMBROKESHIRE

TENBY SN10
Well Park Caravan & Camping Site
►►►► 73%
SA70 8TL
☎ 01834 842179 🖹 01834 842179
email: enquiries@wellparkcaravans.co.uk
www.wellparkcaravans.co.uk
Dir: *Off A478 on right 1.5m before Tenby*
* ⊞ £10-£22 ⇔ £10-£22 ▲ £10-£20
Open: Mar-Oct (rs Mar-mid Jun & mid Sep-Oct bar, launderette, baby room may be closed), Booking advisable Spring BH & Jul-Aug, Last arrival 22.00hrs Last departure 11.00hrs

The amenities at this attractive park include launderette, games room, and enclosed play area. A 10-acre site with 100 touring pitches, 14 hardstandings and 42 statics.

Facilities: TV hookups ◀ ⚠ ▢ ♠ ⊙ � ✳ ⓈⒺ ⊟ ᕦ **Services:** 🛢 ⍩ 🔧 🛢 🛢 ⍾ ⌀ ᴟ 🛒 **Facilities found within 3 miles:** ∪ ♨ 18 ⳨ ℐ ◎ ⌘ Ⓢ Ⓖ **Notes:** Family parties only ⊜

TENBY SN10
Wood Park Caravans ►►► 74%
New Hedges SA70 8TL
☎ 0845 129 8314
email: info@woodpark.co.uk
www.woodpark.co.uk
Dir: *At rdbt 2m N of Tenby follow A478 towards Tenby, then take 2nd right & right again*
* ⊞ £10-£19.50 ⇔ £10-£19.50 ▲ £9-£16
Open: Spring BH-Sep (rs Etr-Spring BH & Sep-Oct bar & launderette may not open), Booking advisable Spring BH & Jul-Aug, Last arrival 22.00hrs Last departure 10.00hrs

This peaceful site nestles in countryside a 15-minute walk away from Waterwynch Bay. The slightly sloping touring area is partly divided by shrubs into three paddocks. A 10-acre site with 60 touring pitches and 90 statics.

Facilities: ◀ ⚠ ♠ ⊙ ℙ ✳ Ⓔ ᕦ **Services:** 🛢 🛢 🛢 ⌀ 🛒 **Facilities found within 3 miles:** ∪ ♨ 18 ⳨ ℐ ⌘ Ⓢ Ⓖ ⊗ **Notes:** Only 1 car per unit, only small dogs accepted, no dogs Jul-Aug & bank hols ⊜

TENBY SN00

Trefalun ►►►► 77%

Devonshire Drive St Florence SA70 8RD

☎ 01646 651514 📠 01646 651746

email: trefalun@aol.com

www.trefalunpark.co.uk

Dir: *1.5m NW of St Florence & 0.5m N of B4318*

* 🚐 £11-£19 🚌 £11-£19 ⛺ £9.50-£16.50

Open: Etr-Oct, Booking advisable bank hols & Jul-Aug, Last arrival 20.00hrs Last departure noon

Set within 12 acres of sheltered, well-kept grounds, this country park offers level grass pitches. Activities available at the nearby Heatherton Country Sports Park, including go-karting, indoor bowls, golf and bumper boating. A 7-acre site with 90 touring pitches, 29 hardstandings and 10 statics.

Facilities: 🛝 🏃 ⊙ 🚿 ✻ ☏ 🐕 ♿ **Services:** [T] 🚽 🧼 🛢 🍃 🧊 🛒 **Facilities found within 3 miles:** 🐴 ⛳ 18 🎣 🏄 🎯 🚤 🧼 [$]

BRECON SO02

Brynich Caravan Park ►►►► 88%

Brynich LD3 7SH

☎ 01874 623325 📠 01874 623325

email: holidays@brynich.co.uk

www.brynich.co.uk

Dir: *2km E of Brecon on A470, 200mtrs from junct with A40*

* 🚐 £13-£18 🚌 £13-£18 ⛺ £8-£13

Open: 24 Mar-28 Oct, Booking advisable bank & school hols, wknds Jun-Sep, Last arrival 20.00hrs Last departure noon

Attractive well-managed park. Family facilities include toddlers' play area, play-barn, field and adventure playground. A 20-acre site with 130 touring pitches and 35 hardstandings.

Facilities: Off licence 🛝 🏃 ⊙ 🚿 ✻ ☏ [$] 🐕 🪑 ♿ **Services:** 🍴 [T] 🚰 🚽 🧼 🛢 🍃 🧊 **Facilities found within 3 miles:** 🐴 ⛳ 18 🎣 🏄 🚤 🧼 [$] **Notes:** No rollerskates, skateboards or motorized scooters, only environmentally friendly ground sheets

POWYS

BRECON SO02
Bishops Meadow Caravan Park
▶▶▶▶ 74%
Bishops Meadow Hay Road LD3 9SW
☎ 01874 610000 📄 01874 614922
email: enquiries@bishops-meadow.co.uk
Dir: *From A470 (just N of Brecon) take B4602. Site on right*
* 🚐 £10–£15 🚎 £10–£15 ⛺ £6–£12
Open: Mar-Oct, Booking advisable bank hols
A family site with most pitches enjoying views of the Brecon Beacons. The site has an outdoor swimming pool. Next door to the park is an all day restaurant with a lounge bar open in the evenings. Facilities include two good quality amenity blocks. A 3.5-acre site with 82 touring pitches and 24 hardstandings.
Facilities: 🚿 🔌 ⚠ 🏪 ⊙❋ 🕒 🗑 🐕 ♿
Services: 🚰 🍽 🛒 🚽 🔌 🛁 🧴 ⛽ 🚮
Facilities found within 3 miles: ∪ ⚓ 18 🎣 ✐ 🗑 🏧

BRECON SO02
Pencelli Castle Caravan & Camping Park ▶▶▶▶ 92%
Pencelli LD3 7LX
☎ 01874 665451
email: aa@pencelli-castle.co.uk
www.pencelli-castle.co.uk
Dir: *Turn off A40 2m E of Brecon onto B4558, follow signs to Pencelli*
* 🚐 £17–£20 🚎 £17–£20 ⛺ £14–£20
Open: 29 Dec-2 Dec, Booking advisable bank & school hols, Last arrival 22.00hrs Last departure noon
This charming park is in the heart of Brecon Beacons National Park, bordered by the canal. Heated toilets with en suite cubicles, drying room, laundry and shop. A 10-acre site with 80 touring pitches and 40 hardstandings.
Facilities: Bike hire, Wi-fi & internet access ⚠ 🏪 ⊙ ℗❋ 🕒 🗑 🐕 ♿ **Services:** 🚽 🛁 🔌 🗑 🛁 🧴 ⛽ **Facilities found within 3 miles:** ∪ 🎣 ✐ ⊗ **Notes:** Assist dogs only permitted, no radios or music

CHURCH STOKE S029

Mellington Hall Caravan Park

▶▶▶ 77%

Mellington SY15 6HX

☎ 01588 620011 🖷 01588 620853

email: info@mellingtonhallcaravanpark.co.uk

www.mellingtonhallcaravanpark.co.uk

Dir: *Leave A489 1.5m W of Churchstoke turn onto B4385 to Mellington*

* 🚐 £15-£17.50 🚙 £15-£17.50

Open: Open All Year Booking advisable BHs, Last arrival 20.00hrs

A small touring park in grounds of Mellington Hall Hotel, with its attractive bistro. The 270 acres of park and farmland guarantee peace. Offa's Dyke footpath runs through the grounds, and this park is ideal for walking, cycling and fishing. A 4-acre site with 40 touring pitches, 40 hardstandings and 95 statics.

Facilities: Hiking maps ⛺ 🚿 ⊙ 🚰 ☎ 🐕 ⛩ ♿ **Services:** 🍴 🍷 🚐 🧺 🔒 **Facilities found within 3 miles:** ∪ ⛳ 🧺 $

Notes: 🚭

LLANGORS S012

Lakeside Caravan Park ▶▶▶ 72%

Brecon LD3 7TR

☎ 01874 658226 🖷 01874 658430

email: holidays@lakeside.zx3.net

www.lakeside-holidays.net

Dir: *Exit A40 at Bwlch onto B4560 towards Talgarth. Site signed towards lake in Llangors centre*

* 🚐 £8.50-£10.50 🚙 £8.50-£10.50

⛺ £8.50-£10.50

Open: Jun-Sep (rs Mar-May & Oct clubhouse, restaurant, shop limited), Booking advisable Etr, May week, summer school hols, Last arrival 21.30hrs Last departure 10.00hrs

Next to Llangors common and lake, this park has launching and mooring facilities, shop, clubhouse/bar and café. Boats and windsurf equipment can be hired on site. A 2-acre site with 40 touring pitches and 72 statics.

Facilities: Bike hire, windsurfing, fishing from boats 🔍 ⛺ 🚿 ⊙ 🚰 ✲ ☎ $ 🐕 🍖 ⛩ **Services:** ☕ 🍷 [T] 🚐 🧺 🔒 🌿 🛒 **Facilities found within 3 miles:** ∪ 🏄 ⛳ 🏄 🧺 $

POWYS

POWYS/SWANSEA

MIDDLETOWN SJ21

Bank Farm Caravan Park ▶▶▶ 76%

Welshpool SY21 8EJ

☎ 01938 570526

email: gill@bankfarmcaravans.fsnet.co.uk

www.bankfarmcaravans.co.uk

Dir: *13m W of Shrewsbury, 5m E of Welshpool on A458*

* 🚐 £12 🚓 £10 ▲ £8

Open: Mar-Oct, Booking advisable BHs, Last arrival 20.00hrs

An attractive park on a small farm, maintained to a high standard. There are two touring areas, one on either side of the A458, and each with its own amenity block, and immediate access to hills, mountains and woodland. A pub serving good food, and a large play area are nearby. A 2-acre site with 40 touring pitches and 33 statics.

Facilities: Coarse fishing pool, jacuzzi, snooker room 🔌 🅰 🏠 ⊙ ❄ 🕔 🛒 🎌 🚻 &

Services: 🔌 🏠 🛒 **Facilities found within 3 miles:** ⌁ 18 ⌀ ⓢ **Notes:** 🔞

RHOSSILI SS48

Pitton Cross Caravan & Camping Park ▶▶▶ 74%

SA3 1PH

☎ 01792 390593 📠 01792 391010

email: enquiries@pittoncross.co.uk

www.pittoncross.co.uk

Dir: *2m W of Scurlage on B4247*

* 🚐 £12-£18.95 🚓 £12-£18.95 ▲ £12-£18.95

Open: Feb-Nov, Booking advisable Spring BH & Jul-Aug, Last arrival 20.00hrs Last departure 11.00hrs

Surrounded by farmland close to Menslade Bay, which is within walking distance, this grassy park is divided by hedging into paddocks. Nearby Rhossili Beach is popular with surfers. A 6-acre site with 100 touring pitches and 21 hardstandings.

Facilities: Motor caravan service bay & baby bath 🅰 🏠 ⊙ ⊙ 🅿 ❄ 🕔 🛒 🎌 &

Services: 🆃 🔌 🔌 🏠 🛢 🏠 ⊘ 🛒 🚜 **Facilities found within 3 miles:** ⌀ ⓢ ⓢ **Notes:** Dogs must be kept on leads, quiet at all times

SWANSEA SS69

Riverside Caravan Park 67%

Ynys Forgan Farm Morriston SA6 6QL
☎ 01792 775587 📠 01792 795751
www.riversideswansea.com
Dir: *Exit M4 junct 45 towards Swansea. Left into private road signed to park*

Open: Open All Year (rs winter months pool & club closed), Booking advisable bank & main school hols, Last arrival 24.00hrs Last departure noon

A large and busy park close to the M4 but in a quiet location beside the River Taw. Family orientated, with club, bar and entertainment. There is a choice of eating outlets and the park has a good indoor pool. A 5-acre site with 90 touring pitches and 256 statics.

Facilities: Fishing on site by arrangement
🐕 🔌 🛶 🗐 🏪 ⊙ 🗔 ⚒ 🕒 🎱 🔥 🚻 ♿
Services: 🛒 🛢 🗎 🔌 🗑 🚿 ⌀ 🗄 🍺 **Facilities found within 3 miles:** ∪ ⚓ 18 ⚑ 🎣 🗗 🗖
Notes: Dogs by arrangement only (no aggressive dog breeds permitted)

LLANTWIT MAJOR SS96

Acorn Camping & Caravan Site
►►► 79%

Ham Lane South CF61 1RP
☎ 01446 794024 📠 01446 794024
email: info@acorncamping.co.uk
www.acorncamping.co.uk
Dir: *B4265 to Llantwit Major, follow camping signs. Approach site through Ham Manor residential park*

* 🚐 £9-£9.50 �। £9-£9.50 ▲ £9-£9.50
Open: Feb-8 Dec, Booking advisable BHs, school hols, wknds May-Sep, Last arrival 22.00hrs Last departure noon

A peaceful site in level meadowland, a mile from the beach. Internet station and a full size snooker table. A 4.5-acre site with 90 touring pitches, 10 hardstandings and 15 statics.

Facilities: 🔌 🛶 🗐 🏪 ⊙ 🗔 ⚒ 🕒 🗄 ♿ 🎱
Services: 🛒 🛢 🗎 🔌 🗑 🚿 🍺 **Facilities found within 3 miles:** ∪ 🎣 🗖 **Notes:** No noise between 23.00hrs & 07.00hrs

WREXHAM/CO ANTRIM

EYTON   SJ34

The Plassey Leisure Park

▶▶▶▶▶ 86%

The Plassey LL13 0SP

☎ 01978 780277 🖻 01978 780019

email: enquiries@theplassey.co.uk

www.theplassey.co.uk

Dir: *From A483 at Bangor-on-Dee exit onto B5426 for 2.5m. Park entrance signed on left*

🚐 £11-£19.50 🚍 £11-£19.50 ▲ £11-£19.50

Open: Jan-Nov, Booking advisable wknds, bank & school hols, Last arrival 21.00hrs Last departure 18.00hrs

A lovely park set in several hundred acres of farm and meadowland in Dee Valley. Superb toilet facilities; also a restaurant, coffee shop, beauty studio, and craft outlets. A 10-acre site with 110 touring pitches and 45 hardstandings. **Facilities:** Sauna, badminton

🌲🍴🏕️🌳⚙️🏊🕐🔥🚪🚿🛁🚻 **Services:**
🍺🍽️🔌🔲⚡🔌🍴🚮♿🚰🏪 **Facilities found within 3 miles:** ∪↯18🎣◎🐴🎱

Notes: No footballs, bikes or skateboards, dogs must be kept on leads

BALLYMONEY

Drumaheglis Marina & Caravan Park ▶▶▶▶ 75%

36 Glenstall Road BT53 7QN

☎ 028 2766 6466 🖻 028 2766 7659

email: helen.neill@ballymoney.gov.uk

www.ballymoney.gov.uk

Dir: *Signed off A26, approx 1.5m outside Ballymoney towards Coleraine, off B66 S of Ballymoney*

* 🚐 £15 🚍 £15 ▲ £11

Open: 17 Mar-Oct, Booking advisable BHs & summer months, Last arrival 20.00hrs Last departure 13.00hrs

Exceptionally well-designed park beside the Lower Bann River, with spacious pitches and two quality toilet blocks. A 16-acre site with 55 touring pitches and 55 hardstandings.

Facilities: Marina berthing, table tennis & volleyball 🏕️🌳⚙️🏊🕐🔥🚪🚿🛁🚻♿

Services: 🍺🚮 **Facilities found within 3 miles:** ↯9🎣🏊◎🐴🎱 **Notes:** Dogs must be kept on leads

BUSHMILLS

Ballyness Caravan Park ▶▶▶▶ 89%

40 Castlecatt Road BT57 8TN

☎ 028 2073 2393 🖹 028 2073 2713

email: info@ballynesscaravanpark.com

www.ballynesscaravanpark.com

Dir: *0.5m S of Bushmills on B66, follow signs.*

* 🚐 £15 ⛺ £15 ⛺ £10-£14

Open: 17 Mar-Oct, Booking advisable Jun-Aug & Etr, Last arrival 21.00hrs Last departure noon

A quality park with superb toilet and other facilities, on farmland beside St Columb's Rill, the stream that supplies the nearby Bushmills distillery. There is a pleasant walk around several ponds, and the park is peacefully located close to the beautiful north Antrim coast. A 16-acre site with 36 touring pitches, 30 hardstandings and 50 statics.

Facilities: 🖾 🖎 ☉ ℗ ✕ ☾ ☞ & **Services:** 🔲 � 🚐 🖸 🔋 🖉 🖴 🛒 **Facilities found within 3 miles:** ↓ 9 ℘ 🖸

LARNE

Curran Court Caravan Park

▶▶▶ 60%

131 Curran Road BT40 1BD

☎ 028 2827 3797 🖹 028 2826 0096

Dir: *On A2, 0.25m from ferry. From town centre follow signs for Leisure Centre, opposite Curran Court Hotel*

* 🚐 £11-£12 ⛺ £11-£12 ⛺ £5-£6

Open: Apr-Sep, Booking advisable main season

A handy site for the ferry. When the reception is closed, the owners can be contacted at the Curran Court Hotel across the road. A 3-acre site with 30 touring pitches.

Facilities: Bowling & putting greens 🖾 🖎 ☾ 🖸 ☞ 🚻 🖵 **Services:** 🔯 🚐 🖸 🖉 **Facilities found within 3 miles:** ↓ 9 ⅏ ℘ ◎ 🖸 🖸

CO ANTRIM

CO FERMANAGH

IRVINESTOWN
Castle Archdale Caravan Park & Camping Site ▶▶▶ 79%
Lisnarick BT94 1PP
☎ 028 6862 1333 🖹 028 6862 1176
email: info@castlearchdale.com
www.castlearchdale.com
Dir: *Site off B82 (Enniskillen to Kesh road). 10m from Enniskillen*
🚐 £16.50-£18.50 🚙 £16.50-£18.50 ▲ £10-£15
Open: Apr-Oct, Last departure 14.00hrs
On the shores of Lower Loch Erne amidst very scenic countryside, this site is ideal for watersports enthusiasts with its marina and launching facilities. Other amenities available on the site include pony trekking, pedal go-karting, cycle hire and coarse fishing. An 11-acre site with 158 touring pitches and 139 statics.
Facilities: � ⊙✕⊙ 🛒
Services: ⚡🍴🚽 📶🔌 🛒🚿
Facilities found within 3 miles: ∪ᴊ🚣 🎣🛶🏌

KESH
Loaneden Caravan Park ▶▶▶ 79%
Highgrove Muckross Bay BT93 1TZ
☎ 028 6863 1603 🖹 028 6863 2300
Dir: *From Enniskillin on entering Kesh follow site sign on left over bridge*
* 🚐 £16 🚙 £16 ▲ £12
Open: Feb-Nov, Last arrival 20.30hrs Last departure 13.00hrs
A purpose built caravan park with good facilities and friendly owners. The touring area is part of a much bigger static park. It lies within a few minutes of the marina and beach, and fishing, boating and windsurfing are all available nearby. A 35-acre site with 298 touring pitches, 36 hardstandings and 262 statics.
Facilities: Mini golf ◖⊙✕ 🛒 ⚐ **Services:** 🍴 📶 🔌 **Facilities found within 3 miles:** ∪ᴊ19🏌🎣🛶🏌
🏪 **Notes:** 🐕

COLERAINE
Tullans Farm Caravan Park

▶▶▶ 66%

46 Newmills Road BT52 2JB

☎ 028 7034 2309 🖹 028 7034 2309

email: tullansfarm@hotmail.com

www.tullansfarmcaravanpark.co.uk

Dir: *Exit A29 (ring road) at rdbt between Lodge Rd rdbt & Ballycastle Rd. Follow sign for Windyhall*

* 🚐 £15 🚎 £15 ▲ £8-£12

Open: 18 Mar-Sep, Booking advisable BHs & wknds, Last arrival 21.30hrs Last departure 13.00hrs

A lovely rural site off the beaten track in quiet farmland, but handy for the beaches at Portrush and Portstewart. Good clean facilities are maintained by the friendly family owners. A 4-acre site with 35 touring pitches, 35 hardstandings and 20 statics.

Facilities: Snooker 🔍 🏔 ⬜ 🎣 ⊙ ❄ 🕒 🚻 🚿

& Services: 🔌 🖂 🛢 🖉 🍴 🚮 **Facilities found within 3 miles:** ∪ ≽ 🎣 ⚓ 🗄 🛒

Notes: Dogs must be kept on leads 🐕

BALLINSPITTLE
Garrettstown House Holiday Park

▶▶▶▶ 74%

Kinsale

☎ 021 4778156 🖹 021 4778156

email: reception@garrettstownhouse.com

www.garrettstownhouse.com

Dir: *6m from Kinsale, through Ballinspittle, past school & football pitch on main road to beach. Beside stone estate entrance*

🚐 €18-€21 🚎 €18-€21 ▲ €16-€21

Open: 4 May-9 Sep (rs Etr-1 Jun shop closed), Last arrival 22.00hrs Last departure noon

Elevated park with tiered camping areas and panoramic views. Plenty of on-site amenities; close to beach. A 7-acre site with 60 touring pitches, 20 hardstandings and 80 statics.

Facilities: Children's club, crazy golf, video shows, snooker 🔍 🏔 ⬜ 💈 🎣 ⊙ ❄ 🕒 🛒 🚻 **& Services:** 🖂 🔌 🛢 🖉 🍴 🚮 🚽

Facilities found within 3 miles: ∪ ≽ 18 ⚓ 🎣 ◎ ⚓ 🗄 🛒 **Notes:** 🐕

CO DUBLIN/CO KERRY

CLONDALKIN
Camac Valley Tourist Caravan & Camping Park ►►►► 73%

Naas Road

☎ 01 4640644 🖹 01 4640643

email: info@camacvalley.com

www.camacvalley.com

Dir: *M50 junct 9, W on N7, site on right of dual carriageway after 2km. Site signed from N7*

🚐 €20-€27 🚌 €20-€27 ▲ €10-€27

Open: Open All Year Booking advisable Jul & Aug, Last arrival anytime Last departure noon
A pleasant lightly wooded park with good layout, facilities and security, within an hour's drive or bus ride of city centre. A 15-acre site with 163 touring pitches and 113 hardstandings.

Facilities: ⌂⍰🏠⊙☂🅿🛇🖪🚻👫🖢

Services: 🖪🗑🖉🎔 **Facilities found within 3 miles:** ∪🛆18🖉◉🗑🖪

CAHERDANIEL
Wave Crest Caravan and Camping Park ►►►► 70%

☎ 066 9475188 🖹 066 9475188

email: wavecrest@eircom.net

www.wavecrestcamping.com

Dir: *From Sneem on N70 (Ring of Kerry road), 1m before Caherdaniel on left*

* 🚐 €12 🚌 €12 ▲ €11

Open: 15 Mar-15 Oct (rs 15 Mar-1 May & Sep-15 Oct shop closed), Last arrival 22.00hrs Last departure noon
Seaside site, with pitches tucked away in the natural contours of the hillside, and offering plenty of privacy. Very good facilities, and an excellent shop. A 5.5-acre site with 120 touring pitches, 65 hardstandings and 2 statics.

Facilities: Boat anchorage, fishing, pool, foreign exchange 🔦⌂⍰🏠⊙☂🅿✖🛇🖪👫🚻🛗👫 **Services:** 🖴🗉🖪🗑🖉🎔🖢 **Facilities found within 3 miles:** ∪🛆18 🖢🖉🖢🗑🖪 **Notes:** Dogs must be kept on leads

KILLORGLIN
West's Caravan Park & Static Caravan Hire ►► 56%
Killarney Road
☎ 066 9761240 🖹 066 9761833
email: enquiries@westcaravans.com
Dir: *From Killorglin on Killarney road, site in 1m*

* 🚐 €5 🚚 €5 ▲ €5
Open: Apr-Oct, Last arrival 21.00hrs Last departure noon
Pretty little site on banks of, but safely fenced off from, the River Laune, which offers trout and salmon fishing. There are good facilities for families. A 3.5-acre site with 10 touring pitches, 3 hardstandings and 50 statics.
Facilities: 🔊 🔍 ♨ ☐ 🕃 🕅 ⊙ 🏱 ✳ ⊙ 🛱
Services: 🔌 🖥 🚿 🚽 Facilities found within 3 miles: ♻ 🛁 18 ✐ 🖥 🖪 **Notes:** Dogs must be on leads (charged)

KNOCK
Knock Caravan and Camping Park
►►► 70%
Claremorris Road
☎ 094 9388100 🖹 094 9388295
email: info@knock-shrine.ie
www.knock-shrine.ie/accommodation
Dir: *From rdbt in Knock, through town. Park entrance on left 1km, opp petrol station*
🚐 €19-€21 🚚 €19-€21 ▲ €19-€21
Open: Mar-Nov, Booking advisable Aug, Last arrival 22.00hrs Last departure noon
A pleasant, very well maintained caravan park within the grounds of Knock Shrine, offering spacious terraced pitches and excellent facilities. A 10-acre site with 88 touring pitches, 88 hardstandings and 12 statics.
Facilities: 🔍 ♨ ☐ 🕅 ⊙ 🏱 ✳ ⊙ 🛱 🛱 ♿
Services: 🕂 🔌 🖥 🍴 ⌀ 🚿 **Facilities found within 3 miles:** ♻ 🛁 9 ✐ 🖥 🖪
Notes: Dogs must be kept on leads

CO ROSCOMMON/CO WATERFORD

BOYLE

Lough Key Forest Park ▶▶▶▶ 70%

☎ 071 9662363 📄 071 9663266

email: seamus.duignan@coillte.ie

www.coillte.ie/tourism_and_recreation

Dir: *Follow Lough Key Forest Park signs, site within grounds. Approx 0.5m from entrance. Park 3km E of Boyle on N4*

* 🚐 €14-€16 🚃 €14-€16 ⛺ €11-€14

Open: 14 Apr-10 Sep (rs pre-booking essential), Booking advisable 3 weeks before arrival, Last arrival 22.00hrs Last departure noon

Peaceful and very secluded site within the extensive grounds of a beautiful forest park. Lough Key offers boat trips and waterside walks, and there is a viewing tower. A 15-acre site with 72 touring pitches and 52 hardstandings.

Facilities: 🄰 ⌷ ⋔ ⊙ ⓢ ⌁ 🝤 &

Services: 🖭 🖸 **Facilities found within 3 miles:** ↯ 18 ≩ ⋒ ≋ 🖸 **Notes:** 😄

CLONEA

Casey's Caravan Park ▶▶▶ *74%*

☎ 058 41919 📄 058 41919

Dir: *From R675 (Dungarvan road), follow signs to Clonea Bay. Site at end of road*

* 🚐 €22-€24 🚃 €22-€24 ⛺ €22-€24

Open: 6 Apr-9 Sep, Booking advisable May-Jun (ex BH wknds), Last arrival 22.00hrs Last departure noon

Spacious, well-kept park with excellent toilet facilities, next to beach. A 4.5-acre site with 108 touring pitches and 170 statics.

Facilities: Crazy golf & games room 🔍 🄰 ⌷ ⋔ ⊙ ℘ ⋇ ⓢ ⓢ & **Services:** 🖭 🔋 ⌀ 🔌 **Facilities found within 3 miles:** ↯ 18 ≩ ⋒ 🖸 **Notes:** Dogs must be on leads at all times 😄